Philosophy and Revolutions in Genetics

Renewing Philosophy

General Editor: **Gary Banham**

Titles include:

Kyriaki Goudeli
CHALLENGES TO GERMAN IDEALISM
Schelling, Fichte and Kant

Keekok Lee
PHILOSOPHY AND REVOLUTIONS IN GENETICS
Deep Science and Deep Technology

Jill Marsden
AFTER NIETZSCHE

Celine Surprenant
FREUD'S MASS PSYCHOLOGY

Jim Urpeth
FROM KANT TO DELEUZE

Martin Weatherston
HEIDEGGER'S INTERPRETATION OF KANT
Categories, Imagination and Temporality

Renewing Philosophy
Series Standing Order ISBN 0–333–91928–9
(*outside North America only*)

You can receive future titles in this series as they are published by placing a standing order. Please contact your bookseller or, in case of difficulty, write to us at the address below with your name and address, the title of the series and an ISBN quoted above.

Customer Services Department, Macmillan Distribution Ltd, Houndmills, Basingstoke, Hampshire RG21 6XS, England

Philosophy and Revolutions in Genetics

Deep Science and Deep Technology

Keekok Lee
Visiting Chair in Philosophy
Institute for the Environment, Philosophy & Public Policy
University of Lancaster

First published 2003 by
PALGRAVE MACMILLAN
Houndmills, Basingstoke, Hampshire RG21 6XS and
175 Fifth Avenue, New York, N.Y. 10010
Companies and representatives throughout the world.

PALGRAVE MACMILLAN is the global academic imprint of the Palgrave Macmillan division of St Martin's Press, LLC and of Palgrave Macmillan Ltd. Macmillan® is a registered trademark in the United States, United Kingdom and other countries. Palgrave is a registered trademark in the European Union and other countries.

ISBN 0–333–96458–6

This book is printed on paper suitable for recycling and made from fully managed and sustained forest sources.

A catalogue record for this book is available from the British Library.

Library of Congress Cataloging-in-Publication Data

Lee, Keekok, 1938–
Philosophy and revolutions in genetics: deep science and deep technology/Keekok Lee.
    p. cm. – (Renewing philosophy)
  Includes bibliographical references and index.
  ISBN 0–333–96458–6
  1. Genetics–Philosophy. 2. Molecular genetics–Philosophy. 3. Genetic engineering–Philosophy. I. Title. II. Series.

QH438.7 .L44 2003
576.5–dc21

                                                                                    2002026950

10 9 8 7 6 5 4 3 2 1
12 11 10 09 08 07 06 05 04 03

Printed and bound in Great Britain by
Antony Rowe Ltd, Chippenham and Eastbourne

Contents

Series Editor's Preface

Renewing Philosophy is intended as a space in which various philosophical projects are tested and their cogency both as assessments of the traditions of modernity and as revealing contemporary developments are presented. Keekok Lee's contribution to this is to provide a new light on the history and concepts of genetic science.

Within the hundred years since Mendel we have witnessed an explosion of research. There are a number of confusions attendant upon the understanding of this domain, not least of which is the general failure to understand how far the very area of research has been transformed during this time. It is part of the mission of this book to instruct those working in the humanities and social sciences in the profound alterations of scientific theory and practice within the supposedly unitary history of 'genetics'.

Focusing on revealing to us the basis of scientific theory and practice of different models of 'genetics' is only one aspect of Keekok Lee's endeavour. This book also contains a parallel investigation of the types of technology that have accompanied and transformed the nature of scientific theory. From the concern with 'hybrids' which Darwin shared with Mendel and whose history in natural philosophy is long, Keekok Lee sketches the development of biotechnology and its relation to the notion of a 'molecular' genetics. While rejecting many of the current philosophical accounts of these developments, the nature of them and their consequences for environmental and legal thought are sharply brought out in Keekok Lee's thorough study of the notion of patenting.

This book is unlike many others within this series. It is written by a veteran author contributing to a novel discipline in a manner which requires careful exposition and explanation for readers whose familiarity with many concepts can certainly not be taken for granted. As this aspect of the work is vital for the communication between natural scientists and those whose background is solidly in the humanities and social sciences, the form of presentation of the argument includes elements of pedagogic attention. These qualities should, however, enable the work to have a much greater chance of provoking and enabling the development of responses from within philosophy to an important aspect of the contemporary world at present under-theorized by philosophers.

The forceful presentation of an argument in relationship to a vast array of historical and scientific matters is always difficult for a philosopher, as it is open to objection from those whose work is more overtly grounded in an appreciation of 'facts'. But uncovering the meaning of such 'facts' requires an analysis that supersedes the empirical realm, while basing itself on the findings there given. It is this type of practice, a pre-eminent practice within philosophy, which is provided here.

The revelation of the way in which this most contemporary of scientific developments has grown out of the Modern Project is a matter of deep interest to anyone concerned with the legacy of modernity. As such, it is hoped that this material and this argument will be part of what is weighed in contemporary discussions not merely of the philosophy of technology or environmental ethics but also within the circles that are seriously engaged with a cultural discussion of the limits of the modern and its relationship to nihilism.

Gary Banham
Series Editor *Renewing Philosophy*

Acknowledgements

I wish to thank Ian Oi, my nephew, for having drawn my attention to certain references in Chapter 5. For technical assistance, I am very grateful to David Shotton and Ann Sharrock.

Introduction

An artefact, to the lay mind, may conjure up a house or a car, but not the family dog or the rose bush in the garden. In other words, the paradigm of an artefact involves something which is made out of what was once alive but is now dead (like a statue sculpted out of wood), or something which has never been alive (like a house constructed out of stone). A living organism, however, fails readily to spring to mind as an artefact: on the contrary, it is regarded *par excellence* as a naturally occurring being. In this view, what is alive (the biotic) is natural but what humans have built or constructed, out of what is inanimate or inert (the exbiotic or the abiotic), is artefactual.

But this implied criterion used by the lay person to distinguish what is natural from what is not is too simplistic to do justice to the long history of humankind in its attempt to transform living organisms into what may be called artefactual beings. At best, as we shall see, it might have been appropriate when Aristotle propounded his philosophy of nature around the 5th century before the present era, but would be highly inadequate in late modernity at the beginning of the 21st century. This long history dates from the first domestication of plants and animals.[1] It will be shown that all cultivars are ipso facto biotic artefacts, including what today is sometimes referred to as the landraces still cultivated by peasant farmers in developing economies or traditional societies. However, this point is not the main concern of the book, which will, instead, focus on the role played by modern science and its technology in creating biotic artefacts. The book will argue that although traditionally bred plants and animals are artefactual living beings, their degree of artefacticity is much less than their counterparts of the 20th/21st centuries. This is because while they have been created using what may be called craft-based technology, their modern counterparts are created by technologies that are science-induced, such that the more basic and the deeper the discoveries at the level of theoretical science, the more powerful the technology they induce. In 20th century biology, there have been two such fundamental discoveries regarding the nature and the mechanisms of genetic transmission from parent to offspring. The first is Mendelian genetics; the second molecular

1

or DNA genetics. The insights of Mendelian genetics led eventually to the technology of double-cross hybridisation, while those of molecular genetics to biotechnology.[2]

Molecular genetics is said to be at a more basic, and therefore, deeper level of understanding of genetic material than Mendelian genetics. It goes beyond genes and chromosomes to tell us about the molecular components of the genes themselves. Theoretical understanding at such a level permits genetic engineers to manipulate genetic material in a way radically different from that permitted by Mendelian understanding only. As a result, biotechnology today can create what are called transgenic organisms whose genomes have incorporated genetic material from another organism belonging to a totally different species, be it plant or animal – in other words, such a technology can cross both species and kingdom boundaries. Such organisms may then be said to possess a greater degree of artefacticity than Mendelian hybrids (which cross no species or kingdom boundaries) which may, themselves in turn, be said to possess a greater degree of artefacticity than the domesticated plants and animals produced by traditional craft-based breeding technology.

The history of such transformation is part and parcel of the history of modernity itself and of the central role which homo faber plays in it, aided and abetted by modern science and its induced technologies. In other words, it is about the project initiated by 17th century Western Europe of humanising nature and, in the process, of naturalising humanity itself.[3] After four hundred years of effort, we begin to see more clearly than ever before the success it has so long promised. Today, biotechnology is poised to render redundant natural evolution through its ability to turn non-human organisms into near complete biotic artefacts, thereby systematically humanising nature. But it simultaneously has the ability to turn humans themselves into near biotic artefacts, thereby naturalising humanity itself.

The book is primarily concerned with this Modern Project. Chapter 1 sets out the transformation from the philosophical point of view.[4] It argues that when humankind alters the status of living organisms to become biotic artefacts, the shift of status is an ontological one. Ontologically speaking, the genetically manipulated plant or animal is a different kind of being from its original naturally occurring counterpart. The tulip in the garden or the chicken in the factory farm is an artefact; as an artefact, it is the embodiment of human intentions and ends, and would not have come into existence or continued to exist but for such human intervention and manipulation. In contrast, the orchid in the rainforest is a naturally occurring being, whose coming into existence and whose continuing to exist, is (in principle) independent of human intention and manipulation.

Chapter 2 looks at the relationship between theoretical science and its technology in order to establish the central thesis that modern technology is science-led and science-induced. It will also seek to draw out the corollary of that thesis, namely, that the deeper the theoretical understanding given by the basic science, the more powerful is the technology its insights would generate. While it is true that theoretical science seeks to establish so-called laws of nature, and technology seeks to establish rules of efficacy in an opportunistic way, it remains true that these rules of efficacy are ultimately grounded in the laws of nature. The deeper the laws, the more potent are the rules both in the scope and precision of their application.

Chapters 3 and 4 respectively set out in outline the science of Mendelian genetics and its technology of hybridisation on the one hand, and the science of molecular/DNA genetics and its biotechnology on the other.

Chapter 5 teases out the implications of the ontological dimension for decision making by governmental bodies with regard, in particular, to the issue of patentability of genetic material such as transgenic organisms, as well as DNA sequences.

Chapter 6 examines the Modern Project in terms of the humanisation of nature and the naturalisation of humanity via its central notion of homo faber. In turning other living organisms into biotic artefacts, humankind is now able, in principle, to turn itself also into a biotic artefact. Humans and non-human living organisms alike are, by virtue of the possibility of tech- nological manipulation, at least in principle, but the material embodiment of human intentionality.

Notes

1 A brief account of it will be given at the beginning of Chapter 3.
2 It is interesting to note the astounding speed with which biotechnology had come to be perceived as a dominant technology towards the last two or three years of the 20th century. For instance, in 1998, Jeremy Rifkin published *The Biotech Century*. Yet, only two years before that, in 1996, when *Scientific American* put out a special issue entitled *Key Technologies for the 21st Century*, there was no section devoted to the subject of biotechnology and, even more surprisingly, there were very few references in the entire issue to it, apart from one chapter – 'Gene Therapy' – which occurred in the section under 'Medicine'. (The index in the edition published by W. H. Freeman and Company in 1996 contains only two such references.)
3 How these terms are used will be made obvious in Chapter 6.
4 An earlier version of Chapters 1 and 2 may be found in Keekok Lee (1999).

1

Living Organisms: Their Philosophical Transformation from Natural to Artefactual Beings

The Introduction has pointed out that the distinguishing criterion between what is an artefact and what is not does not lie in the distinction between the inert or the inanimate (the abiotic or the exbiotic) on the one hand, and the living or animate (the biotic) on the other. It may turn out that living organisms are just as susceptible to being transformed into arte-facts as non-living matter. As the long history of domestication of plants and animals shows, it is not a misnomer to call the products of domestica-tion 'biotic artefacts'. But in order to see why it is not so, particularly today, one must first examine the notion of artefact itself.

Artefact

Very briefly, an artefact may be defined as a material object which is the embodiment of human intention, a physical entity which does not exist in the absence of human manipulation and intervention, but is deliberately created by humans, according to explicit designs to fulfil specific ends.[1] The reference to material embodiment rules out other forms of inventions like concepts, such as that of mass marketing, or techniques such as that of the division of labour as a method of mass production. Concepts and techniques may be deliberately created and may lead to the production of artefacts but they are themselves not artefacts.[2] To produce artefacts, they need a specific technology which itself may be an assembly of artefacts. The conveyor-belt technology is an application of the technique of the division of labour to increase productivity as articulated by Adam Smith. In turn, the conveyor belt and other components of the technology which are artefacts (in economist's terms, these artefacts are plants) are used to produce further artefacts (in econ-omist's terms, these are consumer goods), such as cars and refrigerators.

Artefacts and technology may be said to go hand in hand.[3] A particular kind of artefact requires a specific technology for its production. The Shang ritual bronzes of ancient China required a somewhat different technology from that which produced later Song or Ming porcelain bowls. Today,

4

worldwide, china is produced by a different technology from that used in the China of the Song, Ming or Qing Dynasty.

Another way of elucidating the notion of artefacts is to lean on Aristotle's four causes. For Aristotle, a complete explanation of a phenomenon is given in these terms. For ease of exegesis, Aristotle himself used artefacts to illustrate them. Take a statue, clearly an artefact. It is made of stone – its material cause. It is carved by a particular sculptor(s) – its efficient cause. It is sculpted as an image of Queen Victoria – its formal cause. It was commissioned by the Town Hall of Manchester to celebrate the golden jubilee of Victoria's accession to the British throne – its final cause. The formal, final and efficient causes involve human intentionality in this kind of artefact. The sculptor intended to sculpt an image of Queen Victoria because the Town Hall officials intended to pay homage to their sovereign, and the sculptor intended to make himself the efficient agent in carrying out the intention of his commissioners.

In this example, only the material cause, that is, the stone, is 'given', in the sense that it, per se, has not come into existence because of prior human intention and manipulation. In that sense, the stone is a naturally occurring entity, although after it has been requisitioned by the commissioners and the sculptor and turned into a statue of Queen Victoria herself, the worked-upon-stone has become the material embodiment of human intentionality. In other words, an artefact made out of the stone has been created, although the original stone itself is not an artefactual entity.

However, the example may be misleading. As we shall see, in a society whose technology is craft-based, the material cause is usually 'given' or 'found'. But as societies and their technologies develop, the efficient agent may today be able to create an artefact out of matter which is not found in nature.[4] Instead of making a rocking horse from wood, today one can make a rocking horse out of plastic. Plastic as such is not 'naturally' found. It is technologically derived from something which is naturally given and found, namely oil. Plastic, as a material, is itself an artefact. From this one can see that the plastic rocking horse is an artefact with a much deeper degree of artefacticity than a wooden rocking horse. In the case of the latter, apart from chopping down the tree and seasoning the wood, the artesan would not have manipulated and altered its character in any relevant or significant way. However, in the case of the former, without the developments in theoretical chemistry and the technology they induced, plastic would just not exist as a substitute material for wood as a resource in production.

Biotic artefact

We have done the easy bit, elucidating the notion of an artefact in terms of an abiotic (or exbiotic) product. Aristotle, too, had made things to some extent too easy for us by using, in the main, abiotic artefacts to illustrate the four causes. However, this could give rise, as we have seen, to the misleading impression that only abiotic or exbiotic matter can be turned into artefacts. However, it is obvious that domesticated plants and animals are biotic artefacts. The human, as the efficient cause, deems certain characteristics in a plant or animal to be desirable or undesirable, and accordingly, attempts to breed out or remove the undesirable, while making sure that the desirable features would be retained or become exaggerated in the final product. No conceptual constraint exists but, at best, only technological ones. A black tulip or a Pekinese is as much a human creation as a silk rose or a wax figure of Winston Churchill, as their formal, final and efficient causes lie in humans and with humans. The difference amounts to this. A silk rose is imitative and ersatz; it is simply not a 'real' rose but tries to pass off as one in terms of its visual characteristics. Unlike a real rose plant, no matter how much it might look like one under certain conditions, it would not grow if its stem were planted in the soil, because it cannot perform photosynthesis as a real rose plant can. For clarity's sake, it is best to call this sense of artificial 'artificial[2]'. In contrast, the black tulip plant is capable of performing photosynthesis as it grows and changes. However, it is not a naturally evolved entity and would not be growing but for human design and manipulation. This sense may be called 'artificial[1]'. The silk rose plant is artificial in both senses, unlike the black tulip or the Pekinese which is artificial only in the first sense. This book is not really concerned with artefacts like the silk rose plant or statues of the famous, but with artefacts like the black tulip, the Pekinese or the geep (shoat), which are not naturally occurring or evolved beings but are artefactual beings.[5]

After this clarification, we need to go back to Aristotle's four causes. The reason why he was tempted to use the abiotic artefact to elucidate his explanatory schema is that the four causes can be separated out conveniently in practice, and each assigned to a particular external agency.[6] The stone as the material cause of the statue, for instance, can be identified independently of the other three. In turn, the efficient cause could be identified in terms of the sculptor; the formal cause, in terms of the plan or blueprint which the sculptor could be said to be 'carrying in his head' or have drawn on a piece of paper; the final cause, in terms of the purpose of the town hall officials.

But Aristotle said that in the case of a natural phenomenon, such as a living organism, the four causes are inextricably intertwined so that they can only be separated out for the sake of intellectual clarification and no more.[7] In a living organism, form and matter go together – the matter which constitutes the eagle cannot be grasped independently of the form which that matter takes, that is, of the eagle. This integral fusion of form and matter enables Aristotle to recognise the reality of substances, which could change. From this, he was further able to conclude that the primary or proper meaning of 'nature' is the 'essence of things which have in themselves (qua themselves) a principle of motion' (Aristotle, *Physics*, 2.8.199b15–16) present in them either potentially or actually. By invoking the distinction between potentiality and actuality, he was able to explain substantial change. The former refers to the ultimate, radical possibility of change inherent in matter; the latter, to the manifestation of that potency. This actuality he called 'form', what makes a thing what it is by definition.

Furthermore, living organisms not merely manifest change but also change in certain clearly defined ways. In other words, change involves development, which in turn implies a nisus, a direction towards which the changes are orientated. The acorn, in germinating and pushing its way through the soil, may be said to be striving to become an oak, the whole process of which tends towards the form of the mature plant. If this is so, the formal and final causes (in living organisms) become identical. In living organisms, too, the formal and final causes themselves are also identical with the efficient cause. 'Aristotle ... conceives the notion of a final cause which not only directs but also excites or awakens the energy which it controls, by arousing in the appropriate object a nisus towards its own realization in bodily form' (Collingwood, 1945, p. 84).[8] The efficient cause, then, is an immaterial cause.

But before continuing, one red herring needs to be disposed of. It is a mistake to accuse Aristotle himself of committing anthropomorphism. The end-directedness he was talking about is not meant to be the conscious, intentional variety which is displayed in the human creation of artefacts. He did not say that the plant knew what it was it was doing, and that it planned its development in the same way the sculptor did when he chipped away at the block of stone. The sculptor chipped according to a blueprint he carried in his head, or according to the instructions he had received from the commissioner of the artefact, or in accordance with the conventional requirements of the activity of sculpting objects. However, it is not unintelligible to say that the plant strives, albeit in the absence of consciousness, to get to the source of sunlight so that it could grow properly.[9] Conscious intentions do not exhaust the notion of purposiveness and end-directedness.[10] Aristotle's final cause does not in general entail conscious intentionality, although in the context of creating human artefacts it does refer to conscious intentions and purposes. While purposiveness as end-directedness is what humans and plants have in common, conscious intentionality is a crucial point of difference between them.[11]

For Aristotle, 'those things are natural which, by a continuous movement originated from an internal principle, arrive at some completion' (*Physics*, 2.8.199b15–16). In contrast, artefacts are 'those things which, by a movement originated from an *external* source, arrive at some end'. The end comes from outside the thing itself and is imposed upon it by an outside source, namely, human agency. The Taj Mahal came into existence, and took the shape and character it did, because of the intention entertained by

Shah Jahan, in the light of which he set in motion certain actions leading to its ultimate realisation.

Theses of teleology

Another way of making clear the points above is to distinguish between different theses of teleology. For the purpose of this elucidation, three must be delineated, namely, external, intrinsic/immanent and extrinsic/imposed teleology.

Two forms of external teleology may be identified. In its unmodified form, the classic formulation may be found in Aristotle's *Politics*. In his hierarchy of beings, humans are higher than animals because they possess reason to a greater or different degree. Furthermore, he also believed that the purpose of beings further down the hierarchy of rationality is to serve those higher up:

> we may infer that, after the birth of animals, plants exist for their sake, and that the other animals exist for the sake of man, the tame for use and food, the wild, if not at all, at least the greater part of them, for food, and for the provision of clothing and various instruments. Now if nature makes nothing incomplete, and nothing in vain, the inference must be that she has made all animals for the sake of man (*Politics*: 1.8.1256b16–22).

This is what underlies the medieval notion of The Great Chain of Beings. However, the modern version involves a more streamlined hierarchy – all other non-human natural beings only have instrumental value for humans who alone possess intrinsic value. We shall see, in a moment, that the two different versions have quite different implications for the relationship of humankind to biotic nature. But at this point it may be relevant to draw attention to a possible critique of the thesis of external teleology in either form. This says that it is both an illusion and a fallacy to hold that whatever we humans happen to find useful (whether living or non-living) in the light of our technology must have come into existence just for the purpose of serving our ends, and that its existence is to be justified solely in terms of such a purpose.

Aristotle also subscribed (implicitly) to what may be called intrinsic/immanent teleology as far as biological beings are concerned. We have seen that their formal, final, efficient and material causes are inseparable in practice. For Aristotle, and those influenced by his account of intrinsic/immanent teleology, extrinsic/imposed teleology is then confined to abiotic artefacts. Ex hypothesi these have no intrinsic/immanent teleology as they would not, and could not, have come into existence or continue to exist, but for the fact that humans have designed them to serve specific purposes. Take samurai swords. Should all humans suddenly die out, there would no longer be samurai swords (whether to serve the historic purpose of killing one's enemies, or an aesthetic purpose today, long after Japanese society has outlived its feudal samurai class). There would be only bits of physical matter, which are subject to the laws of eventual decay.

The Aristotelian world-view outlined above may be called Old Teleology. Under it, extrinsic/imposed teleology is restricted only to abiotic artefacts; furthermore, intrinsic/immanent teleology takes precedence over external teleology. This is to say that living organisms, which are naturally occurring beings, primarily exist as ends for themselves unfolding their respective *tele*, and only secondarily serve the purposes of humans. Before they can serve human ends, logically and empirically speaking, they must first grow and develop according to their own *telos*. An oak has first to germinate from an acorn and then grow into an oak tree before we humans can chop it down to make tables and chairs out of it.

If this world-view is anthropocentric, then it remains true that its anthropocentrism is a much less aggressive or more passive form than its modern counterpart, as it can recognise the priority of intrinsic/immanent teleology over external teleology.[12]

The New Teleology of modernity is different. It rejects intrinsic/immanent/ teleology while embracing the simplified version of external teleology. As we shall see, the rejection of the former is a requirement of modern science, its methodology, its ontology of materialism and mechanism as well as its goal, both epistemological and ideological, of controlling nature. The implication of jettisoning intrinsic/immanent teleology and adhering to simplified external teleology leaves the way open for modernity to embrace wholeheartedly extrinsic/imposed teleology, helped by modern science and its technology. While the craft-based technology of earlier times presented more limited and less systematic opportunities to draw living organisms into the domain of extrinsic/imposed teleology, this constraint had been eased since the beginning of the 20th century, and has been overcome by its closing decade. In so doing, New Teleology brings forth a more aggressive form of anthropocentrism and instrumentalism with the means of systematically transforming, in principle, all living organisms into entities with near total degree of artefacticity.

Degrees of artefacticity

Let us observe that for the reasons cited above, and given the technology of domestication in ancient Greece, it was entirely appropriate for Aristotle to regard the humanly created abiotic entity as the paradigm of an artefact, contrasting it with a living organism as the paradigm of a naturally occurring being. In the former, as we have seen, three of the four causes can be separately assigned in principle to external human agency with its intentions and purposes, while the material cause itself is usually given or found in nature (at least this was so in Aristotle's time). In the latter, the four causes are inextricably fused and can only be separated out for the purpose of intellectual clarification, while its formal, final and efficient causes are primarily internal to the material cause. But today's technology, as we shall see, has succeeded in undermining this Aristotelian account of the difference between the abiotic artefact and the living organism. Biotechnology can, in principle if not already in practice, transform a living organism into an artefact such that, like the abiotic artefact, its four causes are no longer fused and internal to it but can be separated out and assigned to an external, human agency and its intentionality. The transgenic organism is then no different from the plastic rocking horse, as they are both artefacts possessing a similar degree of artefacticity. Transgenic organisms are constructed out of existing natural kinds and so are derived from them.[13] Similarly, plastic toys are constructed out of an existing natural kind and so are derived from it. Transgenic organisms have lost their own intrinsic/immanent *telos*, while plastic toys have none of their own to start with. The *telos* of such organisms has been designed and imposed on them by humans. Humans are their creators. They have become creatures to serve human ends in much the same way as humans have created plastic tables to further other human goals. That they are alive, that is, breathe, ingest nutrients, reproduce, is, from this perspective, totally irrelevant, as these capabilities of theirs have been captured by humans so that as 'designer' organisms they no longer live out their own respective *tele*.

Abiotic artefacts, in their ascending order of artefacticity, may be displayed as follows:

1. A granite statue, for instance, may be produced by a technology of blasting, chipping, using tools such as hammer, wedge, and so on. The material, however, is granite, a natural kind, found in nature and is not, therefore, itself an artefact.
2. A plastic statue, on the other hand, is produced by an altogether different technology, which is informed by the sciences of chemistry, geology, and so on. The material, plastic, is not found in nature but is itself an artefact, although it is derived from a natural material, namely, oil.
3. A statue made, in the future, out of a material which is created through molecular nanotechnology; unlike plastic, this kind of material is not derived from a naturally occurring material such as oil or sand, but constructed *de novo* from atoms and molecules of one of the elements, such as carbon.[14]

In the case of biotic artefacts, in ascending order of artefacticity, the following levels may be identified:

1. Produced through the trial and error method of traditional selection and breeding by farmers and horticulturists.
2. Produced through the combined contribution of Mendelian genetics and hybridisation technology by scientists.
3. (a) Produced through the combined contribution of molecular genetics and genetic engineering; (b) to be produced through the combined contribution of molecular genetic engineering, molecular nanotechnology as well as microcomputer technology and the various sciences which underpin them.

This book is not really concerned with technological possibilities per se which may lie just over the horizon, such as molecular nanotechnology. But from the philosophical point of view these possibilities are of relevance, and a few words involving them are in order. The account just given above shows that the degree of artefacticity of an object depends on two related things:

1. The matter or stuff (the material cause) of which the object is made – whether it is found as natural kinds, such as wood or stone, derived from something found in nature, like plastic from oil, or constructed *de novo* using atoms and molecules of elements provided by nature in abundance. In other words, it depends on whether the material is a natural kind (what Aristotle calls second matter), derived from a natural kind, or directly synthesised by humans, as an artefactual kind from an analogue of what Aristotle called first matter, or what we call atoms and molecules of the elements.
2. The degree of artefacticity is, therefore, at its highest when humans succeed in designing the artefact from scratch, from atoms themselves. Such artefacts may then be said to be the near total product of human design and technology. But such a level of artefacticity is only achieved by deep science generating the appropriate technology to go with it; but that moment is not quite with us yet.[15]

But what is already with us is biotechnology (backed up by the theoretical sciences of molecular genetics and biology) which permits humans to use genetic material at the level of DNA molecules to create living organisms according to their own (human) design. Ex hypothesi the genetic materials that constitute transgenic organisms would not have come together without an extremely high order of precision and control involved in such a form of deliberate human manipulation.[16]

By comparison, organisms which are the products of Mendelian genetics and its accompanying hybridisation technology may be said to possess a relatively lower degree of artefacticity. Although their formal, final and efficient causes may be the work of humans, at least humans have not designed their genetic matter in the way molecular genetic engineering has succeeded in doing. Hybridisation as such could and, indeed, does occur without human intervention, that is, naturally, whereas transgenic organisms by their very nature could not have come about without deliberate human design and execution. Mendelian genetics has given rise to a technology which improves the efficiency of hybridisation under the traditional technology of domestic and field breeding. It leaves less to chance than the method of trial and error it replaces, but from the point of view of precise human manipulation and control, it also leaves much to be desired.

Because the control is not so precise (relatively speaking), there is still something, even though diminished, left to the intrinsic *telos* of such organisms. At least it could be said that even if certain traits have been bred out of their genotype, it still remains true that they retain something of what their forebears had before humans intervened. They may be artefacts but they are not the embodiment of an imposed/extrinsic teleology to the same extent that transgenic organisms appear to be. Their minimal intrinsic *telos* is preserved in so far as Mendelian genetics and its hybridisation technology operate within the theoretical framework of the inheritance of genetic material. In radical contrast, molecular genetics and molecular genetic engineering, at a stroke, replace such inheritance by direct human manipulation and rearrangement of genetic material across individual organisms and species. This is why transgenic organisms may be said to possess a much higher degree of artefacticity compared with those organisms produced through the traditional methods of breeding – their efficient, final and formal causes are humanly inspired, imposed and executed, while their material cause is technologically derived from existing natural kinds.

Organisms as beings 'for themselves' and 'by themselves'

We have seen that under Old Teleology, intrinsic/immanent teleology takes precedence over external teleology. Living organisms, first and foremost, do not exist in order to be of use to humans, although for Aristotle it seemed eminently acceptable to argue that beings with a lower level of rationality should serve the purpose of those with a higher level of rationality. But today we can rewrite the Aristotelian prioritising of intrinsic/immanent over external teleology in a different way in the light of the understanding given to us by the theory of natural evolution. That theory provides a naturalistic explanation of how living things have evolved. Natural selection of variations among individual organisms, in the long run, accounts for how species evolve and how the multiplication of species takes place. Humankind is itself such a historically evolved species.[17] This means that no species could be said to have come into being for the sake of some other species, be this human or non-human. The plant (as species and as individual organism) did not come into existence for the sake of providing seeds for the insect. The insect did not come into existence for the sake of providing food for the bird. Neither did the bird come into existence for the sake of providing food or aesthetic satisfaction for the human. However, the plant, the insect, the bird, having come into existence, happen to find themselves to be of use to one another and to humans. But primarily the plant or the bird lives for itself. The bird in eating the insect does so for no other end than that of sustaining its own functioning integrity. In other words, the bird does not eat the insect in order to assuage the hunger of the human, but its own hunger. The fact that it could be of such instrumental value to the human is only a happenstance, albeit an important one. This then shows that the bird may be said to have a 'good of its own', namely, striving to sustain its own functioning integrity. The bird exists, first and foremost, to unfold its own *telos*, and only secondarily to be of use to foxes or humans. It has not come into existence, nor does it continue to exist, to be of use to these other beings, whether non-human or human.

However, standing behind the prioritisation of intrinsic/immanent over external teleology is another fundamental issue, which must now be brought to the forefront. Biotic nature has not come into existence for the sake of humankind; the same is also true of abiotic nature. The atmosphere, water, rocks, carbon or oxygen (in whatever form) have not come into existence for the benefit of humankind, although without them humankind could not have evolved and/or continue to survive.

In this fundamental sense any particular entity, whether abiotic or biotic, which constitutes a part of the whole of nature, has come into existence not to serve the goals (whether consciously entertained or otherwise) of other entities. This fundamental sense of existence may be called existing 'by itself' and logically follows from rejecting the thesis of external teleology, either in its original Aristotelian or modern simplified form. It focuses on the following salient facts:

(1) The already mentioned point that the usefulness of any entity to humanity is a happenstance which has nothing to do with its coming into existence.

(2) Its genesis is independent of the genesis of humankind and, in nearly all cases, predates it.

(3) Its continuing to exist is also independent of humankind, in the sense that if humans were to vanish from earth, earth itself would continue in much the same way as it had done before the emergence of humankind itself.

(4) Human survival is dependent on the survival of nature as a whole, but as just commented upon, nature as a whole is not dependent on human survival.

Furthermore, each entity follows its own trajectory.[18] Each entity displays both permanence and change. Neither Parmenides nor Heraclitus was right, as either asserted only the one aspect of existence while denying the other. A plant grows from a seed to become first a sapling, then a mature tree, which eventually dies and decays. A lake is formed, for instance, by glacial action; but it, too, will one day dry out to become first a swamp, then perhaps a meadow. Indeed, according to geological understanding, lakes are the most transient of all the geological forms. Each (kind of) entity follows its own manner of persistence, change and demise. This rhythm is totally independent of humankind.

But as we have seen, while all entities, whether abiotic or biotic, have trajectories (and in that sense, may be said to exist 'by themselves'), biotic entities as individual living organisms also strive to maintain their functioning integrity and to unfold their respective *tele*. In that sense they may be said to have 'a good of their own', or to have interests (or even needs) which, if thwarted, would cause them harm. Abiotic entities, on the contrary, cannot meaningfully be said to have interests or 'a good of their own' which they strive to maintain or to realise.[19] Their trajectories, unlike the trajectories of biotic beings, cannot be said to be end-oriented. But this is not to deny, however, that humans can damage them, or alter their own rhythm of change and decay without moral limits whatsoever. For instance, we can quarry a whole hill away with our present day technology within a few days, weeks or months, whereas the hill, left to itself, might have taken millennia to weather away.

Given this fundamental difference between the biotic and the abiotic, one must mark it by saying that while both exist 'by themselves', only biotic beings can be said to exist 'for themselves'. This latter sense involves the notion of striving to maintain their functioning integrity and to realise their own respective *tele*. Although one may in certain limited contexts detect a direction to geological/chemical/physical processes in nature, it is not obvious that such teleomatic phenomena display 'direction' in quite the way biotic phenomena do.[20] What is distinctive about biological phenomena is that the organisms keep entropic increase at bay through maintaining their structure and their functioning integrity to stay alive and to reproduce successfully. Take the emperor penguins in Antarctica. When the female has hatched its egg, both the female and male penguins strive to ensure that the egg is successfully transferred from the former to the latter. This operation must be completed within a very short period as the egg would not survive the cold if exposed for more than two minutes. When the transfer has taken place, the male then protects and hatches it during the next four months, while his female partner travels about a hundred miles or so to get to the sea in order to feed and fatten herself. At the first stirring of the Antarctic spring, the egg is hatched. The hatching is timed to coincide with the return of the chick's mother from the sea. But in spite of the long separation, the partners successfully recognise and locate each other. At this point, another intricate transfer begins – the mother takes over, and straightaway, and must feed the chick as any delay would cause it to die of cold and hunger. When the offspring has been handed over, then it is the turn of the male partner to walk the hundred miles or so to the sea to feed himself – he has endured hunger and extreme cold for four months, all through the depth of the Antarctic winter, protecting and hatching the egg.[21]

A plant, too, strives or 'takes steps' to ensure that its leaves grow in such a way as to be exposed to sunlight; to conserve moisture when the ambient temperature is too hot or too dry, by varying its rate of evapotranspiration; to get water at lower levels of the soil by sending its roots to tap a deeper source of moisture – all in order to maintain its own functioning integrity.[22] It is true that a plant is not mobile and cannot literally uproot and transport itself to another place when its environment becomes inhospitable, unlike an animal which can. When a water hole dries up, or the winter is too harsh with thick snow on the ground preventing forage, an animal can migrate to another water hole or to slightly warmer climes. But even a plant is not entirely helpless, as we have just mentioned.

But is there an analogue to striving in the case of abiotic (or teleomatic) phenonema? Take a mountain. When it is being eroded by natural forces, whether physical, chemical or biological, does it strive to maintain its integrity in the way life forms do? Apparently not, as it 'sends out' no recognisable signals to another part of it to replace what is being eroded. Whereas, in the case of a plant, if its leaves are ripped off by the wind, it would 'send out' signals to replace them (and provided the damage is not too great or too persistent, the plant stands a good chance of recovery). In the case of the mountain or rock, there is no known mechanism of self-repair or self-maintenance, whereas plants are known to be capable of such activities.

But a mountain may be considered an unfair example to cite. Would not a wild river be more relevant in making the point? Maybe not. The wild river, too, lacks any known mechanism for self-repair or self-maintenance when its integrity is being assailed, whether the assailing comes from an anthropogenic source or not. Suppose humans dam the river or divert its water in some way which tames it. It is not capable of self-rejuvenation. If it regains its former status, it is because the humans involved have constructed an inefficient dam, which the weight of its water washes away. It is different with a plant such as a dandelion. A gardener may chop off its stem, but so long as its roots are intact, it could renew the stem. And if the gardener removes its roots as well, that is not necessarily the end of the matter, as even some remnants may be sufficient for regeneration. Some plants are capable not only of renewing their own tissues and cells but also of reproducing themselves through cloning. But if a plant propagates by seeds, these could be disseminated by wind or animal; these will start to germinate and grow when suitable circumstances occur. Some could lie dormant for years till conditions are ripe. A river does not spawn another like itself; at best, it branches when it meets a particular set of circumstances.

The difference between biotic and abiotic entities argued above has bearing on the respective notions of biotic and abiotic artefacts. We have seen earlier that if humans were to become extinct, their abiotic artefacts would become extinct with them. Their houses or tables would just simply be no more than the stone or wood that they were made of – stone or wood has its own trajectory with its own rhythm of change and decay. But the story would be different in the case of biotic artefacts. Many would die in the absence of humans sustaining and maintaining them. Others might be tougher and succeed in fending for themselves. Of the survivors, those incapable of reproduction without the direct intervention of humans would die out. But those that can reproduce themselves, through mating on their own, would leave descendants. Over the generations, these offspring would lose more and more of the characteristics deemed desirable by humans which were bred into them or spliced into their DNA. Although the genesis of these organisms would have been anthropogenic, in time, they would lose more and more of their artefacticity, and thereby their status as biotic artefacts, reverting eventually to more or less naturally occurring beings. This is because, as living organisms, they are beings which also exist 'for themselves', unlike abiotic entities, which only exist 'by themselves'.[23] Even as artefacts they have a residual sense of their own *telos,* which has to be surpressed, in order that they realise human ends. But when their extrinsically imposed *telos* is removed, their own residual *telos* could reassert itself in spite of their anthropogenic genesis.

The ontological shift in status

The framework within which the philosophical transformation of the living organism from the status of a naturally occurring being to that of an artefact is delineated implies a sense of what is natural which acts as a counterfoil to what is artefactual.

That sense may be called 'nature$_{fa}$'; the subscript is short for 'foil to what is artefactual'. What is artefactual has itself been defined in terms of what is brought into material existence deliberately because of human intention and manipulation. This fundamental sense of what is natural may in turn be defined as 'what is not the material embodiment of deliberate human intention' and is, therefore, independent of humans both in terms of its origin and its continuing existence. John Stuart Mill recognises it as a key meaning and has obliquely referred to it in his essay 'Nature', as follows:

> It thus appears that we must recognize at least two principal meanings in the word Nature. In one sense, it means all the powers existing in the outer or the inner world and everything which takes place by means of those powers. In another sense, it means, not everything which happens, but only what takes place without the agency, or without the voluntary and intentional agency, of man. This distinction is far from exhausting the ambiguities of the word; but it is the key to most of those on which important consequences depend. (Mill, 1969, p. 316)

The first principal meaning which Mill talks about may be called the cosmological sense of nature, or 'nature$_c$' for short – its opposite is the Supernatural.[24] Everything which happens within the spatial–temporal material domain is natural. As Mill has pointed out, it is all-encompassing – on this definition, the Great Wall of China is as 'natural' an entity as the Great Barrier Reef. As such, it obliterates the distinction between culture/human on the one hand and nature/non-human on the other. The Great Wall of China is an artefact and ought, therefore, to fall within culture; the Great Barrier Reef is not an artefact and ought, therefore, to fall within nature.

The second sense referred to by Mill hints at 'natural$_{fa}$', namely, 'only what takes place without the agency, or without the voluntary and intentional agency of man'. This implies that 'what takes place with the voluntary and intentional agency of man' is not 'natural' but is artefactual.

This sense of the natural appears to be similar to what C. S. Lewis has identified as one of the oldest, and, therefore:

> one of the hardiest senses of *nature* or *natural*. The nature of anything, its original, innate character, its spontaneous behaviour, can be contrasted with what it is made to be or do by some external agency. A yew-tree is *natural* before the topiarist has carved it; water in a fountain is forced upwards against its *nature*; raw vegetables are *au naturel*. The *natural* here is the Given.
>
> This distinction between the uninterfered with and the interfered with will not probably recommend itself to philosophers. It may be held to enshrine a very primitive, an almost magical or animistic, conception of causality. For of course in the real world everything is continuously 'interfered with' by everything else; total mutual interference (Kant's thorough-going reciprocity) is of the essence of *nature* [...]. What keeps the contrast alive, however, is the daily experience of men as practical, not speculative, beings. The antithesis between unreclaimed land and

the cleared, drained, fenced, ploughed, sown, and weeded field – between the unbroken and the broken horse – between the fish as caught and the fish opened, cleaned, and fried is forced upon us every day. That is why *nature* as 'the given', the thing we start from, the thing we have not yet 'done anything about', is such a persistent sense. *We* here, of course, means man. If ants had a language they would, no doubt, call their anthill an artifact and describe the brick wall in its neighbourhood as a *natural* object. Nature would be for them all that was not 'ant-made'. Just so, for us, *nature* is all that is not man-made; the *natural* state of anything is its state when not modified by man. This is one source of the antithesis (philosophically so scandalous) between *nature* and Man. We as agents, as interferers, inevitably stand over against all the other things; they are all raw material to be exploited or difficulties to be overcome. This is also a fruitful source of favourable and unfavourable overtones. When we deplore the human interferences, then the *nature* which they have altered is of course the unspoiled, the uncorrupted; when we approve them, it is the raw, the unimproved, the savage. (Lewis, 1967, pp. 45–6)

But this sense of what is natural is not only born out of the experience of practical, rather than, speculative beings: it is also the case that, from a philosophical point of view, it crucially embodies a category of being which is ontologically different from that of artefactual beings. We will take up this point a little later.

In his understanding of the artefactual, Mill also points out correctly that 'We (humans) move objects, and by doing this, bring some things into contact which were separate, or separate others which were in contact: and by this simple change of place, natural forces previously dormant are called into action, and produce the desired effect' (Mill, 1969, p. 316). Such moving about of objects, as we have seen, has been accomplished since the 17th century, beginning in Western Europe, by modern science, its method, its goal of controlling nature and eventually its technology. Earlier, it was observed that the deeper the science and its accompanying technology, the greater the degree of artefacticity in the artefacts produced. This 'moving about' is what ultimately changes the ontological status of a living organism from that of a naturally occurring being to that of an arte-factual being.

Whatever has come into existence and continues to exist, which is not the result of deliberate human design and creation, is, ontologically speak-ing, a different kind of being from whatever has come into existence and continues to exist, precisely as a result of deliberate human manipulation in terms of its efficient, formal, final and even material causes. Artefacts are the material embodiments of human intentional structures. A world without humans and human consciousness is a world without (human) artefacts; but a world without humans is world which contains nothing but naturally occurring beings, including living organisms.

The distinction between the natural and the artefactual as here understood can only be made by assuming that humans as a species are not a part of nature but of culture. 'Nature' in this sense, then, means 'non-human nature' or 'nature$_{nh}$', and is opposed to 'culture'. Human activities, even of the most basic physiological kinds, are severely circumscribed by cultural norms, such that there is a right and a wrong sort of things to eat, even though from the nutritional point of view, both may be edible and equally nutritious. However, in spite of this fundamental opposition, it remains true that humans are living organisms and organisms are part of nature. But this other sense of nature is not what is referred to in the context of distinguishing between 'the natural' and 'the artefactual', and so must be distinguished from 'nature$_{nh}$'.[25] As a result of culture impregnating and determining all consciously controlled human functions and activities, clearly, humans as organisms are part of nature only in the 'cosmological' sense, or 'natural$_c$'.

Nature$_{fa}$ constitutes the non-human 'Other'. However, the culture/nature$_{nh/fa}$ dichotomy should not be understood as an ontological dualism but an ontological dyadism. Plumwood has given a clear account of dualism; this book follows it. It involves what she calls 'hyperseparation', which is more than a mere dichotomy or a plain distinction.[26] It systematically and pervasively construes the dualised other as inferior – humans and their culture lord over and denigrate what is non-human (which is only of instrumental worth to the privileged master category). As we shall see, ontological dyadism, far from denigrating the Other, recognises that it has ontological worth.

Modern science and its technology are predicated upon nature as the dualised other. Its goal of controlling nature presupposes the inferior status of the dualised other. The successful execution of the modern scientific/technological programme leads inexorably to the increasing elimination of that dualised other. In this view, then, the dualism between human and non-human may finally liquidate itself, if science and technology can in principle systematically and at a deep level transform the natural into the artefactual. Such transformation also produces ontological impoverishment, which is an inevitable part of modern anthropocentrism.

Dualism – and hence also the scientific/technological programme based on it – is unacceptable because it denigrates 'the Other' and leads to its elimination both at the ontological and empirical levels. But one should not throw out the baby with the bath water. To prevent ontological impoverishment, and to save the natural from being systematically transformed into the artefactual through the activities of homo faber, rightly requires throwing out dualism, but not the very distinction itself between the natural and the artefactual. As Plumwood has emphasised, differences should not be obliterated, distinctions not overlooked and respect for 'the Other' should be based on the recognition of relevant differences, not necessarily of similarities.

Respect for nature in this deep sense requires two distinct ontological categories, the non-human and the human. Far from de-emphasising the differences between the latter and the former, this argument requires that their differences be put centre stage. After all, the present predicament arises primarily and precisely because humans as a species are so different from other species on earth. Humans, given their peculiar kind of consciousness, brain and other capabilities, have evolved in such a way as to possess, today, extremely powerful technologies with which they interact with the non-human environment. Moreover, as has been argued, their science and technology enable them systematically to transform the natural into the artefactual, thereby imperilling the very existence of what is non-human.

Unpacked in greater detail, this ontological dichotomy, though not dualistic, includes the overlapping distinctions shown in Table 1.1.

To appreciate 'the ontological distance' that humankind has travelled since the inception of the modern Scientific Project in the 17th century in Western Europe, one must go back again to Aristotle, with whom we began the chapter. This distance may be gauged by the fact that by the late 20th and the beginning of the 21st century, science and its technology have so advanced that what Aristotle argued was relevant only in the case of abiotic artefacts has now been rendered relevant also in the case of biotic nature. Readers have been reminded that Aristotle maintained that in explaining all phenomena, the four causes must be invoked and distinguished, even in the case of naturally occurring beings such as individual organisms. However, in reality, he admitted it was very difficult to separate out these causes where biotic nature was involved, as the individual organism qua organism, while exhibiting them all, did so in a way which rendered them inextricably entwined with one another. Although explanatory cogency and intelligibility demanded that one identify these four causes, the

Table 1.1   The non-human and the human ontological dichotomy

The non-human	The human
nature	culture
$nature_{nh}$	
$nature_{fa}$	the artefactual
beings by themselves	
abiotic beings	abiotic artefacts
beings for themselves	
biotic beings	biotic artefacts

distinctions between them could only be made intellectually rather than empirically. Aristotle realised that it was only with artefacts that the four causes could be externally identified and assigned each to its source. However, since the late 20th century, humankind through biotechnology has been able to create artefacts in the form of living organisms whose degree of artefacticity goes well beyond that achieved by the earlier technology of selective breeding or by the Mendelian-induced technology of hybridisation. The immanent *telos* of a naturally occurring organism under which the four causes are inextricably entwined is replaced by an external *telos* imposed by humankind, under which its four causes, as an artefact, can be externally identified and assembled. Under biotechnology, the material cause of the artefactual organism can be introduced from another species, whether it belongs to the plant or animal kingdom. Its efficient cause is, thereby, anthropogenic. Its formal cause is the external *telos* imposed on it by its anthropogenic efficient cause, such as the desire for genetically engineered sheep to produce milk containing human rather than sheep hormones. Its final cause is to serve the end of its human creator whatever that may be.

Such an individual organism can no longer be said to exist 'by itself' although it does exist 'for itself'. A being that exists 'by itself' is a being that has not come into existence, and does not continue to exist, in order to serve human ends. A biotic artefact has lost that status. But a biotic artefact continues to exist 'for itself', that is to say, it continues to strive to maintain its own functioning integrity, just as a naturally occurring organism does. Humankind has learned to use its science and its technology, especially in the last thirty odd years, precisely to capture the status of a naturally occurring organism, a being capable of existing 'for itself', to render it into a being which is no longer capable of existing 'by itself'. Just as the four causes in a naturally occurring organism are so inextricably entwined that they can only be distinguished intellectually, in the same way a naturally occurring organism in existing 'for itself' is at one and the same time inextricably also existing 'by itself'. But modern science and its technology have succeeded spectacularly in prising apart these two inextricably entwined modes of existence. This transformation of the biotic as a naturally occurring being into an artefactual being has taken more than two thousand years to reach this most recent deep level of artefacticity. And we have just seen that such a transformation involves a revolution at once at two levels, the philosophical and the technological. It now makes sense, both empirically and conceptually, to separate out the four Aristotelian causes, assigning them to external anthropogenic sources, and to destroy the being which exists 'by itself' without destroying also the being which exists 'for itself'. This achievement enables theoretical biologists such as Francisco Varela and Humberto Maturana to conceptualise naturally occurring organisms as mere machines. Such a revolution is awesome but, above all, deeply ontologically worrying.

Are living organisms machines?

In the pre-modern world, houses or statues are ready paradigms of an arte-fact. But in the modern world, a machine is the ready paradigm. A definition of a machine may be given as follows: any system, usually of rigid bodies, formed and connected to alter, transmit and direct applied forces in a predetermined manner to accomplish a specific objective, such as the performance of useful work.[27]

Three elements that constitute its make-up may be distinguished:

1. The rigid components.
2. The arrangement of these components via parts such as a crank or shaft such that the ensemble can perform useful work.
3. The force or power, which moves the parts, to perform the work in question.

But to the above, a fourth implicit assumption may be added.

4. The three elements listed are abiotic. Where all three are biotic in char-acter, by this account, the entity in question does not count as a machine. For instance, a punka wallah does not count as a machine, although the punka wallah has rigid or semi-rigid parts, linked by other rigid parts to perform useful work – the useful work in question being to drive away flies and mosquitoes, which would otherwise make the life of the sahib and memsahib insufferable, by waving a fan intermittently (usually a large dried leaf). A punka wallah is a human, a biotic being, *not* a machine. (This point will be discussed later.)

Machines are meant to be the substitutes or part substitutes for humans in performing useful work for humans. Animals historically provide the most obvious motive force to move the prearranged parts, as in a cart and horse arrangement. The motive force of a windmill is a force of abiotic nature, namely, the wind. Sometimes, as with a bicycle, humans provide the motive force which, acting on the machine, enables it to perform a greater amount of work than the human power on its own could do. But a car relies on the energy which is released from the combustion of petrol – the human driver merely provides direction rather than motive force. The newest arrival in the family of machines is the automated machine in which humans are no longer needed even to provide direction and regula-tion as it has been constructed to be self-regulating.

Having sketched a skeletal account of machines in the mechanical engineer-ing sense, the discussion will now turn to the question whether, given this perspective, organisms of one kind or other can at all be regarded as machines. Drexler (usually regarded as the father of molecular nanotechnology) says that dandelions and rabbits are machines, because they are capable of performing work, that is, putting atoms and molecules together in a certain way to maintain their own structures and their functioning, as well as to reproduce themselves – see Drexler et al. (1992, p. 98). But are they? For a start, organisms, like dandelions and rabbits outside a cultivated, domesticated context, are not artefacts – they are naturally occurring beings. What they do when they eat (absorb nutrients), defecate (expel waste generated in the processes of metabolism), mate and reproduce, as we have argued, they do entirely *for* themselves, although it is true that we humans may find them and/or the products of their activities of use to us. From this perspective, not even biotic artefacts are machines, although they may have been genetically engineered today to advance a human goal.

There is an ambiguity in the expression 'useful work' which Drexler and others (including Maturana and Varela, who will be discussed later in this section) appear to have overlooked. A machine, in the mechanical engineering sense, is a device with certain characteristics designed 'to perform useful work'. 'Work' in this context is a term in physics, 'a measure of the result of transferring energy from one system to another to cause an object to move' (*Hutchinson Dictionary of Science*, 1993, p. 643).[28] Work is done when a spring is being stretched or compressed, a weight is being raised or lowered, or a gas is being compressed in a cylinder. But 'useful work' also refers to an activity leading to an outcome which we consider to be desirable. For instance, if the plates are dirty, they have to be washed should we want them clean. The washing-up is the work that has to be done. Someone has to do the work, and members of a group may squabble as to whose turn it is to perform that work. In principle one could calculate the amount of work (in the technical sense) that is done whenever a human washes a dirty plate, although in practice there would not be much point to the calculation. The washing-up in many households today (at least in certain segments of society in the advanced industrial economies) is done by a machine. The dishwasher performs 'useful work' both in the technical as well as in the lay sense. The link between the two senses lies in this – any activity, on our part, necessary for achieving a desired result requires the expenditure of energy, which we today tend to regard with disfavour. So we design machines with an external energy source to perform the activity which we otherwise would have to undertake ourselves. The machines deliver us the desired result, dispensing with any input of our own energy. So they necessarily perform useful work understood both in terms of physics and in terms of doing a job of work for us. In a slave society, slave owners had slaves to perform useful work (understood in the lay sense) for them. In modern society, it is said machines have become the substitutes for slaves. Slaves, no matter how wretched their predicament, were (are) not machines – they were (are) humans, suffering degradation and indignity through being treated as if they were (are) machines, with no goals or projects of their own independent of those imposed upon them by their masters. Machines, ex hypothesi, as artefacts, have no goals of their own but merely embody the ends and projects of their human designers.

Up to now, a machine understood in the conventional sense, that is, what conforms to the mechanical engineering sense of the term per se, is not ontologically threatening, although it could turn out to be environmentally worrying. A car as a machine-artefact does not, as such, encroach upon the ontological status of other beings as natural beings. It is true it threatens their existence, not directly but indirectly, but not their very ontological status. Cars require roads to run on. They use up space, which might otherwise be left for other human purposes and/or to non-human natural beings. The fossil fuel they use produces toxic substances of one kind or other which could harm both human and non-human living beings. Cars today, in general, embody a type of technology that poses pollution problems to the environment, and is nature-damaging. But machines as such, up to now, do not render non-human natural beings necessarily redundant.

Such machines, however, are only one type of artefact. Ever since its invention to the present, the mechanical clock has been a very powerful and potent referent of the notion of machine as well as that of artefact. Biotechnology, in the last quarter of the last century, has established that an equally potent alternative referent of the latter notion could be the transgenic organism. In other words, from now on, the language of the artefactual does not need to coincide with the language of the machine, as the biotic itself could be transformed into near-total, if not total, artefacts. However, the very predominance of the language of the machine itself, as well as its identification with the language of the artefactual have, as we have seen, distorted Drexler's account (Drexler, 1992) of organisms like rabbits, as machines, or like bacteria, as nanomachines. As a result, Drexler maintains that nature has already successfully designed its own machines – these are simply individual organisms. But naturally occurring organisms are just not artefacts. Ex hypothesi, they are not and cannot be machines, whether nano- or not. They are *the ontological foil* to machines. Drexler's troubled account of what constitutes nanomachines is the result of muddled, erroneous reasoning:

1. He mistakes nature's organisms for artefacts. He fails to grasp and, thereby, implicitly destroys the ontological distinction between the natural $(_{fa})$ and the artefactual.
2. By doing so he also seems to have overlooked that the transformation of the natural into the artefactual is effected via tools/technology (which since the mid-19th century has been backed by fundamental scientific advances). This is ironic, given his own vision of the nanotechnological future.

3. He fails, too, to appreciate that the biotic can be transformed into arte-facts, without becoming machines, as machines are only one type of artefact, among others.

Drexler, of course, is not alone in confusing organisms with machines and in being obsessed with the language of machines. He is simply following a well-established tradition – Karl Ereky, considered to be the father of the term 'biotechnology' (which he used in a series of statements he wrote in the years 1917 to 1919), distinctly regarded the pig as a machine. For him, the difference between the industrial and the peasant approaches to pig rearing was not that the former used electrical pumps and automated feeding and the latter did not. Rather it was because, under the former, the pig was regarded solely as a converter of so much feed input into so much meat output. In a similar vein, even earlier, Max Delbrück began a lecture in 1884 with the statement 'Yeast is a machine' – see Bud (1993, pp. 28–34).

The language of machines, as used by Delbrück, Ereky and Drexler, betrays a deep-seated strong anthropocentrism in their attitude to biotic nature. Naturally occurring organisms are regarded as merely possessing potential instrumental value for us humans. To say that yeast is a machine amounts to casting an exploitative eye on the micro-organism as a being whose value lies in doing a job of work for us. Biotechnology, either in the older or newer senses of the term, is precisely that kind of technology, which harnesses the metabolic and/or reproductive capabilities of organisms to carry out tasks we have set for them. A pig eats food, and, through its metabolism, converts nutrients into a form which can be absorbed by its physiology to sustain, maintain and reproduce itself – the pig, as an indi-vidual organism qua organism, eats primarily for itself, not for us. But humans are like a virus. The virus injects its DNA into the bacteria to get the latter to reproduce on its behalf. It hijacks the bacteria's reproductive capability for its own end. Under biotechnology (the new use of the term, referring to those techniques induced by molecular genetics and molecular biology) we, too, inject alien DNA into bacteria and other organisms, thereby also hijacking their reproductive and/or metabolic capabilities to perform tasks for us.[29] To call such organisms, thus rendered artefactual, 'machines' because they carry out our ends amounts to yet another affirmation of at least two of the theses which make up strong anthro-pocentrism, namely, that humans are the sole loci of intrinsic value, and that non-human nature has mere instrumental value for us humans.

However, defining organisms (whether naturally occurring or modified through biotechnology to perform useful work on our behalf) as machines goes beyond merely treating them as possessing only (potential or actual) instrumental values for us. The procedure at the same time involves a misconstrual of the ontological status of organisms as naturally occurring beings, and reflects a determination to change their status to that of artefactual beings. The two aspects – their sole instrumental status in terms of use-values for humans and their ontological status as artefactual beings – are clearly, inextricably linked. In other words, the anthropocentrism, so deeply embedded in the philosophy which underpins modernity, must be grasped, via not only its axiology, but also its ontology.

One could say that the modern human ultimately does not feel at ease among natural beings or entities, be these biotic or non-biotic. We only feel at home when home is the world of humanised nature – in other words, only when the natural has become transformed into the artefactual. Artefacts embody our labour, our intentions and purposes. By creating them, we have imparted and infused our own value into them. As a result, they could even be said to be an extension of ourselves and part of our own identity. We are most at home when we and the artefactual world have become one. If so, this amounts to nothing less than the elimination of nature as 'the Other'. Ontological impoverishment is the price that has to be paid to enable humankind to be thoroughly at home.

So deep-seated is this modern world-view that it has infected theoretical biologists who fall prey to using the language of machines even in their explanatory account of how organisms are organised as living entities. Just one example will be examined to illustrate this tendency, namely, the work of Humberto Maturana and Francisco Varela (1980) in theoretical biology.[30]

In Maturana's and Varela's writings, a key concept is 'autopoiesis', which in turn enables them (paradoxically, as we shall see) to talk about living organisms as 'autopoietic machines'. The word itself comes from the Greek *autos*, 'self', and *poiein*, 'to produce' or 'to bring forth'. It is used to characterise that property peculiar to a living entity, existing as an organisational unity and maintaining its identity through self-renewal, self-regeneration and self-generation. However, although the term 'autopoiesis' may be new, the concept itself is shared by a lot of theorists outside biology. The concept may be traced, for instance, to systems analysis – see Erich Jantsch (1980). It is also related to the notion of dissipative structures as introduced by the physicist Prigogine and others – see Ilya Prigogine and Isabelle Stenger (1984). Fritjof Capra relies on it in his influential book *Turning Point*:

> an organism is primarily engaged in renewing itself; cells are breaking down and building up structures, tissues and organs are replacing their cells in continual cycles. ... All these processes are regulated in such a way that the overall pattern of the organism is preserved, and this remarkable ability of self-maintenance persists under a variety of circumstances, including changing environmental conditions and many kinds of interference. (1982, pp. 271–2)

But is the autopoietic approach to biotic nature truly reconcilable with the language of machiness built into it by Maturana and Varela? May not the latter fundamentally distort the former?

Maturana and Varela assert, in no uncertain terms, that all living systems are machines. By this they mean to make clear the following:

> First, we imply a non-animistic view which it should be unnecessary to discuss any further. Second, we are emphasizing that a living system is defined by its organization and, hence, that it can be explained as any organization is explained, that is, in terms of relations, not of component properties. Finally, we are pointing out from the start the dynamism in living systems and which the word 'machine' connotes. (1980, p. 76)

Their exclusion of vitalism is clearly uncontroversial. But one cannot be so sure with regard to their second and third theses.

They start off by giving a standard account of machines: 'Machines are usually viewed as concrete hardware systems, defined by the nature of their components and by the purpose that they fulfill in their operations as man-made artefacts' (ibid., p. 77). They then go on to reject it as a naive account, as it concentrates on the nature of their components rather than on the relations between the components which integrate the machine as a unity, as an organisation. The shift from structure (which is concerned with the properties of the components) to organisation enables them to give an abstract generalised account of machines, which is applicable to all machines, irrespective of the type of machines they are and of the components which enter into their concrete realisation as machines. As a result, machines, under their dispensation, need no longer be 'concrete hardware systems, defined by the nature of their components'. In other words, machines are no longer necessarily objects constructed out of abiotic or exbiotic nature. This leaves room presumably for extending the notion of machines to living organisms, to regarding dandelions and yeast as machines.

Next, they go on to remove the second element which constitutes the conventional, but in their opinion, naive account of machines, namely, 'the purpose that they fulfill in their operations as man-made artefacts'. According to Maturana and Varela, their purpose in this crucial sense is not part of the organisational unity of the machine and is relegated to what they call 'the domain in which the machine operates', 'the domain of observation'. Furthermore, they also contend that the notion of purpose, aim or function of a machine is simply an invitation to invent the machine one is talking about, but is irrelevant to a characterisation of the machine's organisation. In other words, they seem to imply that to understand a car as a machine with a certain organisational unity there is no need to talk about the function, end or purpose it supposedly serves in inventing and manufacturing it.

This surely should strike one as rather odd, even a 'naive' reaction from their perspective. A car's organisational unity is controlled by the purpose it is designed to serve, namely, to get us from point A to B by moving both itself and us, the driver and passengers, through a certain portion of space. The machine's organisational unity, one would have thought, would be different – the components would be differently related to one another – if the purpose it is designed to serve were different. Moreover, if the purpose were indeed different, even the components themselves and their properties might have been different. Suppose the machine were not designed as a conveyor of people and their possessions from one place to another but for some other purpose, such as to drill a hole underground. Would the machine have the same components with the same properties and be connected up with one another in the same way as the components which enter into the make-up of a car? Far from the standard account being naive, it is Maturana's and Varela's account which appears to be so. An artefact's purpose or function is not detachable from its organisational unity. On the contrary, its function or purpose informs the very way in which its components are put together as such a unity. Its construction as well as its existence as an organisational unity cannot properly be grasped without reference to its purpose or function, which enters intrinsically into any adequate account of it, both at the conceptual and explanatory levels.

The point may be pursued further via a thought experiment. Imagine an archaeologist in the distant future, after our industrial civilisation has crumbled away, excavating an object, such as a car, buried in one of today's landfills. An approximate account of its organisational unity could probably be arrived at by careful experimentation using models which are reconstructions of it. But the experimentation itself must be guided by a series of hypotheses about the object, one of which surely is that it is a machine-artefact designed to serve a particular end in mind, namely, to convey people from one point to another over land, but not across water, or through the air. Moreover, there are cars and cars. Some are designed and constructed as racing, others as family, cars. In the case of the former, as maximum speed is of the essence, this purpose is built into the organisational unity of such a machine. In the case of the latter, as speed is not the dominant desideratum, others more important, such as capacity for passenger-load, comfort, safety, economic costs and so on, together with a compromise between these relevant desiderata are similarly built into their organisational unity. In other words, the purpose a machine serves is not a factor that can be detached from, or considered as extraneous to, any adequate or complete attempt to explain and account for its organisational unity. That aspect of a machine cannot be relegated simply to the domain of observation, as Maturana and Varela maintain.

Furthermore, when a machine, such as a car, breaks down, it is facile to say that its failure to discharge its purpose also belongs merely to the domain of observation. The disintegration of its organisational unity – a broken crankshaft – manifests itself as failure to discharge its function, that is to move at all. The broken crankshaft is the cause of the car's inability to move, and therefore of its failure to carry out its function. The cause and the effect together constitute the disintegration of the car's organisational unity. To restore the latter, the mechanic must be guided by the purpose the machine is designed to carry out, which leads her/him to identify the broken crankshaft as the cause of its immobility.

Maturana and Varela define allopoietic machines, such as cars as 'machines that have as product of their functioning something different from themselves' (1980, p. 135). That 'something different from themselves' is precisely, in the case of a car, its ability to move across space over land, carrying people in it, the very purpose it has been designed to serve. Its success or failure as an entity with a certain organisational unity can only be judged in terms of the purpose conceived by the humans who construct the artefact in accordance with it. Moreover, in engineering terms, no machine can be designed simply from the point of view of its organisational unity – whatever that might mean – but is, and must be, designed with a whole host of other considerations in mind. For a start, as Chapter 2 will show, technology, unlike pure science, works under a different epistemological target. Pragmatism and efficiency, rather than truth or approximation to the truth, guide its choice of solutions to a problem. It is also opportunistic in using knowledge and theories from any domain. Compromise with scientific purity apart, technology also works under other crucial constraints already mentioned, such as the cost of the end product, its aesthetic aspects, its 'user-friendliness', its safety and so on. All these are woven into the make-up of the technological product, which cannot be detached from its so-called organisational unity. Or to put the same point differently, the organisational unity exemplified in a machine is not pure in the way Maturana and Varela seem to think it is.

The two theoretical biologists have seemingly failed to appreciate that their revised definition of the term 'machine' has destroyed what is most distinctive about it. A machine in the standard view is an artefact, designed, constructed by humans to serve a distinctive human end. By their account, a machine is no longer an artefact, designed for a specific purpose. Instead, it is any system with an organisational unity to it but physically expressed. (A system with an organisational unity but conceptually expressed would, presumably, not be a machine in their view.) As such it is by no means clear from their account that their term 'machine' cannot meaningfully be used to refer to a static organisational unity such as a crystal – see Maturana and Varela (1980, pp. 79–80). However, from their remarks, this much is clear – that they are interested in dynamic machines, not static ones, and in particular, autopoietic dynamic machines, not allopoietic dynamic ones, such as cars. We have seen how they define the latter. They define the former as follows:

> a machine organized (defined as a unity) as a network of processes of production, transformation and destruction of components that produces the components which: (i) through their interactions and transformations regenerate and realize the network of processes (relations) that produced them; and (ii) constitute it as a concrete unity in the space in which they exist by specifying the topological domain of its realization as such a network. (ibid., p. 135)

It is also clear from their remarks that the individual organism is a living system, that all living systems are physical autopoietic machines, and that all physical autopoietic machines are living. In other words, 'autopoiesis is a necessary and sufficient condition for a system to be a living one' (ibid., p. 84).

We have so far argued that in the case of machines, standardly understood, such as cars (but in Maturana's and Varela's termininology, they are allopoietic machines), no complete or adequate account of them in explanatory/organisational terms can be given without reference to the purpose or use to which they have been designed. Such a purpose cannot simply be relegated to the domain of observation or description. At first sight, it might appear that even if the two theorists are wrong in their account of allopoietic machines, they must surely be right with regard to what they call autopoietic machines, that is to say, living organisms, when they maintain that the notion of purpose plays no part whatsoever. However, on closer examination, it might not be so easy to dispense with the notion of end, if not of purpose, altogether.

But to prevent confusion, several meanings of end or purpose need to be borne in mind. An earlier section has anticipated this problem by clarifying the notion of teleology itself in terms of three different theses, namely, external, intrinsic/immanent and extrinsic/imposed teleology. In the context here, the crucial point to emphasise is that Maturana and Varela implicitly have jettisoned the thesis of intrinsic/immanent teleology. To recall, the thesis states that the four causes in the case of living beings are fused, and may only be separated for the purpose of intellectual analysis. Every living being possesses its own *telos* which informs its identity, and governs its attempts at self-renewal, self-maintenance, its processes of growth, maturity, reproduction and finally decay. In other words, they are paradigmatic autopoietic beings, to use Maturana's and Varela's terminology. But having identified them correctly as such, they, nevertheless, feel impelled to undermine that very status, as they see their theoretical task to be that of preparing the way for turning living organisms, which are naturally occurring beings, into artefactual living beings via technological means. In other words, ultimately, they have substituted extrinsic/imposed teleology for intrinsic/immanent teleology.

The *telos* of an artefact is endowed by humans and, as we have argued, it is this, contra Maturan and Varela, which informs its organisational unity, and renders it intelligible. In the case of biotic artefacts, the organism's own intrinsic/immanent *telos* has been displaced by just such an extrinsic *telos*. Biotechnology, operating at a more fundamental level of manipulation than Mendelian whole-organism biogenetic technology, enables us to fabricate living organisms. Parts of their genetic components – their material cause – come from another organism, that is to say, an external source. As a result their form may also alter – wingless chickens could be genetically engineered. Their ability to grow and maintain themselves has also been commandeered by humans to carry out our ends. To all intents and purposes, humans are their efficient cause.

To understand and explain a living organism in terms of theoretical biology alone, external teleology is irrelevant. So is the thesis of imposed extrinsic teleology, as it is a presupposition underpinning all techniques of selective breeding as well as biotechnology in the creation of biotic artefacts. However, biologists (other than genetic engineers), qua biologists cannot dispense with the thesis of intrinsic/immanent teleology. They do not have to subscribe to Aristotle's four causes, but they do have to presuppose that the organism they are studying is organised and functions in certain ways in implementing its own *telos*. In other words, ironically, the definition given by Maturana and Varela of an autopoietic machine cited above serves to characterise, in part, even if not wholly, the *telos* of any one organism. The term *telos* may be replaced by 'purpose', provided the latter is not confused with its cognate 'purposeful' and its implications of being conscious and intentional. 'Purpose' in the sense of being end-directed may be said to inform the activities, the behaviour and the processes underpinning these, of an organism, without attributing to it consciousness and intention whatsoever, as we have seen.

In this sense of *telos*, an organism's *telos* is self-given and self-manifest. As such the term 'autopoiesis', coined by Maturana and Varela, is most apt. What is unfortunate is their use of it in conjunction with the term 'machine'. In this analysis, their resulting term 'autopoietic machine' amounts to a self-contradiction, while their other term 'allopoietic machine' amounts to a tautology – a machine, as we have seen, is an entity or a system without an intrinsic/immanent *telos*, as it is an artefact embodying a human purpose designed into it. Such a human purpose is necessarily deliberate and intentional, involving full consciousness.

In other words, to labour an important point, there is need yet again to remind oneself of the two very different contexts in which the term *telos* may be used:

1. The self-given and self-manifest *telos* in the case of naturally occurring living organisms is totally independent and autonomous of human activity and intervention. Such a *telos* is to be understood as 'end-directedness' without reference to the conscious and the intentional on the part of the organisms themselves, as they are incapable of conscious intentional activity in the way we humans are.
2. The *telos* of an artefact, such as a machine, is a deliberate, intentional structure designed, created and imposed by humans. The end it serves is a conscious human one as it itself, by its very nature, has no self-given ends.

It is ironic that some environmental philosophers who are Deep Ecologists, such as Fox and Eckersley, should welcome Maturana and Varela as unproblematic allies; on the contrary, they should be extremely wary of their standpoint, as it embodies serious confusions about the respective ontological status of natural and artefactual beings. The language of 'autopoietic machines' sits far better with the programme of biotechnology, underpinned by the reductive sciences of molecular biology and molecular genetics, than with the preoccupations of Deep Ecology. The reasons for saying so are as follows:

1. By removing *telos*, understood as intrinsic/immanent teleology, and purpose, as end-directedness, from talk about organisms, it makes it possible for Maturana and Varela to confine their account of the organisational unity of organisms to the processes, that is to say, the mechanisms involved in their ability to transform matter into themselves, in such a way that the product of their operation is their own organisation.
2. Focusing on mechanisms makes it easy for the two theorists to slide into talk about machines (as standardly understood), for machines, too, operate through mechanisms to maintain their own organisational unity. In this way talk about organisms is subtly assimilated to talk about machines via the common notions of mechanisms and organisational unity.
3. In the hands of Maturana and Varela, the characterisation of machines standardly understood is *pari passu* being restructured – *telos* in the sense of imposed, extrinsic teleology as human intention is removed, as we have seen, from an account of their organisation.
4. The two theses just mentioned above (in points 2. and 3.) then prepare the way for transforming the assimilation at the level of language into an assimilation of ontological kinds – organisms *are* machines. Let us

call this use of the term '(MV)machine', where 'MV' stands for 'Maturana and Varela'.

5. Any entity with an organisational unity may be said to be a system; (MV)machines are systems which may now be divided into living and non-living ones.

6. As the standard use of the term 'machine' connotes dynamism, and as organisms exhibit dynamism, it is fitting that (MV)machines are said to be dynamic systems – see Maturana and Varela (1980, p. 76).

7. The difference, then, between living dynamic systems and non-living dynamic ones is to be marked by calling the former 'autopoietic machines' and the latter 'allopoietic machines'. While the mechanisms involved in the former operate to produce the components that constitute their own organisation, the mechanisms involved in the latter operate to produce something other than the components that constitute their own organisation.

8. When the characterisation of organisms has finally been transformed into that of autopoietic machines or living dynamic systems, when *telos* in the sense of intrinsic/immanent teleology has been expelled, this reductive transformation clears the way for further transforming organisms into (near-total) artefacts by biotechnological means, without touching their essential status as 'living dynamic systems'.

9. Far from worrying about such a prospect, Maturana and Varela positively welcome it. A long quotation from them on this point may be justified:

> Machines are generally viewed as human made artifacts with completely known deterministic properties, which make them, at least conceptually, perfectly predictable.[31] Contrariwise, living systems are *a priori* frequently viewed as autonomous, ultimately unpredictable systems, with purposeful behavior similar to ours. If living systems were machines, they could be made by man and, according to the view mentioned above, it seems unbelievable that man could manufacture a living system.[32] This view can be easily disqualified, because it either implies the belief that living systems cannot be understood because they are too complex for our meagre intellect and will remain so, or that the principles which generate them are intrinsically unknowable; either implication would have to be accepted *a priori* without proper demonstration. There seems to be an intimate fear that the awe with respect to life and the living would disappear if a living system could be not only be reproduced, but designed by man. This is nonsense. The beauty of life is not a gift of its inaccessibility to our understanding. (1980, pp. 82–3)

10. Indeed, it is the very understanding of such 'living systems', given to us by molecular biology and molecular genetics, which enables biotechnology to design and create artefactual living systems. Transgenic

organisms are precisely that. Their fabrication substitutes an extrinsic/imposed *telos* for their own intrinsic/immanent *telos*.[33] This then amounts to an assault on their ontological integrity as naturally occurring beings. Homo faber, through biotechnology, has hijacked the mechanisms of such 'living dynamic systems' to sustain and reproduce themselves for the purpose of performing chores for us, of fulfilling our intentions while eliminating their own ends. Maturana and Varela have indeed distorted and altered their ontological status as natural beings, by characterising them as (MV)machines, so that biotic natural beings can then more readily be turned into biotic artefacts.

To conclude: Maturana and Varela have embedded the notion of autopoiesis in a discourse whose very language subverts the ontological integrity of organisms as naturally occurring beings. Moreover, although they themselves are not aware of it, underpinning their account is the world-view of homo faber and of fabrication.[34] The very explanatory framework they advocate as theoretical biologists for the understanding of living organisms is infused by an uncompromising instrumental attitude to biotic nature which, thereby, renders the framework itself suspect.

However, their ontological misconstrual of living organisms is in keeping with the biotechnological attempt to convert organisms which are naturally occurring beings into artefactual beings.

Notes

1   Or to put it more technically, as Hilpinen has done:

> By an 'artifact' I mean here an object which has been intentionally made or produced for a certain purpose. According to this characterisation, an artifact necessarily has a maker or an author, or several authors, who are responsible for its existence. ... Artifacts are products of *intentional making*. Human activities produce innumerable new objects which are entirely unintentional (or unintended); such objects and materials are not artifacts in the strict sense of the word. When a person intends to make an object, the content of the intention is not the object itself, but rather some description of an object; the agent intends to make an object of a certain kind or type. Thus what I want to suggest is that artifacts in the strict sense can be distinguished from other products of human activity in the same way as acts are distinguished from other movements of the body; a movement is an action only if it is intentional under some description ... and I take an object to be an artifact in the strict sense of the word only if it is intentionally produced by an agent under some description of the object. The intention 'ties' to the object a number of concepts or predicates which define its intended properties. These properties constitute the *intended character* of the object. I shall denote the intended character of an object *o* by '*IC(o)*'.
>
> Thus an object *o* is a proper artifact only if it satisfies the following *Dependence Condition*:

... The existence and some of the properties of *o* depend on an agent's (or author's) intention to make an object of kind *IC(o)*. (Hilpinen, 1995, pp. 138–9)

Note, however, that Hilpinen's definition of 'artefact' is much wider than that used by this book, which stipulates that the human intentionality be embodied in a material medium. By this account, unlike Hilpinen's, belief systems are not artefacts.

Artefacts are the ontological foil of naturally occurring entities. While the former are products designed by humans, the latter are not. See also Andrew Brennan's way of marking the difference between them (1984). Brennan says that the latter lack what he calls 'intrinsic functions' because they have not been designed. This book, however, characterises the difference between the artefactual and the natural in terms of the theses of intrinsic/immanent and extrinsic/imposed teleology – see sections which follow.

2   In Chapter 6, when we look at the distinction between reproduction and production in the context of human birth, we shall see that techniques of reproduction do not necessarily lead to the production of biotic artefacts.

3   It follows that the technological as the artefactual is part of what is created by humans. Among other things, humans have created (i) paintings, (ii) computers and (iii) songs. The first two are clearly artefacts, but what about the third? Someone just singing may use certain techniques but does not rely on any technological object. The song and the singing are the expressions of human intentions but these are expressed through an endosomatic organ, that is, the human voice, and not through an ensemble of technological objects. But if the singer were doing karaoke, the performance clearly is inextricably entwined with that particular ensemble of technological objects that may collectively be referred to as the karaoke machine; such singing falls then into the technological and, therefore, artefactual domain.

The distinction between creating via techniques and creating via technologies which issue in material objects is sometimes marked by the distinction between 'making' things and 'doing' things. To sing with one's own voice, using certain techniques, falls into the latter. To use clay, and then bake the moulded clay in the sun to make a bowl, falls into the former; however, its level of artefacticity is much lower than in a case where the potter uses a potter's wheel and then a kiln to make the piece of pottery.

4   But even in the ancient world of craft-based technology, artisans had very early on invented and fabricated alloys such as bronze, made from copper and tin, which themselves are naturally occurring metals.

5   The geep or shoat is a transgenic organism, the cross between a sheep and a goat. Sheep and goat do not normally interbreed. Another is the liger or tiglon. Lions and tigers in the wild do not mate, but they could be made to produce offspring with human intervention. The offspring whose father is a lion is called 'liger', and that whose father is a tiger is called 'tiglon'.

6   For the purpose of this book, the term 'abiotic', for ease of exposition, will be used also to cover the exbiotic, that is, dead organic matter; nothing of philosophical significance arises from such a terminological extension.

7   Aristotle was not only a philosopher but also a biologist, among other things. For an assessment of Aristotle's empirical research in his biology, see Lloyd (1987). For detailed discussions of his philosophy of biology, see Preus (1975) and Gotthelf and Lennox (1987). For a shorter, more recent, assessment of his science and his philosophy of science, including his biological thought, see

Hankinson (1995a,b). See Barnes for a recent account of his life and work (1995a), and of his metaphysics (1995b). For an account of Aristotle's concept of nature, see Weisheipl (1982) and Collingwood (1945, pp. 80–92).

8   See also Gotthelf (1987).

9   The biologist Ernst Mayr introduced the term 'teleonomic' to characterise the end-directedness of biotic activity, and the term 'teleomatic' to characterise the lack of end-directedness in abiotic phenomena, while reserving the term 'teleological' to characterise human activity – see Mayr (1988).

10 As plants (and animals) are end-directed in their activities, they can be said to possess interests. To grasp this point, one needs to distinguish two logically distinct senses of the notion 'interest' which are reflected in the following two propositions:

(a)   Peter takes an interest in keeping fit and eating healthily.
(b)   It is in Paul's interest to keep fit and to eat healthily.

Proposition (a) implies that Peter cares about his health, and he really wants to live healthily. Proposition (b) is true even if Paul is indifferent to the matter, if he remains in ignorance about it, and/or if he lives a lifestyle which is diametrically opposed to it. While (a) is mediated via conscious desires and beliefs, (b) is not. In the case of (a), if conscious desires and beliefs are not understood as being linguistically expressed, then animals could be said to possess them, but plants still would not qualify as they lack consciousness altogether. However, when 'interest' is understood as in sense (b), 'plants' could substitute for 'Paul' and the proposition would still be meaningful if suitably amended to read: 'It is in the plants' interests to receive light and warmth'. Plants, then, may be said to possess interests. Furthermore, it makes sense to say that plants could be made better or worse off when they lack something that is instrumentally valuable to them. For instance, a plant is worse off in the absence of water, sunlight or a particular nutrient, and is clearly better off when such items are available to it. An entity that could be said to be better or worse off under certain determinate conditions could be said to possess interests.

Another way, perhaps, of making the same point is to say that plants have needs which, if not satisfied, could result in their suffering harm. The notions of needs and interests overlap such that entities with needs are also entities with interests, and vice versa.

For a detailed account of how every living organism has an interest in fulfilling the biological function of each of its component organs and subsystems, see Varner (1998). Varner anchors his account of how living organisms can be said to have interests/needs in terms of their aetiology via natural selection under evolution. Varner is right in arguing that while all living organisms have interests, not all of them have desires, and that it is the possession of interests, not desires, which ground their moral considerability. To tie interests to desires conceptually is unnecessarily too strong a claim for grounding moral considerability.

11 Animals too are conscious. But for the purpose of this discussion, the issue whether animal consciousness differs from human consciousness qualitatively is irrelevant.

12 Furthermore, as far as Aristotle himself was concerned, the ancient Greek culture in which his type of anthropocentrism was embedded placed severe constraints on the instrumental use of nature to advance human ends. As we shall see in

Chapter 6, the ancient Greeks despised the life of fabrication (or manufacture) but celebrated the life of contemplation, which cultivated reason, the divine aspect of human nature. One lived not in order to fabricate things out of nature (whether non-living or living) and to use them, but to advance *bios theoretikos*, although in living at all, one cannot refrain altogether from appropriating nature in an instrumental way.

13 Transgenic organisms are genetically modified organisms in which the genetic engineer has inserted a gene from the DNA of an organism belonging to a totally different species, even kingdom, into the organism's genome. For instance, a human gene may be introduced into the DNA of a mouse, an animal gene into the DNA of a plant. This differs radically from a hybrid organism, as we shall see. The hybrid organism bears genes from two individual organisms belonging to different varieties or species which can interbreed and successfully reproduce, even if, as a matter of fact, they may not do so in nature in the absence of some form of human intervention. DNA genetic engineering, unlike hybridisation technology, can cross species barriers, not merely between one plant species and another, or one animal species and another, but also between a plant and an animal species. (This account presupposes the so-called biological-species concept, which, though not without problems, is accepted by most biologists – for further discussion, see Keekok Lee, 1998).

The subject of transgenic organisms will be raised in detail in Chapter 5.

14 This technology of the near future promises to construct material at the nano level, which is the level of atoms, be these carbon or nitrogen. Such materials will replace natural kinds, such as wood, which we use today for fabrication. (Note that atoms of carbon or nitrogen are themselves natural, though not natural kinds such as wood made out of, in the main, carbon, what Aristotle called second matter. Atoms are analogous to what Aristotle called first matter – see Keekok Lee, 1999. For artefactual, non-naturally occurring atoms, see below in this note.) Unlike bulk manufacture, which is polluting, molecular nanotechnology is said to be virtually non-polluting (in relative terms) and could be regarded as a 'green technological fix'. For a popular account, see Drexler (1992).

15 But actually modern science today has gone beyond the level of nanotechnology to the even deeper one of creating artefactual elements. The project concerns attempts to create elements in the periodic table beyond those naturally occurring on earth which have all been found, from the lightest, hydrogen, to the heaviest, uranium. In the periodic table, elements are classified according to their atomic number, that is, the number of protons as well as neutrons, which stabilise the nucleus. For instance, hydrogen has one proton, while uranium has 92 protons. Plutonium, with 94 protons, as we know, was first manufactured in 1941. But physicists, up to 1970, had thought that the 'superheavy' elements, between 96 and 105 onward, would not be stable, and would probably last only a fraction of a second. Element 108 would, by their calculations, last only a billionth of a second. But the situation has changed since. Theorists have now calculated that elements around the atomic number 114 could be much more stable (indeed lasting for billion of years), and in the 1980s made elements 107, 108 and 109 one atom at a time. At the end of 1994 German physicists at the GSI heavy ion research laboratory in Darmstadt succeeded in manufacturing elements 110 and 111. The leader of the team said that they were now hoping to make element 112. The present calculations of physicists show that it is possible to carry on until they reach element 116, which they regard as the true end of the periodic table – around element 118 the decay rates become really too

fast to be stable at all. Yet until 1970, it was thought that the periodic table would peter off at about element 108.

The artefactual elements are constructed by combining nuclei of lighter elements, with physicists carefully calculating the right number of protons and neutrons to use to build the new atom. A beam of atoms of one of the elements used is aimed at a thin foil made of the other in a vacuum. In this process, when a nucleus belonging to the beam collides with a nucleus in the target material, they fuse and a new compound nucleus is formed. Element 110 was created by firing a beam of nickel atoms at a lead foil. The physicists at Darmstadt were hoping to make element 112 using a zinc beam – see Hall (1995); see also Armbruster and Hessberger (1998). The above shows that, strictly speaking, in the history of science and technology, the ability to create non-naturally occurring atoms has taken place earlier in time than a technology, such as molecular nanotechnology, which claims to be able (so far, by and large, in principle only) to construct instances of second matter, that is to say, artefatual kinds to replace natural kinds by arranging atoms in certain ways. In that sense the creation and manufacture of plutonium in 1941 and, since then, other 'superheavy' elements have already gone beyond the programmatic pronouncement of modern science from its inception in the 17th century, to manipulate and control matter atom by atom. Such a radical project involves the creation of second matter, or what this author has called 'nature$_{nk}$' – see Keekok Lee (1999), pp. 83–4.

However, nuclear physics is even deeper and more radical than that, as it sees fit to create and manufacture elements in the periodic table which are not found naturally occurring, at least on earth. There are also other labourers in the vineyard, so to speak, whose work has now shown that, by comparison, molecular nanotechnology of the near future could even be said to be 'conservative'. Raymond Ashoori (1993), a physicist, and his co-researchers (1992, 1994) could be said to have created an 'artificial atom', which has established in principle that the electron count of such atoms, from 0 to 60, is perfectly manipulable by their human makers. According to one account:

> The 'atom' in question was actually an empty space within a gallium arsenide crystal to which electrons could be moved one at a time by the application of a light magnetic pulse. In the case of an ordinary, garden-variety atom, electrons were held in space by the nucleus, whose positive charge attracts and binds the negatively charged electrons. In the 'artificial atom,' by contrast, electrons were held, instead, by an externally imposed magnetic field. But in the final effect was much the same: a bunch of electrons whizzing around in a small space. (Regis, 1995, pp. 276–7)

In this way, atoms may be customised to be of any size and shape – long thin ones or big round ones. The next stage would be to try to stick these created atoms together to form artefactual molecules, and these, in turn, to form artefactual solids, liquids or gases.

16 To prevent misunderstanding, some remarks about the notion of 'precision' or 'precise' in this context (and throughout this book) are called for. Its sense is tied up with the philosophy and methodology of reductionism, which imbue the science of genetics, in particular, DNA genetics. The scientist is manipulating nature at the level of the DNA molecule in the cells of the organism, not at the

level of the whole organism (except in the case of bacteria). As Chapter 5 will show, isolating DNA in the laboratory is an immensely complex process, which requires subjecting the initial bit of the organism (such as the thymus or liver of a mammal), or whole organisms (in the case of bacteria), or tissue cultures (such as human white blood cells), to a series of very specific actions involving physical, chemical and electrical forces.

However, (molecular) biotechnology, as it stands at the beginning of the 21st century cannot be said to be precise in another sense, namely, that it fails to guarantee a relatively high success rate in all of its operations. On the contrary, its success rate can be abysmally low – in the case of animals, this is considered as acceptable, but not so if some such, or similar, operations were to be performed on humans. Take the following examples. In the famous case of Dolly the sheep, the experiment involved a total of 277 embryos. The first gene-transfer experiment with cattle, performed in 1991 (by P. Krimpenfort et al.), used techniques pioneered a little earlier to produce sex reversal in mice. This experiment succeeded in producing a mouse with XX chromosomes and with testicles (albeit sterile), but which is perfectly male in its mating behaviour – see Chapter 5 (note 13) for the details of this experiment. The researchers wanted to create cows with human-derived DNA, ultimately to produce an iron-binding protein called lactoferin. If successful, such transgenic cows would eventually be 'pharmed' (a word formed from 'pharmacy' or 'pharmaceutical' and 'farm') for the protein(s) which could, then, be isolated and recovered from their milk. This experiment involved the following numbers at various stages of the procedure (adapted from Holdrege, 1996, p. 112):

eggs (cow) used	2470
eggs which matured	2297
eggs fertilized in vitro	1358
eggs injected with human DNA	1154
eggs which survived this injection	981
embryos which developed from such eggs	687
embryos transferred into oviducts of cows	129
cows which became pregnant	21
calves born	19
calves which are transgenic	2

One can see at once from the figures above that the successful outcome was very low indeed, in spite of the fact that each stage of the procedure was very precisely defined. Furthermore, as Holdrege also points out, only one of the two transgenic calves was truly transgenic after all – in the case of the other, the human DNA could only be detected in the placenta, but not in the body tissues or cells, such as blood, of the calf.

At present there are two ways of viewing this very low rate of success in many of these procedures. Those who adhere to the reductionistic framework in which the science and the experiments are conducted take it that these are technical glitches, which sooner or later will be overcome, and that the success rate would go up suitably. Furthermore, scientists who wish to exploit the technology will not necessarily be bothered by such wastefulness, at least in the case of animals. Their one successful transgenic cow, for instance, could be multiplied through breeding (but preferably cloning), building up a herd of transgenic cows from whose milk the desirable human protein may be isolated and recovered. However, those who are critical of the reductionistic framework altogether argue that the low rate of success is predictable in principle, and therefore inherent, in the kind of science that it is. Such poor results cannot be overcome in principle as they are indicative of the theoretical limits or, indeed, even the wrong-headedness of the fundamental methodological and philosophical assumptions of such kind of genetics – see, for instance, Holdrege (1996) and Ho (1998).

17   Later, in Chapter 6, we shall look at the complexities concerning the continuing evolution of this species.

18   The term 'trajectory' has been introduced to refer to the entire history of any (naturally occurring) entity and/or process, either biotic or abiotic, thereby including its coming into existence, its continuing to exist and its ceasing to exist. As the entity or process is a naturally occurring one, the term is intended to imply that no part or stage of its existence is deliberately manipulated, controlled or produced by humans. Such usage clearly in turn implies an ontological dyadism – though not an ontological dualism – between what is natural, on the one hand, and what is artefactual on the other. For a detailed account of these notions, see Keekok Lee, (1999, especially pp. 177–80).

19   For the view that even abiotic nature may be said to have interests, see Plumwood (1993). But this author has difficulty with such a claim – see Keekok Lee (1999, pp. 169–72).

20   The biologist Ernst Mayr coined the two terms 'teleomatic' and 'teleonomic'. The former refers to those processes at work in abiotic nature, which simply follow physical laws, such as the law of gravity and the second law of thermodynamics. The latter refers to those processes at work in biotic nature as a result of which organisms display programmed behaviour, the programme being the product of natural selection; in other words, it roughly coincides with what this book calls the thesis of intrinsic/immanent teleology. See Mayr, 1988.

21   Admittedly, we are ignorant of the precise mechanisms by which such highly co-ordinated activities take place. But the fact that the birds lack consciousness like human consciousness is neither here nor there; their behaviour is distinctly purposive, that is, end-directed, co-ordinated, non-random.

22   Furthermore, research has recently established that plants can 'smell', 'feel', 'hear', and so on. by means of chemical communication, in spite of lacking consciousness of any kind – see Coghlan (1998, pp. 24–8).

23   However, this does not mean that abiotic beings have no value other than instrumental value for humans – see Keekok Lee (1999).

24   For the emergence of the notion 'nature$_c$' in ancient Greek thought, see Lloyd (1992).

25   For slightly different overlapping definitions, see Ferré (1992, pp. 26–9).

26   By 'hyperseparation' or 'radical exclusion', Plumwood (1993) means the following:

> The relation of radical exclusion has special characteristics. For distinctness, for non-identity or otherness, there need be only a single characteristic which is different, possessed by the one but not the other, in order to guarantee distinctions according to the usual treatment of identity (e.g. in Leibniz's Law). Where items are constructed or construed according to

dualistic relationships, however, the master tries to magnify, to emphasise and to maximise the number and importance of differences and to eliminate or treat as inessential shared qualities, and hence to achieve a maximum separation. ... Denial or minimisation of continuity is important in eliminating identification and sympathy between members of the dominating class and the dominated, and in eliminating possible confusion between powerful and powerless. ... A major aim of dualistic construction is polarisation, to maximise distance or separation between the dualised spheres and to prevent their being seen as continuous or contiguous. ... A further important feature of dualistically construed opposition is that the underside of a dualistically conceived pair is defined in relation to the upperside as a lack, a negativity. (pp. 49–52)

Also: 'The upperside is an end in itself, but the underside has no such intrinsic value, is not for-itself but merely useful, a resource. The identity of the underside is constructed instrumentally, ... the underside is not part of the sphere to be considered morally, but is either judged by a separate instrumental standard ... or seen as outside morality altogether' (ibid., p. 53).

27   Alternative definitions are: 'a device consisting of two or more resistant, relatively constrained parts that may serve to transmit and modify force and motion in order to do work' (Alexander Cowie in *New Encyclopaedia Britannica*, Macropaedia, 1975, 11, 231); or 'a device for transforming or transferring energy' (George H. Martin, *Kinematics and Dynamics of Machines,* New York: McGraw-Hill, 1969, 3). (These definitions are cited by Mitcham, 1994, p. 327.)

28   Another account reads: 'In physics, the term work refers to the transference of energy that occurs when a force is applied to a body that is moving in such a way that the force has a component in the direction of the body's motion' (*McGraw-Hill Concise Encyclopedia of Science and Technology*, 1984 p. 1891).

29   An Edinburgh-based biotech company has of late patented Tracy the sheep, which has been genetically engineered to produce Alpha 1, an anti-trypsin drug used in treating people with emphysema. Herman the bull has had a human gene inserted into his germ-line so that his daughters may produce, in their milk, an antibacterial drug called lactoferrin. This would then make breast-milk substitutes more like human milk – see John Vidal and John Carvel (1993, p. 25).

30   Maturana, Varela and Uribe published an earlier version in English entitled 'Autopoiesis: The Organization of Living Systems' in *Biosystems*, 5 (1974) 187–96. Francisco J. Varela published *Principles of Biological Autonomy* (1979). This was followed by Humberto R. Maturana and Francisco J. Varela, *Autopoiesis and Cognition: The Realization of the Living* (1980). A nontechnical presentation is found in Maturana and Varela (1988), especially in chapter 2. This popularised version has influenced significantly a strain of environmental thinking. Warwick Fox (1990, pp. 165–76) introduced the concept 'autopoiesis' to environmental philosophy. See Eckersley (1992, pp. 60–1, 70–1) for a direct endorsement, and Gare (1995, p. 129) for an oblique endorsement. But see Plumwood (1993, p. 210) for a more critical response. Freya Mathews, while saying that her 'idea of self-realizability matches up, in essential respects, with Maturana's notion of autopoiesis', nevertheless recognises that hers 'differs from Maturana's in the following fundamental respect

... [Where] Maturana considers that autopoiesis dissolves the apparent telos of living systems, I see the capacity for self-realization, understood in systems-theoretical terms, as definitive of telos' (1991, p. 173).

31   The term 'machines' here refers to the standard understanding.
32   These are (MV)machines, not machines as standardly understood.
33   For a critique of biotechnology along these lines, see Michael Fox (1990); Henk Verhoog (1992); Keekok Lee (1999).
34   See Chapter 6 for further exploration.

2
Philosophy, Modern Science and Modern Technology

Modern science originated in Western Europe; it would not be arbitrary to date its beginning in the 17th century. But science, modern or pre-modern, is unintelligible without the understanding that it can only take place within a certain philosophical framework, and in particular, a particular type of metaphysics and epistemology. The philosophy of modern science may be called empiricism-cum-positivism and its metaphysics, Scientific Naturalism.[1] But to understand modern science, one must first turn to pre-modern science and its philosophical presuppositions which were displaced by its successor.[2]

Pre-modern philosophy and its science

The dominant European world-view during the late Middle Ages, up to the 17th century, was Aristotelianism, the result of that grand Thomist synthesis between Catholic theology against a history of Augustinianism in the Church and the Church's exposure to Platonism.[3] What Thomism had done was to co-opt some of Aristotle's theses, his categories and his logic to lay down a cosmological framework within which the universe was conceived to be finite and hierarchically ordered, as well as purposefully ordained by God. Its centre was the earth; its outermost boundaries were the fixed stars. Everything in the space between had its proper place. In a nutshell, it was this conception of the universe which Copernican heliocentrism, as championed by Galileo, challenged and ultimately displaced. The new astronomy thus threatened not merely the old Ptolemaic astronomy but also the old cosmology and philosophy which underpinned it.

It challenged it in a truly radical manner, not because it downgraded Man but because, as would soon be made clear, it replaced qualitative differences with quantitative ones. R. G. Collingwood has pointed out that it is 'both philosophically foolish and historically false' (1945, p. 96) to construe its significance as that of dethroning Man and his planet from the centre of the universe, and of diminishing his importance in the cosmic scheme of things. After all, Boethius in his *De Consolatione Philosophiae*, considered to be the most widely read book of the Middle Ages, had long acknowledged the cosmic insignificance of man and earth.[4] Copernicus and Galileo (two of the famous founding fathers of modern science) were, therefore, not likely to risk the charge of heresy for merely affirming a commonplace belief. For the same reason, when Copernicus's posthumous publisher wrote that heliocentrism, for the purpose of studying and calculating the orbits of the planets, would be a convenient device, his remark need not be interpreted as one of mere caution and timidity, as if he admitted that the established view was true and correct. On the contrary, those who championed heliocentrism were aware that it would amount to a revolution in cosmology. Collingwood holds that it amounted to denying that the universe has a centre and, by so doing, thoroughly undermined the view, inherited from Greek thought, of spherical world-organism – the earth in the centre, surrounded by water, air, then fire, and for Aristotle, the *quinta essentia* which constituted the outermost layer. But with no centre, differential parts would not be required either. This then left the way open to the rival paradigm that the universe is homogeneous as far as the kind of matter it is made out of is concerned. The stars do not possess a divine substance. The laws of terrrestrial physics, like the law of gravitation, apply to both the sublunary regions as well as celestial space. Terrestrial and celestial physics could become one. Nature is not made of heterogeneous substances differing in quality, as Aristotelians taught. There is one qualitatively uniform substance. The differences it displays are differences of quantity and of geometrical structure. This, as we shall see, enabled Galileo and others to develop and bring to maturity the mechanistic world-view via the new scientific method.

But the Aristotelian philosophical world-view was not merely entwined inextricably with Ptolemaic astronomy but also laid down the terms in which terrestrial science was conducted. In outline, its main points are: [5]

1. The human intellect is concerned to explain why things are as they are (why a dog is a dog and not a cat), why they could not be otherwise (why a dog does not become a cat), and why it is best that they be as they are. A satisfactory explanation consists of (a) giving the causes of things, and (b) comprehending the purpose behind events in nature.
2. There are four causes – borrowed directly from Aristotle as indicated in Chapter 1 – in terms of which a thing or event would be satisfactorily explained.
3. Nature (as already mentioned) is composed ultimately of four elements – earth, water, air and fire. Each of these may have two qualities attributed to it in terms of the pairs hot/cold, and wet/dry – earth is cold and dry; water, cold and wet; air, hot and wet; fire, hot and dry. Each of these elements has a natural home assigned to it; for earth and water it is the

ground, for fire and air above the ground. Moreover, things which pertain to earth and water possess the natural tendency of gravity enabling them to strive to return to their natural abode if they are removed from it – if a stone is thrown up into the air, it will eventually fall to the ground. Similarly, things pertaining to air and fire possess the natural tendency of levity. Explanations in terms of these natural properties are called teleological. (This sense of teleological refers to the final and formal causes of a phenomenon – see what follows in the next section for further comment.)

4. Causes of things are not ascertained by means of the senses, although their effects could be so perceived. Rules then have to be established by which one could determine causes through their effects.

5. As things perceived in nature both differ as well as are similar to one another in numerous aspects, one needs to distinguish accidental from non-accidental properties. The latter constitutes the inner essences of things, which serve to distinguish them from one another. Definitions capture these essences.

6. Aristotle distinguished between forms of knowledge, each with its respective source and goal – *techne* and *episteme*. *Techne* is concerned with how to do things based on an awareness of, or reasoning about, the proper nature of the thing to be made or the activity undertaken. *Episteme* is scientific knowledge whose source is the understanding of things through their causes. *Phronesis* is practical, that is, moral and political, knowledge.

Modern science, its methodology and its philosophy

Although Galileo (1564–1642) bears the distinction of bringing to maturity the new revolutionary mechanistic paradigm and world-view in his scientific method, others also paved the way.[6] Among these is Kepler (1571–1630), a contemporary. Kepler, building on the work of William Gilbert on magnetism (published in 1600), formulated the principle of inertia, that bodies tend to remain stationary wherever they might be. This challenged the Aristotelian conception of natural movements, as noted in thesis 3 in the section above. Furthermore, Kepler explained gravitation in terms of mutual affection, which draws a body towards neighbouring bodies – the stone falls to the ground because the ground attracts it. In the same way, the tides change because the moon attracts the water. To these innovations, he added a third – that, in physics, the word *anima* be replaced by *vis*. The former embodies the conception of a vital force or energy capable of producing qualitative changes, the latter that of a mechanical energy or force, which is itself quantitative, bringing about quantitative changes. In 1595 Kepler had written:

as the eye was created for color, the ear for tone, so was the intellect of humans created for the understanding not of just anything whatsoever but of quantities. It grasps a matter so much the more correctly the closer it approaches pure quantities as its source. But the further something diverges from them, that much more do darkness and error appear. It is the nature of our intellect to bring to the study of divine matters concepts which are built upon the category of quantity; if it is deprived of these concepts, then it can define only by pure negations. (Caspar, 1959, p. 62)

In other words, Kepler was really referring to the mathematisation of nature, entailing not only a change in scientific method, but also a profound change in world-view, from an organic to a mechanistic one. (Kepler held that the human intellect was created by God to apprehend the world in terms of mass and number. But his theological belief simply underpinned his mechanistic world-view, rather than challenged it.)[7] Galileo is credited with having formulated the new paradigm even more forcefully, especially in that famous remark of his about the 'book of nature':

Philosophy is written in this grand book – I mean the universe – which stands continually open to our gaze, but it cannot be understood unless one first learns to comprehend the language and interpret the characters in which it is written. It is written in the language of mathematics, and its characters are triangles, circles, and other geometrical figures, without which it is humanly impossible to understand a single word of it; without these, one is wandering about in a dark labyrinth. (Drake, 1957, pp. 237–8)[8]

Galileo saw mathematics and mathematical measurement as indispensable to the study and understanding of nature, as well as a tool to make it disclose its secrets to us. The marriage of mathematics to physics constituted a radical departure from Plato's and Aristotle's views of the relationship between the two subjects. Plato disparaged the physical world as being transient and subject to decay – true knowledge is about objects, which are immutable and eternal. Pure mathematical ideas seem to qualify for such a status. Hence Plato thought the forms alone worth studying. Aristotle, on the contrary, inferred from the very abstract character of mathematical procedure that mathematics could have nothing to offer to physics, as the latter is concerned with the study of matter and its motion, which mathematics precisely ignores.

For Galileo, mathematics enables one to make calculations, which could then be tested to see if they fit observation. If they do not, this should not be construed that either calculations are irrelevant (Aristotle) or that observation is not required (Plato). A bad fit could signal that the scientists have not taken something into account and that they should redo their homework. For Galileo, observations and measurements yield scientific facts, and if these conflict with existing philosophical beliefs, it is (orthodox) philosophy and not science that should give way. Careful observation of the moon's surface through the telescope has shown that it is not smooth, but has craters and mountains; dismissing such evidence in the name of Aristotelianism would amount to a mere dogmatic appeal to authority. This would be neither good philosophising nor practising good science, but sterile mouthing of the philosophy of others. Galileo was hostile to the Aristotelians precisely because he was against the dogmatism they displayed.

Mathematical physics soon established itself as the queen of the new sciences. But whether Galileo and others anticipated or intended its implications is immaterial: its success definitively ushered in the mechanistic world-view. The new science and its method imply a new philosophy and cosmology. The mathematisation of nature meant that a new 'reality' emerged, one based on abstraction, isolation, measurement and quantification. Galileo gave expression to it in *The Assayer*, a work which may be read as his attempt to formulate a philosophy of science, albeit not in a systematic manner. The gist of it may be found in the following extract:

> Now I say that whenever I conceive any material or corporeal substance, I immediately feel the need to think of it as bounded, and as having this or that shape; as being large or small in relation to other things, and in some specific place at any given time; as being in motion or at rest; as touching or not touching some other body; and as being one in number, or few, or many. From these conditions I cannot separate such a substance by any stretch of my imagination. But that it must be white or red, bitter or sweet, noisy or silent, and of sweet or foul odor, my mind does not feel compelled to bring in as necessary accompaniments. Without the senses as our guides, reason or imagination unaided would probably never arrive at qualities like these. Hence I think that tastes, odors, colors, and so on are no more than mere names so far as the object in which we place them is concerned, and that they reside only in the consciousness. Hence if the living creature were removed, all these qualities would be wiped away and annihilated. But since we have imposed upon them special names, distinct from those of the other and real qualities mentioned previously, we wish to believe that they really exist as actually different from those. (Drake, 1957, p. 274)

From the above, one may infer the following theses:[9]

1. What are real and reside in (material) substances are what Locke later called 'the primary qualities', namely, shapes, numbers and motions. These alone would be sufficient to excite in us tastes, odours, sounds

and colours, what Locke calls 'the secondary qualities'. Galileo wrote: 'I think that if ears, tongues and noses were removed, shapes and numbers and motions would remain, but not odors or tastes or sounds' (Drake, 1957, pp. 276–7).

2. The elimination of secondary qualities, that is, of qualitative differences between things, is required because what is real and intelligible in nature is what is measurable and quantifiable. The ontology implied consists precisely of holding that what is real is what is measurable and quantifiable, and only what is measurable and quantifiable is real.

3. The elimination of secondary qualities permits the reduction of a complex whole (with its sensuous qualities) to the relatively simple matrix of what could be weighed, measured and counted.

4. Not only are the secondary qualities derivative and dependent upon the primary ones but they are also totally mind-dependent and hence are mere appearances with no objective existence whatsoever. Galileo called them 'mere names' to which there are no referents in the 'objective real' world; at best they refer to mental phenomena residing in living, sensible (human) beings.

5. This means that the natural world studied by the new science is necessarily a world of pure quantity from which living and sensible beings have been excluded. In other words, it is a dead, inert nature that is being studied.

6. As such, the new science concentrates on the overt, the outer, the public, the impersonal, capturing their quantifiable features in laws of nature which are meant to be universal in scope. By the same token, it ignores or downgrades immediate experience (which is of secondary qualities), the qualitative, the covert, the inner, the private, the personal or the particular.

7. Its epistemology consists of holding that what is knowable is what is measurable and quantifiable, and only what is measurable and quantifiable is knowable.

8. Humans, the students of nature, stand outside nature. As Collingwood (1945) puts it:

> Nature, so regarded, stands on the one hand over against its creator, God, and on the other over against its knower, man. Both God and man are regarded by Galileo as transcending nature; and rightly, because if nature consists of mere quantity its apparent qualitative aspects must be conferred upon it from outside, namely by the human mind as transcending it; while if it is conceived no longer as a living organism but as inert matter, it cannot be regarded as self-creative but must have a cause other than itself. (pp. 102–3)

9. The scientists become instruments for recording and analysing the real and the knowable. Apart from the processes of thinking which involve their

intellectual/logical capabilities, their sensory and emotional reactions are neutralised or eliminated both in the design of the experiment and the analysis of its result. Scientific data are emotion- and value-free. Science becomes the most rational, if not the only, form of rational activity.

This amounts to an outline of what is also sometimes called the metaphysics (and epistemology) of Scientific Naturalism. In this mechanistic view of scientific method and of nature, the behaviour of natural entities and their processes of change and maintaining dynamic stability are understood as regularities or uniformities, as mere movements, which are the result of the impact of one body on another body, the attraction of one body towards another body, or the repulsion of one body by another body. Hume's analysis of the notion of cause later in the 18th century articulates this conception most forcefully indeed.[10] Regularities – phenomena of kind A followed by phenomena of kind B – replaced tendencies which are the result of effort on the part of the beings which are studied. Why do plants lean towards light? Because the plants, in order to grow and develop in a way they are capable of (or have the potential to do), require light and so strive to reach it. The new science and its philosophy render this kind of explanation both redundant and unintelligible, but would instead sanction a regularity type of explanation. Whenever plants are found to grow well, they have leant towards light; in the absence of light, plants have not been found to grow.[11]

Indeed, to modern philosophy, the entire Aristotelian conceptual apparatus, in terms of 'wants', 'desires', 'striving to fulfil', and so on, is suspect and must be rejected. It is condemned as 'teleological' as it conceived changes and processes in nature to be directed or dictated by goals or ends which did not yet exist but which would be ultimately realised.[12] As mentioned earlier, for the Aristotelians (and Aristotle), a full and proper explanation has to be in terms of the four causes. But to the new science and the new philosophy, two of them – the final and the formal – smack of the teleological. Only the material and the efficient causes, which lend themselves to measurement and quantification, are retained. To explain why a coastline is indented in the way it is, one needs only to refer to the kind of rock or rocks the coast is made of, the strength and direction of the waves, the force with which the waves hit the shores, the temperature of the water, the direction and strength of the prevailing winds, and so on.

Final and formal causes are suspect because they appear to be tied up with essences. Essences are grasped through reason and given by definitions, according to Aristotelianism. Why does fire rise? Because it is of its essence or in its nature to do so. To Galileo and those who professed the new science and its philosophy, these are mere words, signifying and referring to nothing in reality. For them, only a result obtained through calculation and measurement is to count as scientific knowledge. As essences are not amenable to such treatment, they do not form part of the province of science.

Even worse, in the hands of the Aristotelians, final causes even led to anthropomorphism. For instance, Galileo, as much as the Aristotelians, noticed that a falling object, such as a stone, falls faster and faster in its downward journey. The Aristotelian physicists (or Thomists) would explain the phenomenon thus: a stone belongs to the element, earth, whose natural home is at ground level, the surface of the planet. Suppose you had been away for a long time from your loved ones. As you got nearer and nearer home on the return journey, you would get more and more excited and walk or ride your horse faster and faster. Similarly, a stone would fall faster and faster as it approached nearer and nearer its natural abode – the impetus being the joy of getting there.

Galileo would regard such anthropomorphism to be singularly unhelpful. He preferred to observe and measure the rate of fall and to determine the law of acceleration in precise mathematical terms. The 'why' is of no concern to the scientist. Only the fact that the object fell in the way it did, which could be measured, is of significance.

The new method and the mechanistic world-view ushered in by Galileo and others is necessarily empirical (using mathematics not merely as a tool, but also thereby mathematising nature), anti-metaphysical (no essences in terms of hidden entities and mechanisms) and anti-teleological (no final and formal causes, only material and efficient ones).[13] As we saw, Galileo had complained that Aristotelian doctrines were upheld as dogmas at the expense of empirical evidence. This was because Aristotelianism believed in *episteme*, knowledge arrived at by means which, to Galileo and others, were obscurantist and 'metaphysical'. The spirit of modernity consists precisely in repudiating all such superstitions and 'idols' upheld by traditional authorities of one kind or other. As far as Galileo himself was concerned, the Church as an authority was acceptable, provided it confined itself to matters purely of faith and did not meddle with matters of science, which were outside its jurisdiction. The only authority in matters of science that he would acknowledge was the authority of those who practised the new scientific method, implicitly backed up by the new philosophy, and not that of Aristotelian science and philosophy. In other words, a new epistemological authority replaced the old.

From the account above, we have seen Galileo's contribution towards the articulation of the new philosophy to back up the new science, although Galileo was primarily a scientist, not a philosopher, who set himself the task of systematically constructing such an account.[14] That new philosophy, as mentioned earlier, may be labelled 'empiricism' or 'positivism-cum-empiricism'.

To prevent misunderstanding, perhaps, one should briefly distinguish between 'empirical' and 'empiricist'. Aristotelian science clearly relied on empirical observation, as must all science. But the new philosophy goes beyond merely using observation and indeed even measurement.[15] It lays down that the world as ascertained by the senses is the only world we can come to know: it professes an empiricist epistemology. Furthermore, it holds that anything not grounded in sense experience is not real but is 'metaphysical': it professes an empiricist ontology. Whatever is known by the senses is real and nothing is real unless known through sensory experience. This then involves the abusive sense of the term 'metaphysics', as the metaphysical realm, in the new understanding, came to be identified with what is beyond sensory experience and hence cannot be real. Pronouncements about such a domain would only amount to empty words, if not outright unintelligibility. The new philosophy, in being materialistic and mechanistic, is against the metaphysical mode of explanation – bodies which are real and exist and about which we can have knowledge are material, and motion is the efficient cause of all changes in such bodies.[16] Explanations in terms of essences captured by the definitions of words are pseudo-explanations – to say that opium sends one to sleep because it possesses *virtus dormitiva* is to utter a tautology, namely, that opium sends one to sleep because it sends one to sleep.

The new philosophy is also aggressively anti-teleological, as we have seen, by rejecting the formal and final, while retaining only the material and efficient, causes in its explanatory schema. This hostility to both the metaphysical and teleological modes of explanation is a consequence of its empiricist ontology and epistemology. Philosophers such as Hobbes, Descartes and later Locke, in reinforcing and developing Galileo's limited attempt, fiercely formulated the new world-view of materialism and mechanism, jettisoning the Aristotelian organic cosmos in the process.

The goals of modern science

Let us next move to the goals of the new science in the light of the new philosophy. Today, we commonly identify three such goals – prediction, explanation and control. The positivist methodology and philosophy of science uphold the unity of method thesis and, moreover, that the logic of predicting/explaining an event, as well as testing a theory or hypothesis, is symmetrical.[17] By this conception, the ability of science to make predictions is crucial. To predict a phenomenon is to invoke a law (a regularity or uniformity of sequence) which licenses the prediction; in turn, a law is tested in terms of the prediction it licenses. Prediction, then, is the lynchpin of an epistemology which decrees that the scope of knowledge is delimited by the sensory given. A system of thought that does not issue in testable predictions cannot count as knowledge. This entails a positivist exclusion from the scientific domain any theory which is incapable of issuing in testable (hence precise) predictions; in this view, for instance, geology is in danger of not qualifying to be a science, as its principles or laws permit explanations, but not predictions precise enough to be testable.

Apart from the crucial role of prediction in epistemological terms, the possibility of prediction is also linked to the possibility of control. Comte, certainly, held this to be so. If one can successfully make predictions with the help of laws, then one can take steps to get out of the way of the event predicted, if it is considered to be undesirable (the weak sense of control). Or one could alter or modify the circumstances, so that certain desired results could be brought about and other undesired ones prevented from arising (the strong sense). Astronomical knowledge enables one, for instance, to predict an eclipse of the sun at a certain place and on a certain date. Then one can arrange to be there to observe it, if its observation can be used to further some other task, like Eddington's expedition in 1919 to test Einstein's theory of general relativity. Alternatively, if an eclipse of the sun is considered to have undesirable effects – suppose observing one causes cancer of the eye – then one could take appropriate avoiding action.[18]

The second possibility allows one to interfere more directly with the workings of nature. According to the laws established about plant growth, a certain degree of warmth, and not merely exposure to light, encourages plant growth. If one wishes to encourage growth, then one ought to put the plants in a warm place.

For Comte, the possibility or the lack of direct intervention depends on the type of phenomenon studied; astronomical phenomena are too large in scale and too far away for us to influence, whereas physiological phenomena are not.[19] However, the possibility of control in both the weak and the strong senses provides the link between science and what Comte called 'art', or between science and technology, as we would put it today. In this way, the new science has always been connected up with utility (for humans) – a theme that Francis Bacon had made familiar.

The weak form of control is not the real goal. It is *faute de mieux*, and at best, a prelude to the aspiration of controlling nature in the strong form. Being able to predict the onset of drought or rain is clearly better than not being able to do so at all. But it would be better if scientific theoretical understanding of meteorological phenomena ultimately enabled one either to generate rain (when drought is undesired) or to hold rain at bay (when dry weather is desired).

To Bacon's voice on this matter, Descartes also added his:

> as soon as I had acquired some general notions in physics and had noticed, as I began to test them in various particular problems, where they could lead and how much they differ from the principles used up to now, I believed that I could not keep them secret without sinning gravely against the law which obliges us to do all in our power to secure the general welfare of mankind. For they opened my eyes to the possibility of gaining knowledge which would be very useful in life, and of discovering

a practical philosophy which might replace the speculative philosophy taught in the schools. Through this philosophy we could know the power and the action of fire, water, air, the stars, the heavens and all the other bodies in our environment, as distinctly as we know the various crafts of our artisans; and we could use this knowledge – as the artisans use theirs – for all the purposes for which it is appropriate, and thus make ourselves, as it were, the lords and masters of nature. This is desirable not only for the invention of innumerable devices which would facilitate our enjoyment of the fruits of the earth and all the goods we find there, but also, and most importantly, for the maintenance of health, which is undoubtedly the chief good and the foundation of all the other goods in this life. ... we might free ourselves from innumerable diseases, both of the body and of the mind, and perhaps even from the infirmity of old age, if we had sufficient knowledge of their causes and of all the remedies that nature has provided. (1992, pp. 142–3)

Positivism is a philosophy of order and social reform, not of violent change.[20] Order in the study of natural phenomena takes the form of systematically structuring sense experience into a coherent interconnected body of knowledge, so that knowledge about one phenomenon could ultimately be understood by being derived from knowledge about others within it.[21] Not only does such an axiomatic structure allow explanation, prediction and theory testing to take place, but it also enables us in the end to control nature (in the strong sense earlier identified). And this bears out the Baconian dictum that 'knowledge is power'.

In the light of the above, it would be fair to conclude that built into the new scientific method and its accompanying philosophy from the 17th century onwards is the aspiration to control and manipulate (and in that way to dominate) nature. Bacon, Descartes and Hobbes all unhesitatingly declared it to be so. It does not look as if the ideal of knowledge for its own sake, what Einstein called 'the holy curiosity of inquiry', ever existed in its neat purity at the inception of modernity (or at any time later, for that matter). The philosophical, as well as the ideological, requirements of the new world-view ensure that science, as technology, and science, as theoretical knowledge, go hand in hand. While humans had used and controlled nature in the past, modern science makes it possible for them, more systematically than ever before, to control (to exploit) nature.

This new opportunity for manipulating nature has prompted several radically different responses. The majority holds that the exploitation of nature redounds to the good of all humans. Some argue that the possibility of exploiting nature would displace the exploitation of men by fellow men only when capitalism has been superseded, and envisage, thereafter, a cornucopia for all humans. Others hold that the exploitation of nature is yet another means to sustain the exploitation by some humans of others (whether capitalism is dislodged or not), and that the exploitation of nature and of humans must together be overcome. Yet others recognise even the possibility of exploiting certain humans while emancipating nature from exploitation. Those who subscribe to Adam Smith's 'invisible hand' argument represent the first (which is the dominant) attitude. Marx stands for the second, 'utopian' socialists for the third, and the so-called eco-fascists for the fourth.

The crucially built-in goal of controlling biotic nature in modern science has taken on another dimension in the last thirty years or so with the establishment of molecular genetics as a theoretical discipline, and its accompanying technology, biotechnology. Such a technology permits a kind of control which operates at a far deeper level than the technology of Mendelian genetics. This, in turn, as already hinted at in the first chapter, permits the dramatic introduction of external/imposed teleology upon biotic nature, even with regard to the material cause of a phenomenon. Ironically, at the same time, it also permits the restoration of two of the four Aristotelian causes, which modernity from the 17th century onwards has cast into the outer darkness, namely, formal and final causes, albeit in a revamped form, through altering the ontological status of living organisms as naturally occurring beings to that of biotic artefacts.

Episteme, techne and technology

We have seen how modern Western philosophy has challenged the pre-modern authorities, philosophical and theological, and put in their place a new epistemological authority, given to us by science and its findings. That replacement is reflected, curiously, in the very emergence of the word 'epistemology' in modern Western philosophy to denote that branch of philosophy also referred to as 'the theory of knowledge', dealing with scientific and other types of knowledge claims. But philosophy conducts no experiments nor makes observations and measurements, although it tries to render intelligible the findings yielded by experiments, observations and measurements. The etymological root of 'epistemology' is the word 'episteme'. *Episteme*, as we have seen (for Aristotle) is knowledge, the understanding of things uncovered by the use of reason through grappling with their causes and essences, which is contrasted with *techne*, delineating the domain of know-how. But for Galileo and other moderns, scientific knowledge is not *episteme*, but what is yielded by measurement, quantification, calculation, observation (what is grounded in sensory experience, in the broad sense of the term). Modern scientific knowledge is, therefore, more like *techne* as the latter, too, operates within the realm of experience (but only in this very restricted aspect – see below for the fundamental differences between the two).

From *techne* is derived the word 'technology'. At least in the English language, 'technology' was given its modern usage by the last half of the 17th century, appearing for the first time in a dictionary in 1706 referring to 'a Description of arts, especially the Mechanical'. Later, it was extended to the industrial arts and practical arts in general. Building on this, Jacob Bigelow in the preface to his book *Elements of Technology* (1831) used the word to refer to 'the principles, processes, and nomenclatures of the more conspicuous arts, particularly those, which involve applications of science'. In the German language, as early as 1728, Christian Wolff, in his *Preliminary Discourse on Philosophy in General*, used it to refer to 'the science of the arts and of the works of art', or to the use of physics to give 'the reason of things which occur through art'.[22] Contemporary usage clearly reflects this historical lineage. Today when we speak of science and technology, we roughly mean the distinction between theory and its application ultimately in manufacturing products.[23]

Even more interestingly, 'technology' is derived not only from *techne* but also from its being conjoined with *logos*. Carl Mitcham (1979) reminds us that, strangely enough, when, for the first time in Greek thought, the two words *techne* and *logos* were joined together into a single word by Aristotle, he used it in the context of rhetoric. As such, the Greek term 'technology' meant 'the study of grammar or rhetoric', and the term 'technologist' referred to the grammarian or rhetorician. What could account for the dramatic change in denotation of the words between Aristotle's use of the terms and their modern usage? Mitcham points to a deep ontological divide between the moderns, on the one hand, and Aristotle (and Aristotelians), on the other, in their conception of nature and the world around them.[24]

According to Aristotle (and those who followed his world-view), *techne* involved *logos*, but *logos* had nothing to do with mathematical or quantitative concepts or reasoning: carpentry and flute playing involved great *techne*. What could be grasped by *techne* through *logos* was merely the form or the 'whatness' of the thing that was being made or done. But the matter itself, out of which the thing was made, and the actual processes of making it, fell outside of *logos*. In producing an artefact such as a table, the form is the idea in the head of the artisan:

> its union with matter is, as it were, at the mercy of matter and its specific receptivity. Form cannot be forced into or imposed upon matter; an artisan must let the matter guide the way it will receive form. The ultimate decision in action rests not with reason but with sensation, aisthesis. ... Indeed, on one occasion [*Physics*, 1.9.192a18] Aristotle goes so far as to describe the coming together of form and matter, the becoming of an entity, as dependent on a 'desire' or 'reaching out' on the part of matter for form. (Mitcham, 1979, p. 178)

Aristotle understood matter to be embodied in particulars. Hence the place of *logos* – the logical universal – was necessarily limited in knowledge about particulars. Knowledge of particulars is acquired essentially through imitation, practice and experience – one does not become a builder by reading manuals on building, but by building and thereby coming to know intimately the properties and propensities of the stone that one is building with.

This limitation of the role of *logos* in the case of *techne* would also explain why Aristotle produced a *logos* of the *techne* of persuasion, because language is a rarefied medium, and is not material in the way that blocks of stone are material particulars. Here, one can lay down a systematic discourse about the means and processes involved in the art of persuasion – a recognition that words, even when divorced from reason, are a powerful means to get an audience to accept certain ends or do certain things. There is a logic of means – a set of general rules and devices – irrespective of the ends to which the means may be put, which could be laid down and learnt. Although Aristotle did claim that one could produce similar discourses about every other art, it remains true he never did, except in the case of the *Rhetoric*. As a result, the term 'technology', as noted earlier, comes to mean no more and no less than simply the study of grammar or rhetoric. Aristotle as good as conceded that as far as *techne* in general is concerned, apart from grasping form, there is no *logos* of the activity involved qua activity.

In contrast, modern technology is precisely predicated on the assumption that there is a process of production which has nothing to do with the particular forms of things. Aristotle and Aristotelians regarded matter as taking on forms, and held that there was a desire on the part of matter to unfold itself in accordance with the forms the particulars involved. But with modernity, as it emerged under the influence of Galileo, Descartes, Newton and others, as we have seen, matter becomes inert, dead matter. According to the Cartesian view it is mere extension, which is devoid of form, potentiality or *telos*. Being deprived of any desire or aspiration of its own, it opens the way for what today in environmental philosophy is called strong anthropocentrism, which regards humans as the sole source and locus of intrinsic value, and nature as being of only instrumental value to humans.

As matter is considered to be uniformly inert under modernity, there can, then, be a general procedure of production, which consists ultimately of the rearrangement of the elements of such matter to serve human ends. So technology in modern terms is the study of the manipulation of nature.[25] From the manipulation of words, it becomes the manipulation of matter. Such a drastic change in meaning reflects the revolution in worldview from the Aristotelian (ultimately, ancient Greek) paradigm of living, organic matter to that of mechanism and its conception of dead, inert matter as well as of reductionism. Therein lies the (or at least one very significant) passage from late medievalism to modernity.

Modern science and technology: divergence, then convergence

This section will explore (1) the respective epistemological underpinnings of theoretical science and technology in general, and (2) in the light of that show how technological knowledge, which is informed and engendered by scientific theories, enables us to control nature in the strong form.

But one must first say something briefly about technology in general and its history.[26] It must straightaway be admitted that technology is not peculiar to modernity.[27] Technology had always existed, since the first adze made by our Stone Age ancestors. It should not be understood as merely coterminous with our contemporary variety rooted in so-called modern science.

To do justice to all historical forms of technology and to provide a comprehensive framework for a philosophical analysis of technology, Mitcham (1994, p. 160) proposes a tentative schema, suggesting four modes of the manifestation of technology: (a) technological knowledge, (b) technological volition, (c) technological activities (making and using), (d) technological objects (or artefacts).[28] However, this book cannot hope to be a contribution to this larger and more ambitious project that Mitcham has delineated. Its aims are far more modest and confined. Regarding (b), it will be observed that while pre-modern technology primarily involves the will to survive and to satisfy basic biological needs, technology in modernity is primarily about the will to control and manipulate nature, with the goal of ever improving the material well-being of humans, and/or advancing other more spiritual ends, such as those of freedom and self-realisation.[29] With regard to (b) and (c), Chapter 6 will argue that, in modern thought, the notion of homo faber and its related notion of fabrication best capture the essence of the human species. Through the activity of fabrication, homo faber seeks material affluence, on the one hand, and freedom and self-realisation, on the other. But in the main, it explores the relation between (a) and (d), to show how modern technology ties in with the programme of modern science; that increasingly, since roughly the mid-19th century, scientific theories induce and inform technology; that the 'deeper' the theory, the more powerful the technology generated. The exploration is intended to cast light on the ontological transformation of living organisms as naturally occurring beings into biotic artefacts.

Scholars of (European) technological civilisation have suggested dividing it up into various phases. For instance, Lewis Mumford (1946) proposes a three-fold division (whose edges are meant to be overlapping) in terms of the type of energy and characteristic materials used. The eotechnic phase is a water-wind-and-wood complex; the paleotechnic phase is a steam-coal-and-iron complex; the neotechnic phase is an electricity-and-alloy (as well as synthetic compounds) complex. The first, for him, stretches roughly from AD 1000 to 1750; the second, from 1750 to the 1850s; and the third, from the 1850s to the present.

Mumford's classification is heuristically enlightening in general but, perhaps, less helpful from the standpoint of this book. So a different division is proposed here, not based so much on the conjoint variables of energy and material, but on whether the technology is craft- or science-based. In the case of the latter, it would be argued that what is significant is the relationship between the technology and the kind of science it might (or might not) rely on. The suggested classification in the context of European technological history is as follows (bear in mind, though, that the boundaries between them are not meant to be neat and tidy, but overlapping):[30]

Phase I		Relatively autonomous craft-based (though not necessarily guild-based) technology.
	A	Roughly equivalent to Mumford's eotechnic phase.
	B	Roughly equivalent to Mumford's paleotechnic phase.
Phase II		Science-theory-led technology.
	A	Roughly equivalent to Mumford's neotechnic phase, but ending by the 1940s.
	B	From the 1940s to the present.

Note that this division fails to superimpose neatly upon that which obtains in the history of science itself. There the radical cleavage, as we have seen, is between pre-modern science (up to the 17th century) and the rise of modern science (from the 17th century onwards). Phase IA falls clearly into the pre-modern scientific era, but Phase IB (roughly up to the 1830s) falls clearly into the modern scientific period. In other words, the major cleavage has been drawn between the kind of technology which is theory-led and inspired, in contrast to that which is relatively independent of basic scientific theories and discoveries themselves. Although Phase IB, in terms of temporal location, coincided with the rise of modern science, the technology it represented was, nevertheless, by and large, not a spin-off of theoretical advances.

On the contrary, during this period, it often happened that technology inspired theoretical research, rather than that theoretical advances led the way to new technologies. For instance, this relationship of technology preceding theory is true in the case of the invention of the steam engine, which first appeared, in the form of the steam pump, as a response to the demands of the coal-mining industry to mine seams at deeper levels where flooding occurred. It later, as the steam locomotive, made railway transportation possible, and replaced sailing ships on the high seas in the form of the steamer. Attempts to improve its efficiency eventually led to the establishment of the abstract, fundamental science of thermodynamics. Sadi Carnot, a French army officer and engineer, set out to understand how the steam engine worked, hoping thereby to improve its efficiency. The English had invented the machine, enabling perfidious Albion to be superior both in war and industry. He studied the phenomenon of heat, with the goal of recapturing that superiority for France. He found an intrinsic inefficiency in the conversion of heat to work. The steam engine works because parts of it are very hot and other parts very cold. Heat moves from the hot to the cold and in so doing, work is performed. But when the parts reach the same temperature, that is to say, a state of equilibrium, no further work can be performed. A difference in temperature between parts of the system – a difference in energy concentration – must obtain for work to occur. He also discovered that as energy moves from a higher to a lower level, less energy is available for work on the next round. For example, in a waterfall, the water, as it falls, can be used to drive a wheel, but it is no longer available to perform any further work once it reaches the pool at the bottom.

Later, famous scientists such as Joule, Kelvin, Clausius and Boltzmann added to Carnot's efforts. Boltzmann's contribution consists of linking the behaviour of matter at the macro level to the behaviour of matter at the micro atomic level, thus providing a unifying theory of vast scope to explain the nature of change in the world. It is apt to quote F. W. Atkins (1984) here:

> The aims adopted and the attitudes struck by Carnot and by Boltzmann epitomize thermodynamics. Carnot traveled toward thermodynamics from the direction of the engine, then the symbol of industrialized society: his aim was to improve its efficiency. Boltzmann traveled to thermodynamics from the atom, the symbol of emerging scientific fundamentalism: his aim was to increase our comprehension of the world at the deepest levels then conceived. Thermodynamics still has both aspects, and reflects complementary aims, attitudes, and applications. It grew out of the coarse machinery: yet it has been refined to an instrument of great delicacy. It spans the whole range of human enterprise, covering the organization and deployment of both resources and ideas about the nature of change in the world around us. Few contributions to human understanding are richer than this child of the steam engine and the atom. (p. 7)

Even more remarkably, during Phase IB, technological discoveries that formed the very basis of the Industrial Revolution were made by people who knew no science, had no formal education and, indeed, in some cases, could not even read or write. The most famous of these apprentices and craft-based mechanics is George Stephenson. Later in life, when he became famous and rich, he was only partially successful in overcoming his illiteracy. What is now called the Davy lamp – the safety lamp for miners, which first appeared in 1815 – was also an invention by Stephenson. But because of his humble background, illiteracy and ignorance of physics and chemistry, Humphrey Davy – fellow and later president of the Royal Society on whom a baronetcy was eventually conferred – could not credit Stephenson as a fellow inventor. Instead, he accused him of having stolen his idea. Davy died in 1829, convinced that Stephenson had cheated in spite of all the evidence to the contrary. Eventually, it took a House of Commons committee in 1833 to vindicate Stephenson – see Davies (1980, pp. 19–32).

This incident illustrates not merely the more humble origins of the inventors of many remarkable technological discoveries, but also the class-based difference at the time, at least in Britain, between technology and the practical (those who work with their hands), on the one hand, and science and the theoretical (those who work with their brains) on the other. The ancient universities of Britain, then, did not want to know either science or technology. The Royal Society was established to cater in the main for (pure) science, and was supported and patronised by gentlemen and members of the Establishment. Technology, instead, belonged to the mechanical societies, which grew up in the 18th century in the cities of Britain. It was nurtured and supported by the combined zeal of entrepreneurs, industrialists, engineers, unlettered and untutored mechanics; in other words, of people who dirtied their hands in one way or other with industry and manufacturing.

From this point of view, it is not unreasonable to argue that Phase IB and Phase IA, in spite of differences between them, share the essential similarity of being craft-based and relatively independent of explicit scientific/theoretical input. Phase IA includes inventors such as Leonardo da Vinci (1452–1519), but, in spite of the ingenuity of his many inventions, he is not celebrated in history for his contribution to science, but as a Renaissance genius in the design and execution of artefacts, belonging to both the fine and practical arts. He considered himself to be a 'man without letters'. Other giants of the period, such as Galileo, were hired by rulers, for instance, to improve their weapons of war which, in turn, led them to so-called pure scientific research and to establish new sciences. Yet others, such as Sir Isaac Newton (1642–1727), a Cambridge mathematician and physicist, often hailed as the greatest scientist of all time, concentrated on the theorising, and did not dabble at all in technological inventions. (However, he dabbled a lot in alchemy, so much so that John Maynard Keynes was moved to say that 'Cambridge's greatest son' was 'not the first of the age of reason' but 'the last of the magicians'.) In other words, both Phase IA and IB displayed a split between science and technology – either that science was pursued relatively independent of technology, or that technology led the way to scientific theorising. The causal direction the other way round, of theory inducing technology, by and large, did not occur until much later on.

One difference between the two sub-stages of Phase I worth commenting on is this: IA is, on the whole, as Mumford (1946, p. 108) points out, an era of creative syncretism. Western Europe collected unto itself the technological innovations of other civilisations, and adapted and built upon them. To mention just a few: the water mills, already in place in the earlier part of the Christian era, can be traced back to the water wheel of the Egyptians, who used it to raise water; the windmill probably came from Persia in the 8th century; gunpowder, the magnetic needle and paper came from China, the last two via the Arabs. Europe by AD 1000 was ready to receive these and other discoveries (such as algebra from India, again via the Arabs). Glass technology (known as far back as the Egyptians), improved and developed, laid the foundation for the development of astronomy, and of bacteriology by Leeuwenhoek in the mid-17th century. The former was made possible by the invention of the telescope – by a Dutch optician, Johann Lippersheim in 1605 – which Galileo perfected; the latter by that of the compound microscope (by another Dutch optician, Zacharias Jansen, in 1590).

Mumford (1946) sums up what he has called the paleotechnic phase, and what is called Phase IB here, succinctly as follows:

> The detailed history of the steam engine, the railroad, the textile mill, the iron ship, could be written without more than passing reference to the scientific work of the period. For these devices were made possible largely by the method of empirical practice, by trial and selection: many lives were lost by the explosion of steam-boilers before the safety-valve was generally adopted. And though all these inventions would have been better for science, they came into existence, for the most part, without its direct aid. It was the practical men in the mines, the factories, the machine shops and the clockmakers' shops and the locksmiths' shops or the curious amateurs with a turn for manipulating materials and imagining new processes, who made them possible. (pp. 215–16)

Phase IA was largely based in Western (continental) Europe; in contrast, Britain became the main focus of Phase IB, based on the steam engine, the symbol of the Second Industrial Revolution. But even here it could be said that the conception of the steam engine might ultimately be traced back to Hero of Alexandria, the translations of whose works in the 16th century had made people turn to the steam engine as a possible source of power and energy. As Mumford (1946, p. 152) points out, the relative backwardness of Britain, ironically, made it more ready to welcome and push through the developments associated with Phase IB.

As we have seen, the history of science and the history of technology in modern Western Europe, at one level of understanding, are not neatly harnessed in tandem. In Phase I, technology stood relatively independent of theoretical/scientific input. Phase II shows a marked difference – the major technological innovations are theory-led or -induced. With regard to Phase IIA, on the theoretical side, by 1850, most of the fundamental scientific discoveries had already been made. Regarding electromagnetism, Faraday in 1831 found that a conductor cutting the lines of force of a magnet created a difference in potential. This, together with the work done by Volta, Galvani, Oersted, Ohm, Ampere and Henry, provided the theoretical foundation for the conversion and distribution of energy, as well as for such significant inventions as the electric cell, the storage cell, the dynamo, the motor, the electric lamp. During the last quarter of the 19th century, these were spectacularly translated into industrial terms in the form of the electric power station, the telephone, the radio telegraph, and so on. Augmenting these were the phonograph, the moving picture, the steam turbine, the aeroplane.

That was on the physics front. On the chemistry front, it was the isolation of benzine by Faraday in the 1830s (and later, the use of naphtha) which made the industrial use of rubber possible. Advances in organic chemistry permitted the industrial utilisation of coal beyond using it as a direct source of energy. From 1 ton of coal, one could get 1500 pounds of coke, 111,360 cubic feet of gas, 12 gallons of tar, 25 pounds of ammonium phosphate and 4 gallons of light oils. From coal tar itself the chemist produced new medicines, dyes, resins, perfumes. Metallurgy also took revolutionary steps forward; however, aluminium, discovered by Oersted as early as 1825, had to await the arrival of electricity as a cheap source of energy before its commercial exploitation became feasible in the last decade of the century. Rare metals were incorporated into the industrial processes – for example selenium, whose electrical resistance varies inversely with the intensity of light, was used in automatic counting devices and electric door-openers. To quote Mumford (1946) again, he has aptly written as follows:

> In [this] phase, the main initiative comes, not from the ingenious inventor, but from the scientist who establishes the general law: the invention is a derivative product. It was Henry who in essentials invented the telegraph, not Morse; it was Faraday who invented the dynamo, not Siemens; it was Oersted who invented the electric motor, not Jacobi; it was Clerk-Maxwell and Hertz who invented the radio telegraph, not Marconi and De Forest. The translation of the scientific knowledge into practical instruments was a mere incident in the process of invention. While distinguished individual inventors like Edison, Baekeland and Sperry remained, the new inventive genius worked on the materials provided by science.

Out of this habit grew a new phenomenon: deliberate and systematic invention. Here was a new material: problem – find a new use for it. Or here was a necessary utility: problem – find the theoretic formula which would permit it to be produced. The ocean cable was finally laid only when Lord Kelvin had contributed the necessary scientific analysis of the problem it presented: the thrust of the propeller shaft on the steamer was finally taken up without clumsy and expensive mechanical devices, only when Michell worked out the behaviour of viscous fluids: long distance telephony was made possible only by systematic research by Pupin and others in the Bell Laboratories on the several elements in the problem. Isolated inspiration and empirical fumbling came to count less and less in invention. (p. 217–18)

In other words, it was only roughly from 1850 onwards that modern society began to reap the material benefits promised by modern science, its method, its philosophy and its ideological goal of controlling nature. That promise took more than two centuries to materialise when the paths of pure (theoretical) science and technology no longer diverged, acting, by and large, independently of each other, but began to be harnessed to work as joint forces. However, at least on one level of understanding, the team may be said to be led by pure science, the senior partner, while technology follows. (Yet at a deeper level, this may be an over-simplification – for qualifications, see section below.) In Phase I, when each was relatively autonomous, technology sometimes led the way to theoretical advance – witness the relationship between the steam engine and the fundamental science of thermodynamics. However, under the new settlement, technology has lost that causal initiative and now becomes, much more so than before, the executive arm, so to speak, of pure science.

The philosophy of technology and the philosophy of science

The relatively recent specific partnership between science and technology noted above raises, in the first instance, a terminological issue. One could conceivably distinguish between Phase I and Phase II by proposing that the word 'technology' be confined only to the former, and that some other term, such as 'applied science', be used in connection with the latter. It follows from this proposed usage that (a) the relationship between science and technology in Phase I is a contingent one, while (b) the relationship between science and applied science in Phase II is more than contingent. However, this possible way of defining terms may not find favour as it produces too much of a discontinuity in the history of humans in their attempts to modify nature in order to secure their own ends, be they survival, improvement of material well-being or the pursuit of self-realisation. The new technology is but a form of technology in the long history of that subject. It would be less misleading and distorting in recognising it as such. So it would be clearer to say that science and technology are really two separate, though related, forms of activities. The very intimate relationship which has grown up between the two roughly since 1850 is, nevertheless, a contingent one, in spite of the avowed aim of modern science to produce a technology which can control nature in a thoroughly systematic manner, guided by theoretical understanding rather than crude empirical happenstance.

To prevent misunderstanding of what has just been said, one needs to return to two of the main points raised in earlier sections of this chapter – Modern Science, Its Methodology and its Philosophy, The Goals of Modern Science. There it was argued that (a) modern science from its first beginnings was backed up by the new philosophy, in particular by its metaphysics of Scientific Naturalism, and (b) its ideological goal was the advancement of human material well-being via its technology to control and manipulate nature.[31] These two theses may be said to constitute the Modern Project of Science and Technology. The ideological goal to control and manipulate nature renders the Modern Project *au fond* a technologically oriented one. Under the Modern Project, modern science may be said to be really theoretical technology, a view associated with, for instance, Heidegger and Jonas. From this standpoint, science and technology appear to be inextricably linked – the linkage is more than an accidental one. As such, it is more than merely contingent. It is, then, not surprising that such Science should eventually spawn successful Technology, even though the Modern Project itself took over two hundred years since its inception 'to deliver the goods', so to speak.

To quote Mitcham (1994):

> For Heidegger what lies behind or beneath modern technology as a revealing that sets up and challenges the world is what he calls *Ge-stell*.
>
> *Ge-stell* names, to use Kantian language, the transcendental precondition of modern technology. ...'*Ge-stell*' refers to the gathering together of the setting-up that sets up human beings, that is, challenges them, to reveal reality, by the mode of ordering, as '*Bestand*' or resource. ... '*Ge-stell* refers to the mode of revealing that rules in the essence of modern technology and is not itself anything technological.' ... Not only does *Ge-stell* 'set-up' and 'challenge' the world ... it also sets upon and challenges human beings to set upon and challenge the world. ... 'The essence of modern technology starts human beings upon the way of that revealing through which reality everywhere, more or less distinctly, becomes resource.' (pp. 52–3)

Michael Zimmerman (1990), more or less, also makes the same point:

> Far from being a dispassionate quest for truth, scientific methodology had become the modern version of the power-oriented salvific

methodologies developed in the Middle Ages. Hence, Heidegger argued, even though modern science preceded the rise of modern technology by about two hundred years, modern science was already essentially 'technological' in character, i.e., oriented toward power. ... Science ... seeks not to let the entity show itself in ways appropriate to the entity in question, but instead compels the entity to reveal those aspects of itself that are consistent with the power aims of scientific culture. (pp. 181–2)

Hans Jonas (1966), too, has written in the same vein about Bacon's view of science:

Theory must be so revised that it yields 'designations and directions for works,' even has 'the invention of arts' for its very end, and thus becomes itself an art of invention. Theory it is nonetheless, as it is discovery and rational account of first causes and universal laws (forms). It thus agrees with classical theory in that it has the nature of things and the totality of nature for its object; but it is such a science of causes and laws, or a science of such causes and laws, as then makes it possible 'to command nature in action.' It makes this possible because from the outset it looks at nature *qua* acting, and achieves knowledge of nature's laws of action by itself engaging nature in action – that is, in experiment, and therefore on terms set by man himself. It yields directions for works because it first catches nature 'at work.'

A science of 'nature at work' is a mechanics, or a dynamics, of nature. For such a science Galileo and Descartes provided the speculative premises and the method of analysis and synthesis. Giving birth to a theory with inherently technological potential, they set on its actual course that fusion of theory and practice which Bacon was dreaming of. (pp. 189–90)

In the light of the above and of the points raised in the earlier section, there is, perhaps, some justification in saying that Modern Science is Theoretical Technology. All the same, Modern Technology, nevertheless, is applied science. To see why this latter claim may be justified, one must distinguish the Modern Project, itself embedded in a certain metaphysical and ideological framework, from: (a) the formulation and the testing of specific scientific theories in the history and philosophy of science; (b) the relationship, if any, between a specific theory and a related specific technology; and (c) the epistemic goals of theory formulation and theory testing, on the one hand, and the testing of technological hypotheses on the other. Here, as we have seen, the linkage in the case of any one specific theory and any one specific technology throughout the modern period, in particular during Phase I, appears to be much looser than the postulated linkage between Science and Technology in the Modern Project itself.

(However, in Phase II and especially IIB, the intensely intimate causal relationship between certain specific theories and the specific technologies they induce and render possible does obtain.)[32] Moreover, the epistemic goals of theory formulation and testing are also perceived to be somewhat different and distinct from those of testing hypotheses in the technological domain even in Phase II.

The recognition that their epistemic goals are distinct is reflected by the fact that while the philosophy of science has a recognised and well-established agenda, an analogous philosophy of technology does not obviously exist. Indeed, while the former is an eminently respectable part of philosophical enquiry, the latter may be held at arms length with a degree of suspicion, even if it does not draw a blank – see Bunge (1979).[33] The agenda of the one may be clear, that of the other is not. Bunge feels the need to sketch an outline for that missing agenda. He writes:

> Some of the typical problems in the philosophy of technology are these: (a) Which characteristics does technological knowledge share with scientific knowledge, and which are exclusive of the former? (b) In what does the ontology of artifacts differ from that of natural objects? (c) What distinguishes a technological forecast from a scientific forecast? (d) How are rule of thumb, technological rule, and scientific law related? (e) Which philosophical principles play a heuristic, and which a blocking, role in technological research? (f) Does pragmatism account for the theoretical richness of technology? (g) What are the value systems and the ethical norms of technology? (h) What are the conceptual relations between technology and the other branches of contemporary culture? (p. 263)

The aim of this section is to clarify problem (b) identified above, as far as biotic artefacts are concerned. This section later also addresses (d). But for the moment, what will be emphasised is one crucial difference between science and technology (in both phases), namely, their respective overarching epistemological goals. But before dealing with that, it may be helpful to point out their similarities under Phase II in two essential aspects as Bunge (1979, pp. 265–8) has done:

1. Methodologically, a technological research programme is no different from that of a scientific one. They include the following elements: identifying and articulating the problem, solving it with existing empirical or theoretical knowledge, and, failing that, putting forward new hypotheses and ways to try to solve it, working out a solution within the new framework, testing the solution by experimentation and, in the light of that, amending the hypothesis under test or even reformulating the original problem.

2. Epistemologically and ontologically, technology and pure science (at least in one conspicuous tradition in the philosophy of science) share certain common assumptions: that an external world exists, that we can come to know it partially, though never totally, and that knowledge of such a world can be improved upon and increased, though again recognising that the goal of complete and total knowledge can never be reached.[34] In other words, they both subscribe to what may be called critical realism; technologists would realise, just as the pure scientists, that their theories cannot, literally, be pictures of reality but are symbolic oversimplified representations of a fairly abstract kind of 'the reality' that they are grappling with. (In this conception of the philosophy of science, in Phase I, technologists would have tended to be naive realists, if they had at all confronted themselves with this philosophical issue.)

However, whether under Phase I or II, it is said that the overarching epistemological goal of technology differs from that of science. Even in the latter phase, the critical realism of the technologist is subordinated to the crucial requirement that the solution works – in other words pragmatism is an overriding demand. Unlike pure scientists who often claim that in principle they are interested in knowledge for the sake of knowledge, technologists are primarily interested in scientific knowledge (if it exists) as a mere means to the end of providing a solution to the practical problem in hand. If scientific knowledge is nonexistent or unhelpful, they will look elsewhere for assistance. Nor would they be unduly worried should the viable solution turn out for the moment to lack a proper complete scientific explanation.

To put it even more strongly, scientific knowledge per se seems neither to be a necessary nor a sufficient condition for what counts as a successful technological solution to a problem. An example that it is not the former is the success shown by the traditional methods of artificial selection in breeding plants and animals. Until the so-called rediscovery of Mendelism in 1900, there was no adequate or proper explanation to account for their success. An example that illustrates the latter is plate tectonic theory in geology and seismography, which have not so far, at least, led to a technology of forming new mountains, or of controlling the movements of the earth's crust or, indeed, even of accurate predictions of earthquakes.

Technology's goal of getting practical results also affects its relationship with the concept of truth. To quote Bunge (1979) on this point:

> Although in practice [the technologist] adopts the correspondence conception of truth as adequacy of the intellect or mind to the thing, he will care for the true data, hypotheses and theories only as long as they are conducive to the desired outcomes. He will often prefer a simple half-truth to a complex truth. He must, because he is always in a hurry to get results. Besides, any error made in neglecting some factor (or some

decimal figure) is likely to be overshadowed by unpredictable disturbances his real system may undergo. Unlike the physicist, the chemist, or the biologist, he cannot protect his systems against shocks other than by building shock-absorbing mechanisms into them. For similar reasons, the technologist cannot prefer deep but involved theories when superficial ones will do. However, unless he is a pseudotechnologist, he will not shy away from complex and deep theories if they promise success. ... The technologist, in sum, will adopt a mixture of critical realism and pragmatism, varying these ingredients according to his needs. He will seem to confirm first one and then another epistemology, while actually all he intends to do is to maximize his own efficiency regardless of philosophical loyalties. (p. 269)

The epistemological target of (pure) scientific theorising is truth (or at least, approximation to truth) according to a dominant tradition in the philosophy of science – for instance, see Popper (1969). When technology applies the findings of pure science – for instance, when a theory of flight is based on the theory of fluid dynamics – the epistemological target of such technological theories is efficiency, not truth. Indeed it may be said to adhere to the following methodological rule: only adopt as deep a scientific theory as is adequate for the problem in hand. In this sense, it is theoretically less sophisticated than pure science, although it makes up for this theoretical simplicity by being wholly opportunistic in using knowledge of any kind, from any domain (whether ordinary, older, less sophisticated or the latest sophisticated deep theory in science).[35] For example, in constructing an optical instrument, the technologists would rely, in the main, on ray optics, a theory of optics based on what was known about light round about the middle of the 17th century. They would ignore wave optics except to the extent it could help them understand why certain effects occur, such as the appearance of colours near the edge of the lens which, to them, are considered to be undesirable.

Deeper, more complex and more accurate theories may not necessarily be the most economical to use – imagine using quantum theory to predict or explain car crashes. Efficiency demands that you use less deep theories, with smaller operational costs, to get as much out of them with as little input as possible. From the standpoint of technology, a true scientific theory in principle can be successfully employed, but in practice technologists may have to decline its help, so long as an alternative exists which can do the job satisfactorily, but at less cost operationally and therefore, usually, economically. The alternative may indeed even be a false theory on the whole, but so long as it possesses an element of truth which can be relied on by the technology in question, it would do fine.

To emphasise the distinction between scientific and technological knowledge, Bunge says that while the former attempts to formulate laws (about universal regularities), the latter aims at establishing rules.[36] Laws are descriptive – when conditions *x, y, z* obtain, *A* obtains. Rules, on the other hand, are prescriptive. They are what may be called hypothetical imperatives – if one wishes to achieve *A*, then one ought to do *x*. Phase I technology primarily relied on pre-scientifc rules (rules of thumb used in arts- and crafts-based procedures of production, such as yeast fermentation in brewing and baking). In Phase II, technological rules are grounded in scientific laws. By this is meant that the laws must be capable of accounting for, or explaining, the efficacy of the rules. To prevent water from freezing in the car radiator in the winter, one ought to add antifreeze to it. The rule achieving the desired end is successfully and satisfactorily explained in terms of the differential freezing points of water and methanol or ethanediol (two commonly used antifreeze substances), which in turn could be accounted for by further deeper theories, such as the kinetic and atomic theories.

Phase I rules may be empirically very effective. But because they are not properly grounded in scientific laws, there is always the possibility that their efficacious outcome may be a mere coincidence. Suppose (in temperate climates) one adheres to the rule 'do not plant in the depth of winter but in the springtime': one would indeed get a high degree of horticultural success. But one might mistakenly conclude from this that the plants grow so well because of the warmth that comes with the spring. But one would be wrong, though not totally wrong. The warmth is an important component of success, but only when it is accompanied by an increase of light in the spring and summer, which is vital to plant growth. Today the rule's efficacy is properly grounded in our theoretical understanding of the processes involved in photosynthesis and the conditions under which plant growth obtains.

The above would account for why Phase I rules, though empirically effective, provide one with less than optimal control over nature. Maybe most of the time they work, but there will be cases of failure. Within the framework of technological rules, the failure cannot be explained, just observed. However, it could later be explained in terms of scientific laws when these are discovered. If so, then the laws in turn could lead to the formulation of improved, more efficacious rules (that is under Phase II), whose scope of operation may transcend that of the original rule. Using the plant growth example again, the theoretical understanding of plant physiology, chemistry, and so on, enables the technologist to devise the greenhouse. Such a technological innovation makes it possible for us humans to overcome the constraints imposed by nature through the rhythm of its seasons. Now tomatoes in northerly climes will grow the whole year round under artificially produced conditions of appropriate degrees of warmth and light. Undoubtedly in this way the scope has enormously increased one's control over nature.

It would be helpful to sum up the above as follows:

1. Phase I technology is, by and large, independent of science. It flourished in cultures which lacked explicit systematic scientific theorising of any kind. It could flourish just as readily in cultures engaged in such theoretical activities, but underpinned by a metaphysics and using a methodology which differ from the modern scientific one. Such technology can be empirically efficacious and, indeed, was so historically.

2. However, phase II technology is a much more powerful tool in manipulating nature than its Phase I counterpart. Take the treatment of haemophilia in the history of medicine. Under Phase I, the only alleviation available would have been prevention at the most elementary level, that is, for the sufferer of the condition to take steps to reduce the chances of being bruised, cut or wounded. Under early Phase II technology, haemophiliacs were given whole blood transfusion. Further medical understanding advanced, and the precise nature of the condition became understood. It is now known that there are two different forms of haemophilia: haemophilia A, in which the sufferer lacks a clotting chemical called factor VIII, and haemophilia B, in which the sufferer lacks factor IX. Of the two, the former is more common than the latter. In the light of this understanding, a new technology replaced whole blood transfusion. The missing clotting chemical is injected three times a week to counter the inherited condition. The technology is more specifically targeted than the one it replaces; as a result, it is scientifically more precise. Its emergence is predicated upon advances both in theoretical knowledge and technology, allowing the clotting chemical to be either extracted from human blood plasma or manufactured by genetically engineered organisms. This may be said to constitute the middle stage of Phase II technology.[37]

But today, with the science of molecular genetics and its accompanying technology of genetic engineering in place, there is room to take the treatment of haemophilia to yet another stage of development. This is so-called gene therapy. Indeed, it has been reported that this further stage has already been taken. According to the publication *Science in China*, a team of scientists at the Institute of Genetics in Shanghai had performed it on two teenage haemophiliacs, both suffering from a lack of factor IX.[38] One of them is said, as a result of the treatment, to be now producing the clotting chemical in his own blood. If this were really so, it would be a permanent cure. Using standard gene therapy techniques, the team first isolated the gene for factor IX, then inserted it into a virus. It also removed fibroblasts (cells which form connective tissue under the skin) from the two patients. The treated virus was used to infect these fibroblasts. The infected fibroblasts, now carrying the missing gene, were then injected back into the two patients. An inherited disability is now cured by gene replacement therapy.[39] This admittedly is not as radical as germ-line gene therapy which, if carried out, could in principle eradicate haemophilia by ensuring that no sons would be born with the genetic disorder (not merely that males born with such an inherited condition would be permanently cured of it) or that no mother who is a haemophilia carrier would give birth to daughters who, in turn, will be carriers.[40]

3. Although it is the case that more precise scientific theories are not necessarily always relied upon by technology, which seems to prefer the less precise and complex but still adequate alternative, such theories are, nevertheless, required to ground the efficacy of the rules, giving them the maximum epistemological support possible. Going back to the example of ray and wave optics in the construction of optical instruments, one can see why the former accounts for the instrument's overall success, and the latter, for its being less than totally perfect. As we have seen, while efficacious technological rules may lead to new theoretical understanding, their efficacy, on its own, is not synonymous with truth.

4. Phase II technology, although induced and led by pure scientific findings, is not entailed by them. In other words, theoretical advances and revolutions may be a necessary but not a sufficient condition for its emergence. However, to prevent misunderstanding of this claim, one has to distinguish between two contexts here: (a) pure theory providing the epistemological grounding and direction for the induced technology, and (b) a pure theory being actually used in a particular piece or type of technology. As we have seen, in context (b), there are two possibilities: (i) there could be an alternative, less accurate theory the technology could rely on, or (ii) social, economic and political considerations may be hostile to the emergence of a new technology. The discussion here is confined to (i). As for context (a), when a theory-induced technology does emerge, the efficacy of its technological rules is grounded in, and accounted for, by the laws of the pure theory – in this sense, there is a very strong empirical, as well as epistemological, link between technological efficacy and scientific truth. Furthermore, they have certain concepts in common.

'Deep' theories and their power of control

We have, so far, looked at the differences between Phase I and Phase II technology. One needs to say something very briefly here about the distinction between the 'deeper' and 'less deep' theories in the natural sciences underpinning Phase II technology. 'Deep' may be understood in at least three ways:

1. A less deep theory is ultimately to be explained in terms of a deeper one. The kinetic theory is explained in terms of the atomic theory, and the

latter itself is accounted for by subatomic quantum theory. Relatively speaking, the first is less deep than the second, and the second than the third. Similarly, Mendelian genetics is accounted for in terms of molecular genetics.

2. The deeper theory may also then be said to be more comprehensive in scope, explaining a wider range of data, accounting for more variables in their causal contribution to a particular phenomenon.

3. A less deep theory may contain laws about particles and their behaviour at the macro level of existence and observation, while a deeper theory postulates laws about particles and their behaviour at the micro level of existence and observation. Newtonian macro physics may then be said to be less deep than quantum physics.

All three senses are relevant to the discussion in hand. The Modern Project of Science and Technology is built on an ontology of materialism. Ever since its inception, its central aim has been to penetrate the nature and structure of matter. As we have seen in an earlier section, macro properties of the natural world, such as the so-called secondary qualities, are said not to reside in the object and, therefore, are not real. Objects are constituted by their primary qualities, which are real. Furthermore, matter at the macro level of existence is to be broken down analytically into its component parts at the micro level of existence. Hence the atomic theory of matter – all macro objects are made up of atoms, and molecules, which are themselves combinations of atoms. 20th century science went even beyond that to the subatomic theory of matter.

In this world-view, matter then is ultimately uniform and homogeneous. Its diversity, in the form of different sorts of organisms, of minerals, that is, of different natural kinds, is no more than a difference in the arrangement of the primary qualities involved, of atomic particles which, in turn, are constituted of subatomic particles and their nuclei.[41]

It has been the ideological goal of the Modern Project from its very beginning in the 17th century to use its theoretical advances to engender powerful technologies to control nature in order to serve human ends. This promise has been made good from the middle to the late 19th century onwards. And as its theoretical advances get deeper and deeper into the structure of matter, the theory-induced technologies get more and more powerful.

Take biology as a discipline. In the words of one well-known historian of the subject:

> Contemporary biology is characterized by several important factors. One is the firm belief that all biological problems can ultimately be studied on the molecular level. This view does not maintain that studies at other levels of organization, such as that of the cell, the organ, the whole

organism, or the population are of no value. In fact, there is a growing awareness among some biologists that it is [...] as important to study these higher levels of organization as it is to study the lower, molecular levels. The view that reduction of a complex biological phenomenon to its simpler components (cells or molecules) is a sufficient explanation has become less prevalent among biologists in the early 1970s.[42] Nevertheless, the revolution in molecular biology in the 1950s and early 1960s emphasized the importance of understanding the molecular basis of biological phenomena before trying to approach the larger, higher-level interactions. (Allen, 1979, pp. xiii–xiv)

Biologists on the whole, since the late 1970s, may indeed have resisted strident reductionism of the kind which says that cells are mere collections of molecules, or 'what is true of *E. coli* [a bacterium] is true of the elephant', a view prevalent in the 1950s and 1960s. But it remains true that they unanimously agree that molecular biology provides a deeper level of theoretical understanding than classical Mendelian genetics, leading to much more powerful technologies culminating in the creation of human-made life.

As illustrated by the treatment of haemophilia mentioned above, Phase I technology is perhaps, at best, only a feeble expression of the weak form of control earlier identified. But the Phase II technology illustrates the strong form of control at work. And each of its stages is an expression of a progressively greater degree of such control. These points may be displayed as follows, using haemophilia again as an example:

1.   The technological rule of Phase I, yielding only weak control, may be formulated thus: if unstoppable bleeding is to be avoided, the sufferer of haemophilia ought to avoid being bruised or cut. Call this TRI. The scope of TRI's efficacy is not great, in the sense that it is useless should the sufferer unavoidably become bruised. There are, unfortunately, many such situations arising in the lifetime of a sufferer. Its efficacy is no more impressive than its analogue in a hurricane context, where one could, at best, only advise people to get out of the way of the hurricane when the signs of its imminence are detected, there being no means of deflecting it or defusing its strength. This minimal degree of control is a reflection of the lack of theoretical understanding of the phenomenon in question (although, as noted earlier, from the epistemological point of view, theoretical understanding is only a necessary, not a sufficient condition for the emergence of a more powerful technology).

2(a).   The technological rule of the first stage of Phase II, which is a manifestation of the strong form of control, may be formulated thus: to prevent unstoppable bleeding, the sufferer ought to be given a blood transfusion containing normal blood of the right type. Call this TRIIa.

Undoubtedly, the scope of TRIIa's efficacy is greater than that of TRI, for it can cope when the sufferer unavoidably has bruised or wounded himself. But it is beside the point when the appropriate type of normal blood is not available for transfusion.[43] The increase in control reflects the theoretical understanding that the condition is caused by an inability of the sufferer's blood to clot, owing to its lack of a certain chemical, and that it is a genetic disability, not a functional one.

2(b). The technological rule of the second stage of Phase II may be formulated as follows: to prevent unstoppable bleeding, the sufferer ought to be given the clotting chemical (factor VIII or IX). Call this TRIIb. The scope of TRIIb's efficacy is greater than that of TRIIa, as it overcomes the scarcity in the supply of normal whole blood, especially when the clotting agent in question can be produced via genetically engineered organisms.[44] Also, the clotting agent can be more conveniently introduced into the sufferer's body through injections, rather than the more cumbersome technology of full blood transfusion itself. This greater degree of control is a reflection of the more detailed theoretical understanding of the nature of blood in general, and the specific deficiency isolated in the blood of haemophiliacs.

2(c). The technological rule of the third stage of Phase II may be formulated as follows: to prevent unstoppable bleeding, the sufferer ought to be given gene replacement therapy. Call this TRIIc.[45] The scope of TRIIc's efficacy is greater than that of TRIIb, as it renders repeated and tiresome injections of the clotting agent throughout the lifetime of the sufferer redundant. And even more tellingly, the sufferer, formerly identified as a haemophiliac, is transformed under such treatment into a non-haemophiliac. His status has spectacularly altered. His genetic disability has been removed once and for all (if the treatment is truly successful). This still greater degree of control reflects yet more advanced theoretical understanding of the nature of heredity via molecular genetics.

2(d). The technological rule of the fourth stage of Phase II may be formulated as follows: to prevent unstoppable bleeding in individual males from ever occurring, germ-line therapy ought to be given to the female carriers of the condition. This would yield male genotypes with the gene to produce factor VIII or IX. Call this TRIId.[46] The scope of TRIId's efficacy is in turn greater than that of TRIIc, for it actually tackles the problem at an earlier stage, by ensuring that no males would be born haemophiliac in the first place. This ultimate degree of control is a further reflection of knowledge in molecular genetics and of the nature of haemophilia as a genetic disability.

One caveat should be entered. The correlations between the efficacy of technological rules, their corresponding degree of control, on the one hand, and theoretical advances in the relevant pure sciences, on the other, as set out above, are not meant to reflect actual historical correlations. They are meant to bring out more clearly the epistemological linkage between technological rules and scientific laws, namely, that laws ground the efficacy of rules. And in so doing, one is also laying bare the philosophical foundations for the ideological goal of modern science to control nature in the strongest form possible, to make it serve human ends, be it the alleviation of pain, the promotion of material well-being or of freedom and self-realisation.

Notes

1 This section will concentrate on the empiricist side of the label, while the next will say something about the positivist dimension.
2 The respective accounts of modern philosophy and modern science given in this chapter are not intended to imply that either arose absolutely *de novo* from nowhere in the 17th century and, therefore, to deny that precursory work in medieval philosophy and science based on developments of Aristotelianism might not have paved the way – see, for example, Grant (1997). (Mentioning a date, such as the beginning of the 17th century as the starting point of modernity, is, of course, in one sense arbitrary, though unavoidably so.)
3 See Wick (1967).
4 The crucial passage, which according to Collingwood must be well known to nearly every educated person in Western Christendom, is as follows:

> Thou has learnt from astronomical proofs that the whole earth compared with the universe is no greater than a point, that is, compared with the sphere of the heavens, it may be thought of as having no size at all. Then of this corner, it is only one-quarter that, according to Ptolemy, is habitable to living things. Take away from this quarter the seas, marshes, and other desert places, and the space left for man hardly even deserves the name of infinitesimal (Book ii, Prosa vii). (Collingwood, 1945, p. 97)

5 As noted earlier, medieval Aristotelianism is not to be equated straightforwardly with Aristotle's own system of philosophy. What follows is Aristotelian rather than Aristotle's philosophy.
6 As is the case with all great thinkers, Galileo's writings are subject to different assessments. One interpretation even claims that there is nothing really new about his science. For an account of some of these interpretations, see Shapere (1974). Shapere in his own evaluation also differs from that of Drake (1980). For a selection of Galileo's writings, see Drake (1957). See also Drake and O'Malley (1960).

As for the philosophy of mechanism, it may be taken to embrace any one or all of the following theses:

(a) The (modern) science of mechanical motion as established by Galileo, Newton and others.

(b) Reality is nature mathematised and quantified.

(c) The natural world is actually a machine to be studied and understood by sciences, such as the science of mechanistic motion, using mathematics for the formulation of their laws.

(d) The fundamental stuff of the universe is matter in motion (for instance, Hobbes's materialism) to which everything else in the universe may onto-logically be reduced.

(e) The laws of motion or of physics are the most fundamental laws to which other laws about natural phenomena are to be ultimately reduced.

(f) The universe is a deterministic one – given the laws of nature (discovered under (a), (b) and (c) above) and the positions and velocities of the particles of matter at time t, one could predict precisely their positions and velocities at time t_1 (Laplacean determinism).

In this chapter, the mechanistic paradigm and world-view are discussed primarily in the context of (a) and (b) above. In Chapter 1 the section entitled 'Are living organisms machines?' (pp. 33ff.) touched on an aspect of (c).

For a fuller discussion of the emergence of positivism, especially with regard to Hobbes and Bacon, see Keekok Lee (1989a, pp. 35–66). Positivism itself plays a significant part in formulating the philosophy of mechanism. But another very important contributor is, of course, Descartes, whose dualism between the material and the mental/spiritual makes it possible for science to treat all things in the universe (except humans, in so far as they have minds and souls) as mere objects, subject only to the laws of mathematics and physics.

7 Max Caspar, a biographer, has written:

> Nothing in the world was created by God without a plan; this was Kepler's principal axiom. His undertaking was no less than to discover this plan of creation, to think the thoughts of God all over again, because he was convinced that 'just like a human architect, God has approached the foundation of the world according to order and rule and so measured out everything that one might suppose that architecture did not take Nature as a model but rather that God had looked upon the manner of building of the coming human.' (1959, p. 62)

8 The term 'philosophy' is here used in the sense of 'natural philosophy' to refer to the study of what we call physics today. The ancient Scottish universities still use the term 'professor of natural philosophy' to refer to the professor of physics.
   For a dissenting voice on the overrated significance of this passage, see James Maclachlan (1990).

9 For a related account of the new science, its methodology and its metaphysics, see Richard S. Westfall (1992). In the new order, nature was quantified, mechanised, perceived to be other and secularised.

10 For an account of Hume's analysis within positivist methodology, see Keekok Lee (1989a, pp. 67–71).

11 Such a low-level regularity may in turn be derived from a higher-level regularity, so that ultimately a science consists of a hierarchical or pyramidal structure of regularities – see Lee (1989a).

12 However, one should not overlook that for Aristotle 'for the sake of which' did not imply want, desire or ends separate from the processes themselves.

13 In the history of modern philosophy, the term 'metaphysics' has two meanings. The first refers to that branch of philosophy called by that name after Aristotle

himself, which is concerned with the general problem of being and existence – 'ontology' is often used as a substitute term. (See Barnes, 1995b, for a short account of Aristotle's notion of metaphysics.) The second refers to what may be called the abusive sense, so that anything called 'metaphysical' carries with it the charge of being unintelligible, obscurantist, even meaningless. (This sense will be further raised in the text, a little later see page 51.) Science, whether modern or pre-modern, necessarily presupposes certain metaphysical assumptions from the standpoint of metaphysics in the non-abusive sense; however, champions of modern science have been to known to deny this. Instead, they charge pre-modern science with making 'metaphysical' assumptions in the abusive sense of that term.

14   The first detailed systematic account is given by Hobbes – see Keekok Lee (1990, pp. 11–106). But Hobbes's contribution is frequently, if not invariably, overlooked for the following reasons:

(a)   He had the misfortune to write before Newton; after Newton, physics became the 'queen of the sciences' or the paradigmatic science. For Hobbes the most mature science (except possibly astronomy) was geometry.

(b)   The geometry he celebrated as the paradigmatic science was Euclidean geometry which, since the late 19th and early 20th centuries, has been shown by logicians and mathematicians to be only one geometry among others. The plurality of geometries means that geometrical truths are no longer considered to be both certain and informative and, hence, no longer satisfy what used to be the philosophical Holy Grail, the twin *desiderata* of being informative and certain. As Einstein commented, in so far as they are informative, they are uncertain, and in so far as they are certain, they are uninformative or tautologous.

(c)   He did not coin the term 'positivism', the honour going to August Comte almost two centuries later.

Hobbes's *Leviathan* is regarded as his consummate contribution to political philosophy; but given his ambition to construct a new philosophy systematically, that famous book of his also has a lot to say about metaphysics and epistemology. (On this point, see also Keekok Lee, 1990, pp. 11–106, and McNeilly, 1968, p. 77). As for Comte, his monumental opus is entitled *Cours de Philosophie Positive* (6 vols, Paris, 1830–42); for an accessible selection, see *The Essential Comte*, edited by Andreski (1974).

For a general account of positivism, see Kolakowski (1972); for an account of the relationship between positivism and the social sciences, see Halfpenny (1982).

15   As pointed out by Dijksterhuis (1961): 'The Aristotelian–Thomistic theory of knowledge is markedly "sensationalist": all our knowledge is due to the experience gained during our present lives with the aid of the senses, and there is no room for any knowledge inborn or deriving from an anterior existence' (p. 132). Moreover, Albertus Magnus (another important Dominican thinker who contributed to the so-called Thomistic synthesis) also emphasised the role of experimentation, under all possible circumstances, in gaining scientific knowledge. However, in spite of these 'modern' characteristics, it would not be right to ignore the overall medieval context, social and philosophical, in which they were embedded.

16   Hobbes anticipated Comte's law of intellectual development involving three stages: the theological, the metaphysical and finally the scientific (or positivist)

stage. Proper knowledge (as opposed to pseudo-knowledge) is only obtained in the last stage of intellectual development. See Keekok Lee (1990, pp. 12–20).

17   But there is another thesis which together with that of the unity of method constitutes such a methodology – it is called the unity of science thesis. However, unlike the unity of method thesis, not all who care(d) to call themselves positivists would subscribe to it. It says that all phenomena can ultimately be explained in terms of the laws which obtain in the so-called basic or fundamental science(s), whether physics or chemistry, or physics-cum-chemistry. Philosophers, like Hobbes in the 17th century and Neurath in the 20th century, upheld it. But whether philosophers do or do not, and irrespective of the fashionable distancing of philosophers from positivism today, it remains true that the reductionism implicated in the unity of science thesis provides the metaphysical impulse behind scientific explanations even today – we shall see this clearly when we turn to molecular genetics and biology in Chapter 4. Indeed, the whole thrust of this book, in a sense, is to make obvious the role played by such a reductionistic enterprise in transforming living organisms as naturally occurring beings into biotic artefacts.

18   If it is objected that such a possibility does not qualify as weak control, then only the possibility of control in the strong sense remains as the goal of science.

19   Comte could not possibly have anticipated late 20th century projects such as terraformation.

20   See Keekok Lee (1989a).

21   As far as order in the normative political, moral and legal domains is concerned, it is obvious that such order is entirely human-made. In these, there is no analogue to prediction in the domain of natural phenomena by which one could test a theory or hypothesis. That is why the logic of prediction or explanation or theory testing is transmuted to become the logic of justification – see Lee (1989a, pp. 132–63).

22   On the above points I follow Mitcham (1979, pp. 184–5).
      The dictionary referred to is John Kersey's edition of Edward Phillips's dictionary, *The New World of English Words*, published in 1706.

23   Having said this, one must still point out that in humankind's history of tool-making and tool-using, there are different types of technology, only the latest stage of which is quite so systematically science-induced. This point will be looked at in detail later.

24   The account that follows summarises Mitcham's arguments (without misrepresenting them, one hopes).

25   For a more detailed discussion of the relation between modern science and modern technology, see 'The philosophy of technology and the philosophy of science' (pp. 63ff.). There, two approaches will be mentioned – the more orthodox holds that pure science paves the way for technology which is applied science, and the less familiar, the Heideggerian inversion, namely, that pure science is really theoretical technology. The line of thought developed in this book acknowledges the Heideggerian inversion at the level of the metaphysics and the ideology of Scientific Naturalism, but not necessarily at the more concrete level of theory formulation, theory testing and theory application as technology. But these points will be pursued later.

26   As for the various usages of the term 'technology', a discussion may be found in Mitcham (1994, pp. 143–54).

27   For a recent accessible account, see Pacey (1990).

28 Mitcham lists five philosophies of technology in terms of volition as the will to: survive or satisfy some basic biological need (Spengler, Ferré), control or power (Mumford), freedom (Grant, Walker, Zschimmer), efficiency (Skolimowski) and realise the *Gestalt* of the worker (Jünger) or almost any self-concept (Ortega) – see Mitcham (1994, pp. 247–8).

29 The economic relations of this control are secondary – witness the agreement between both Marxist and bourgeois capitalist analyses on this point.

30 Phase I itself would probably have been preceded by an earlier stage which could be called the phase of 'found technology'. It would have included some degree of shaping and designing the thing found to suit the use it was put to – see Ihde (1993). It would be difficult to conceive of the beginnings of human culture in its absence. It is found also in the case of certain primates such as chimpanzees – in this context, Ihde calls it 'prototechnology' (1993, p. 48). But with humans, unlike other primates, they soon developed beyond found technology and its minimum designing to that of maximum designing.

Human cultures in general, not only Western European culture, have also gone through Phase IA and IB. What is distinctive about Western European culture is that it went on to Phase II from the 17th century onwards.

31 For a discussion of the alternative goal of promoting self-realisation, rather than improvement in material well-being, under the philosophy of idealism, see Chapter 6.

32 In Phase II the causal arrow from theory to technology is not displaced by recognising that technological objects spawned by theory could in turn influence the development of theory. For instance, it has been correctly observed that the design and construction of the cyclotron (and increasingly more powerful ones) have affected and continue to affect theory development itself. The point to grasp here is simply that the cyclotron would not, as a matter of fact, have been dreamt of, designed or constructed in the absence of theoretical particle physics as we know it today. As a technological construct and object, it is, therefore, totally conceptually dependent upon the understanding of subatomic matter, as given to us by the theories and speculation prevalent in contemporary physics.

For an alternative view, see Don Ihde (1991) on what he calls 'technoscience.' He writes: 'Today's Big Science is so closely tied to Big Technology that one can meaningfully speak of a single, complex phenomenon which is both a scientific technology and a technological science: *technoscience*' (p. 138). Ihde may be said to push the Heideggerian inversion to its logical conclusion, namely, that: (a) there is no 'pure' science 'eventually producing some "applied" effect'. Rather there is a *'technology-driven science'*. 'At the highest altitude, such a perspective was suggested most radically by Heidegger ... But at a lower and much more concrete level we also have noted how parts of our world are instrumentally and technologically revealed and even produced' (ibid., p. 137). (b) Theoretical entities are much more like technological than 'natural' ones. They are:

> an interesting crossing of what could be called the convergence of Nature with Culture through laboratory science. The object produced in the laboratory and reified into an independent thing was fabricated, but fabricated in such a way that it takes on the status of 'reality.' ... Reality is what resists, at least until more powerful instruments and laboratory complexes can overthrow them' (ibid., p. 134).

(c) 'Instrumental realism' is the correct account of theoretical entities:

> By turning to the role of instruments and taking account of what they deliver for science, the very territories previously taken as theoretical domains also change – they shrink in size and significance. In short, instrumental realism gives some degree of type of 'reality-status' to entities often taken to be merely theoretical, leaving only small areas to remain theoretical. This means, in turn, that the role of 'pure' theorizing gets reduced to an even smaller area of science's activity than had previously been assumed. Theorizing becomes a special, highly speculative exercise of scientific imagination important, but both reduced in size and open to greater skepticism in regions outside the current reaches of instrumental possibility. (ibid., p. 100)

See also Staudenmaier (1985, chapter 3).

33   According to Mitcham (1994, pp. 37–8), Bunge belongs to what he calls the 'engineering philosophy of technology' school, as opposed to the 'humanities philosophy of technology' school, to which Mumford, Heidegger, Ellul and others belong.

34   Scientists, if pressed, are by and large critical realists, although a few may even be naive realists. A competing tradition in the philosophy of science rejects realism, even of the critical variety. (On another front, Kuhn's *Structure of Scientific Revolutions* (1962), in spite of Kuhn himself, has been *interpreted* as an attack on the rationality of science itself.) Far from it being the case that scientific theories are attempts to capture Reality, Reality is given and constituted by them – see, for instance, Bird (1987, pp. 255–64). Older philosophers of science, such as Duhem and Poincaré, espouse scientific conventionalism or instrumentalism. But see also Ihde (1991) who espouses 'instrumental realism' (not to be confused with the Duhem/Poincaré variety), already mentioned in an earlier note.

35   For an account by an engineer, see Gosling (2000, p. 3). (William Gosling is a past president of the UK Institution of Electrical Engineers.)

36   For a full philosophical discussion, see Bunge (1983, pp. 69–71).

37   Ian Wilmut and his team, which stunned the world in 1998 with the news about Dolly the cloned sheep, are also responsible for Polly. Polly is a cloned sheep too, but she is also a genetically transformed clone, through the technology of nuclear transfer, the technology used also in the creation of Dolly. According to the Wilmut team, their real achievement in creating Polly is to get her to secrete in her milk the human protein factor IX – see Wilmut et al. (2000).

38   See *The Observer* (10 October 1993, p. 13). Western scientific reaction reported in *The Observer* mentioned certain ethical problems that could arise. For instance, using a retrovirus as the vector could conceivably trigger cancers.

39   Another success story of gene replacement therapy concerns the disease known as ADA (adenosine deaminase) deficiency, commonly known as the 'bubble-boy disease'. The boy in question had no choice but to live his short life in a plastic bubble in order to avoid infection to which he could fatally succumb. The condition was caused by some 'misplaced' nucleotides on the DNA of chromosome 20. In 1990 two girls (from Ohio) were treated, when physicians (W. French Anderson, Michael Blaese and Kenneth Culver) at the US National Institute of Health mixed cells containing the right molecular sequences carried by viral vectors with extracts of their own white blood cells, and then introduced the new

mixture into their blood stream. Soon the transformed cells began producing the normal amount of ADA. This showed that gene therapy had worked in the sense that their bodies had begun to produce almost a quarter of the ADA that an average person makes. See Regis (1995, pp. 272–3); Ridley (1999, pp. 249–50).

40　This last step has now been taken. Doctors from the Universitat Autonomia de Barcelona and researchers from the Cefer Institute of Reproduction in Spain published in the journal *Prenatal Diagnosis* the case of a Spanish woman who is a haemophilia carrier, but who has chosen not to have daughters. The medical team involved made sure that the embryos implanted in the woman's uterus were male. (The technique used is PGD, pre-implantation genetic diagnosis.) This goes beyond the stage sanctioned by the British HFEA (Human Fertilisation and Embryological Authority) which allows the elimination of embryos possessing the defective gene for haemophilia before transplantation only in the case where the mother is a carrier; it does not yet permit a woman or couple to choose the sex of an embryo to ensure that no daughter would be born, who might eventually pass the defective gene to her sons, when she in turn reproduces. (See Meek, 17 October 2000, p. 6).

41　The claim that there are natural kinds, or that natural kinds exist, presupposes that there are discontinuities which actually exist in the world and which can be found to be so. This in turn presupposes some version of metaphysical realism. The thesis of metaphysical realism is as follows: that there is a fundamental distinction between the world as it is and whatever thoughts, beliefs, hypotheses or theories we may have about that world. The two are logically independent; sometimes, our beliefs or theories may be quite false, even utterly false, and at other times, they turn out to be true.

　　This book cannot begin to examine this large assumption. Nor can it begin to give an account of natural kinds, which may be said to be comprehensively philosophically grounded. For a recent attempt to give such an account, see T. E. Wilkerson (1995). However, this author does not altogether agree with Wilkerson's analysis.

42　The observation to follow is this author's, not Allen's. One important and interesting area of dispute today is the theory of natural selection in the light of theoretical advances in genetics. Richard Dawkins (1976, 1982) – maintains that the unit of selection is the single gene. Those who disagree – Ernst Mayr (1982); Elliott Sober and Richard Lewontin (1982, pp. 157–80) – hold that selection is of phenotypes, not of genes or genotypes.

43　Furthermore, patients who undergo frequent blood transfusions tend to accumulate an excessive amount of iron, which causes damage to the heart and liver, as well as often interfering with normal growth and development.

44　A later development on this front, reported in late September 1997, was the success of the laboratories of the American Red Cross in Rockville in producing factor VIII in pig's milk. The pigs were genetically modified to do so. Scientists injected pig embryos with an artificial version of the human gene responsible for the liver in making factor VIII. To ensure that the blood-clotting protein would be found only in the pig's milk and nowhere else, the human gene was tied in with a pig gene which only works in its mammary glands. See Coghlan (27 September 1997).

45　Another example of the same progression at work concerns the condition called Gaucher's disease. Philippe Gaucher discovered it in 1882. It is inherited from two carrier parents who themselves may be free of the symptoms. The sufferer's body is unable to break down the chemical glucocerebroside, found in the membranes of white and red blood cells, which enables macrophages containing fatty glucocerebroside globules to accumulate in the liver, blood marrow and spleen. This could lead to brittle bones as well as the liver and spleen swelling up. In the 1980s Dr Roscoe Brady of the National Institute of Health (USA) identified the enzyme, which the patient lacks, responsible for such symptoms. He managed to extract the critical enzyme from placentas, and administer it as a drug to patients. This first-generation drug, called ceredase, is manufactured by a company called Genzyme. But it can only be expensively produced. Dr Brady, in the late 1980s, went on to identify the gene that makes the enzyme that breaks down glucocerebroside. This gene is then inserted into cells isolated from Chinese hamsters. The cells are grown in vats producing unlimited amounts of cerezyme, the biotechnological version of ceredase. In 1994 Genzyme was on the verge of marketing this second-generation drug with the expected approval of the US Food and Drug Administration. Already the next new-generation product on the horizon was being put in place, a device to insert the actual missing gene into the patients' bodies. (See McKie, 1994.)

46   This rule can now be instantiated by means of pre-implantation genetic diagnosis (PGD), using in vitro fertilisation to grow embryos outside the uterus, then testing to check that they do not carry the gene for the disease, and implanting only such embryos. In October 2000 an American couple from Colorado, Adam and Lisa Nash, announced that their infant son, born in August of that year, had been thus conceived, with the precise aim of harvesting cells from his umbilical cord for infusion into his elder sister, who suffered from a rare inherited genetic disorder called Fanconi anaemia, a condition which stops cell production in the bone marrow. The medical team soon afterwards declared the procedure was successful and that the Nashes' daughter had been saved. Shortly following this report, University College Hospital, London, announced that it, too, would be using PGD to ensure that a family afflicted for generations with a form of bowel cancer known as familial polyposis (killing half of those who inherited the condition in their early middle age) would escape the condition. See Browne and McKie (2000).

3
Biotic Artefacts: Mendelian Genetics and Hybridisation

The first two chapters have set out the philosophical foundations for the transformation of the natural into the artefactual, as well as addressing the historical and theoretical relationships between modern science and its technology. Chapter 2 has also introduced the notion of degrees of artefacticity, the different levels of human intervention in the creation and maintenance of their artefacts, and the corresponding erosion of nature's independence of humans. The following two chapters will explore in some detail the scientific/technological transformation of living organisms into biotic artefacts, thereby altering their ontological status of naturally occurring to that of artefactual beings. To demonstrate this, a convenient focus is provided by the history of agriculture and husbandry. The science of classical Mendelian genetics characteristically induces the biogenetic technology of hybridisation of whole organisms (in Phase IIA). However, the even more basic sciences of molecular genetics and biology lead to biotechnology (Phase IIB), which no longer works at the level of whole organisms, but at the molecular and cellular levels.[1]

The first agricultural revolution

The first agricultural revolution is usually associated with Neolithic culture from around 8000 to 3500 BC. But it would be unrealistic to assume that the Neolithic climax in terms of settled agriculture and husbandry could have taken place without the long period preceding it – in particular, the Mesolithic (from 15,000 to 8000 BC), and even the Late Paleolithic (from 30,000 to 15,000 BC), which laid down a foundation of knowledge about food plants and animals. Similarly, nor should one assume that the sedentary mode of existence based on cultivation displaced totally the hunting/gathering mode with the advent of the so-called agricultural revolution. More likely, hunting and gathering carried on, though no longer as the dominant mode. In any case, it could not be entirely dispensed with, given the vagaries in the fortunes of agriculture – after all, even today when there are famine and economic depression in the land, the rural population at least is able to resort to hunting animals and collecting edible (though perhaps not very appetising) plants to stave off starvation.

Paleolithic foragers must have built up and transmitted a vast canon of knowledge about plants and their properties to their Mesolithic and Neolithic descendants. As hunters, they would have done the same with regard to the feeding and breeding habits of wild animals. This knowledge became the foundation for the eventual domestication of plants and animals. Paleolithic humans lived in very harsh conditions during the Ice Age. Although they did invent fire, their severe environment left them with fewer opportunities to bend it to their own ends. Instead, they specialised in one particular mode of adaptation, namely, hunting. However, when the ice melted, and after the flooding that followed, their Neolithic descendants could do much more in altering the environment to suit their will.[2] They could use their stone axe to clear spaces in the thick forest, to chop the wood into suitable lengths and sizes to erect stockades and dwellings, to stake out fields. They could also terrace the hill slopes, build dams and reservoirs, and dig irrigation ditches. In other words, their habitat became increasingly humanised. A cave was no longer the standard form of dwelling, not even one with paintings on the rough and uneven walls. Instead, house walls were made smooth with clay and plaster, or wooden planks were split to create them. Their source of food, in the main, came under their control through careful selection, cultivation and assiduous maintenance, as well as ingenious methods of storing the products of their labour.[3] Work became routinised and planned well in advance, rather than the spasmodic and, relatively speaking, more spontaneous activities under the previously dominant hunting and gathering mode of existence.

In the glades opened up in the forest, Neolithic women (in the division of labour, it usually fell to the women to be the planters and the breeders) created plots around charred stumps and roots, in which favoured herbaceous annuals could be encouraged to grow. And more importantly, under such carefully protected cultivation in the open, plants hybridised with ease.[4] Hybridisation would at first be entirely spontaneous, but perhaps later some plants might be placed in close proximity with others to encourage the process. Promising hybrids would be carefully selected and nurtured so that eventually they contained more accessible nutriment than their wild forebears; in the case of tubers, their roots would swell, and in those valued for their fruit or seeds, these would produce larger, juicier specimens or in greater quantities. This led eventually to agriculture in the narrower sense as normally understood, based on monoculture with an emphasis on high yield. But perhaps even preceding the cultivation of herbaceous annuals was the cultivation and protection of certain fruit- and nut-bearing trees, which could take up to thirty years or more to mature. From this perspective, it might be correct to say that horticulture preceded agriculture and, indeed, rendered it possible. The period of experimentation and accumulation of knowledge about the improvement of plants would have been an extended one, and as such would require a fall-back to prevent starvation if the experiment failed. Fruits and nuts from trees (such as coconut, date palms, breadfruit, durian, and so on. in the tropics and the subtropics) provided the margin of safety, just as hunting did in times of crises and stresses.

Biologists and ethnologists, on the whole, are of the opinion that the first domestication of animals (which preceded the Neolithic period) probably began with the dog, and included such barnyard animals as the pig and the duck. However, it is held that the dog, descended from more ferocious ancestors such as the jackal and the wolf, did not begin its useful life to humans as a hunting companion. Its ancestors were drawn to human settlement by the lure of bones and offal. Such scavenging made them more docile at least towards those humans with whom they came in contact, although still ferocious to other human strangers and intruders. This meant that they would make good 'watchmen'. It was only later that they became helpers in hunting and herding, and ultimately no more than pets in the final stage of their domestication and humanisation. However, in the overall domestication of animals, including herd animals, it is very likely that, originally, religious/magical motivations, rather than economic/ utilitarian ones, would have played a primary role.[5] The veneration of animals is a well-established practice in human culture throughout its history, and it persists, after all, even to this day in some societies.

From the perspective of this book, the most remarkable thing to emphasise about the Neolithic domestication of plants and animals is that it laid down the basic techniques for improvement, leading to the generation of new varieties.[6] This is to select for breeding plants and animals possessing certain desirable characteristics, with the aim of enhancing and improving those properties. Undoubtedly, over the millennia, the techniques were improved upon and further knowledge, information and skills accumulated. But it would not, perhaps, be too simplistic and distorting to say that artificial selection in breeding, relying on craft-based technological rules throughout what has been called Phase IA and IB (Chapter 2) in the history of technology, lasted right up to the 1930s. As we shall see, although Mendelian genetics was rediscovered in the opening years of the 20th century, Mendelian theory, at first, merely generated anticipation and promise of things to come, rather than an ability to deliver new products instantaneously. Writing about the impact of Mendelism on American agriculture, Jack Kloppenburg (1990) says:

> Mendel's work was less a Rosetta Stone providing the key to the mysteries of heredity than a uniquely effective agenda for further research. An understanding of the mechanisms of inheritance was to be a crucial tool

for the control of transmitted characters, but before the new science of genetics could really begin to contribute to breeding practice, a host of inconsistencies had to be clarified, interpreted in a Mendelian frame-work, and unified in a coherent corpus of theory. ... If Mendel was nec-essary for rapid progress he was not sufficient, and despite the hopes of some there was to be no swift outpouring of markedly superior new plant varieties. (p. 77)

Indeed, during a very long period of human history, from Neolithic times onwards to about the 1930s, which mark the coming of age of agricultural genetics, the peasant/farmer/breeder, as far as plants were concerned, used the craft of selective breeding, by and large, relying on open pollination, to develop what today are called landraces. These landraces have sustained for millennia (and still do in the non-industrialised societies of today) human populations throughout the world.[7] The scientific hegemony in agriculture is, therefore, no more than seventy odd years old.

The system of agriculture in which the landraces were developed is, of course, designed to improve the quality of the plants or animals as well as to increase yield, characteristics deemed desirable by the farmer/breeder.[8] Apart from intensive selection, numerous other devices such as crop rota-tion, lying fallow, addition of organic manure, and so on, were introduced to sustain and improve productivity. By definition, cultivars, which are the result of intensive selection and breeding over centuries, if not millennia, are human artefacts. Humans in creating them have shown remarkable ability in controlling – understood in the strong form – the procedure and determining the outcome, even though it is true that luck would also have played a propitious part in their long history of development. However, it is also true to say that compared with post-Mendelian cultivars, the control exercised, though very impressive, could not be as thorough and as great as that presented in the light of the understanding about the mechanisms of transmission of inherited characteristics given by Mendelian genetics and its associated sciences, such as cytology. To see precisely what this new understanding is, let us now turn to Mendel's discovery itself.

Mendelian genetics: the science[9]

Human beings have always been baffled by the inheritance of characteris-tics, particularly from parents to their offspring, prompted in the main by the resemblance that some children bear to their parents. The ancient Greeks had a few hypotheses – that it was a matter of which sex dominated in the sexual act, or that it had something to do with the heat of the womb or even which testis the sperm came from. But, of course, resemblance between parent and offspring is not confined to humans. The issue is a wider one, involving all organisms. Very much later (in European thought at least), Buffon (1707–1788), who lived during the period of the French Enlightenment, held that the male determined the extremities, such as the head, the limbs and the tail, while the female, the overall shape and size, as well as the innards. He backed this by citing the characteristics of the off-spring from seven different crosses, including ass × horse, mare × ass, ewe × goat (the first animal mentioned in each pair is the female). Apparently nearly all of Buffon's examples were based on correspondence he conducted with those who claimed to have knowledge of the hybrids; it is certain he did not conduct or supervise any of the hybridisation himself. With hindsight we can now say that none of these speculations was correct.

However, preceding Mendel were others whose work on hybridisation falls within the methodology of scientific research recognised as modern. This included Joseph Koelreuter (1733–1806) and Joseph Gaertner (1722–1850), who actually conducted very extensive experiments on plants such as pinks, sweet williams, tobacco, maize and, especially, peas. Mendel studied them too, and so did Darwin – see Olby (1966). Koelreuter believed that he had settled the matter for good, that plants do reproduce sexually, a matter considered to be contentious, although it was not thought to be so in the case of animals. He wrote in 1761 that as a result of his work 'even the most stubborn of all doubters of the sexuality of plants would be completely convinced' (ibid., p. 37). In fact, he had also observed in his hybridisation experiments that the original hybrids (what today we would call the F_1 generation) were all alike, and as far as most of their characteristics were concerned, they tended to be intermediate between the parental species. But when these in turn were bred with one another, their offspring (the F_2 generation) were diverse, and in terms of their characteristics, were more like one or other of the original grandparent species than their parental hybrids. But Koelreuter's religious beliefs dictated that God in the Garden of Eden had created all the species there were, and that no new species could be produced through hybridisation. So he interpreted the diversity of the F_2 generation as the result of his own tampering with nature, forcing species to mate when God had not intended them to.

Another forerunner was Charles Naudin (1815–1899), who indicated that segregation could occur in reproduction, based on his observation that the offspring of a hybrid *Primula* had almost reverted to the parental species. However, because he, like others before him, clung to the belief that hybrids were unnatural entities and would produce 'degenerations', he failed to appreciate the implications of his hypothesis. Instead he was content to argue merely that nature was 'eager to dissolve hybrid forms' by separating out the two 'specific essences' (Olby, 1966, p. 63). Darwin, too, read Naudin, but also failed to realise the full implications of Naudin's hypothesis, and dismissed it on the grounds that it could not account for reversion to distant ancestral traits. Given such failure of comprehension, it is said that even if Darwin had read Mendel, he might not have grasped its significance either, and might have dismissed it as irrelevant to the problems facing him.

Darwin clung to a theory of genetics based on blending heredity, which presented him with the following problem.[10] As natural selection works on small deviations or variations exhibited by organisms over generations, and if these were inherited or transmitted from generation to generation, then under blending heredity, after a few generations, the variations would be effectively diluted, if not totally lost. Natural selection could not then stabilise or act in favour of the variation if it were damped out in this way. Francis Galton (1822–1911), a cousin of Darwin and a founder of biometrics, worked out the following formula: heritage $= 1/4\ p + 1/8\ pp + 1/16\ ppp$ (where p = parent, pp = grandparent, ppp = great-grandparent, and so on), which he called the Ancestral Law of Inheritance. In other words, blending inheritance presupposes that (1) parental contributions are equal, and (2) these contributions are halved at each successive generation. This law could account for distant reversion, as it postulated that ancestral contributions were not lost, but only successively halved, and that even a tiny fraction of those contributions could produce a palpable effect in posterity.

However, in Darwin's thinking, variations exhibited by organisms depended on the transmission, to its offspring, of characteristics acquired in the lifetime of the individual parental organism. In other words, he subscribed to a form of Lamarckianism. Variation is ultimately due to the conditions of life, that is, the environment, which acted on the reproductive system and on the individual in its embryonic state, as well as at later stages of its life and development. All these acquired characteristics were inherited. But if so, he needed a mechanism for their transmission. So he postulated 'pangenesis', reviving the Hippocratic theory of inheritance – genetic particles which were called 'gemmules' were thrown up by the body cells, tissues and organs, and then despatched by means of the fluids circulating in the body to the reproductive organs, where they were assembled. The offspring received gemmules from both parents at conception. What characteristics were exhibited by the offspring depended on whether the gemmules for certain traits came from the maternal or paternal contribution. Not all transmitted gemmules necessarily find expression in the new individual. Unused ones could appear in later generations, thus accounting for distant reversion. Galton put this hypothesis to the test of experiment. He mixed the blood of rabbits with differently coloured coats, and transfused it back into the experimental animals to see if they, when in-bred, would produce offspring whose coat colour was tainted. The results were negative and Galton dropped pangenesis. His own account of inheritance combined the thesis of blending heredity with the Ancestral Law of Inheritance, which was later used by the biometricians to resist Mendel's theory.

Mendel (1822–1884) was born Johann, but renamed Gregor, when he joined the Augustinian monastery in Brno, or Brünn, in 1843. His life as a monk gave him the time, the finances and the security to educate himself, as well as to engage in his scientific research on hybridisation. However, unfortunately, this activity ceased by 1871 when his administrative duties as abbot of the monastery – to which post he was appointed in 1868 – increasingly robbed him of his leisure for study.

The achievement of Mendel over his predecessors consists of a combination of the following elements:

1. His methodological approach, it is said, was less that of the naturalist and more that of the physicist of his time. The former tended to be more Baconian, to make as many observations as one could, and then try to detect an underlying pattern to them. The latter first analysed a problem, worked out a solution, and then undertook to test it by means of a suitable experiment. A positive result would confirm (support) the solution/hypothesis; a negative result would refute it. Mendel knew certain salient facts about hybrids, such as uniformity in what, today, we call the F_1 generation, but diversity and reversion in the F_2 generation. What he was looking for was an explanation of these facts. His approach, based on precise quantification and experimentation, fell within what was later called the *Entwicklungsmechanick* conception (enunciated by the physiologist Jacques Loeb in 1912), which held that biological phenomena and their complex processes, such as development, regeneration and fertilisation, could all ultimately be explained in atomic and molecular terms.
2. His other related methodological innovation was to bring statistics to bear on the study of heredity. Although Galton also used statistics, he did not combine it with the rigours of experimentation, which Mendel did. Galton's experimental technique left much to be desired. For a start, he did not grow his own plants but handed out his selected and graded seeds to helpful friends who grew them, then harvested the seeds and returned them to Galton. Mendel counted all the offspring from his hybrids. In seven series of experiments dealing with crosses, which varied by one factor alone, he examined 15,347 seeds – see Olby (1966, pp. 77–8).
3. We have seen that Koelreuter and Gaertner shared the theology of Linnaeus which held that only species created by the Almighty were true, that they had lasted since the beginning of the world, and would continue to last. But garden varieties created by humans were monstrosities, and would have a short existence. Their preoccupation with fixed species and whole entities contrasts with Mendel's analysis in terms of the inheritance of unit-characters.

Mendel was perfectly aware that he was being innovative in his research on plant hybrids. He said that although many had worked on them before, 'not one has been carried out to such an extent and in such a way as to make it possible to determine the number of different forms under which the offspring of hybrids appear, or to arrange these forms with certainty according to their separate generations, or definitely to ascertain their statistical relations' (Mendel, 1965, pp. 8–9).

His famous experiments on peas (*Pisum sativum*) started in earnest in 1856, and concluded in 1863. Prior to that he had already examined 34 varieties of the pea to determine purity of type and their suitability as research material. He said that the 'value and utility of any experiment are determined by the fitness of the material to the purpose for which it is used'. From these he selected 22 for his experiments. He undertook seven series of crosses, which varied by one factor – for instance, the length of the stem, crossing tall pea plants with tall ones or tall plants with short ones. He found that two tall plants, when crossed, always gave tall offspring; and so too did two short ones. But when a tall was crossed with a short, the F_1 generation of offspring were all tall. Yet when he crossed these, the F_2 generation of offspring yielded the famous ratio of 3:1, three tall to one short. When he in turn bred this generation of shorts with other short plants, they all bred true. So it struck him that the shortness characteristic, although it did not appear at all in the F_1 generation of hybrids, surfaced unchanged in the next generation.

This led him to assume that each organism had two factors (today they are called alleles) for each inherited characteristic (such as height or colour in flowers), one from each parent. The individual could have inherited two like factors, say, both for tallness, or it could have inherited two unlike factors, say, one for tallness from one parent and one for shortness from the other. When expressed in an individual, it looked as if, sometimes, one factor masked the other. The masking factor was the dominant one and the masked, the recessive.

He also did two series of crosses which varied by two factors, and one series of crosses which varied by three factors, getting the same results as the uni-factorial crosses. But even then he did not feel satisfied, as he was aware that his work was new and not in line with scientific thinking and knowledge of the time. As such, it ran the risk of being faulted on the grounds that it was the result of an isolated experiment by an isolated experimenter. He tried to see if the results could be repeated for plants other than *Pisum*. They worked when he crossed the French bean (*Phaseolus vulgaris*) with the bush bean (*P. nanus*), but when he crossed the bush bean with the scarlet runner (*P. multiflorus*), the white (of *P. nanus*) and the red (of *P. multiflorus*) did not segregate according to the 3:1 ratio. For the first time Mendel encountered an experimental outcome failing to fit the theory. Later, he spent five years on hybridising *Hieracium* (wild hawkweed) trying to reproduce the results he had got with *Pisum*, but he also failed. Although he was not to know it then, *Hieracium* turns out to be peculiar in that meiosis (the two successive divisions of the nucleus preceding the formation of the sex cells or gametes) and fertilisation do not occur. Its seeds are of purely maternal origin because of apomixis, that is, asexual reproduction.

He reported the outcome of his research to two meetings of the Naturforschenden den Vereins in Brno, and the society published his paper 'Versuche über Pflanzenhybriden' in 1866. He sent a copy to Carl Nägeli (1817–1891), professor of botany at Munich, who was interested in plant heredity. Nägeli failed to grasp the nature and significance of Mendel's work, and dismissed it as 'merely empirical, not rational'. Mendel himself even thought it just that Nägeli should be so mistrustful and cautious about his work. He also sent one to Darwin but Darwin never read it, as shown by the fact that the pages of that reprint remained uncut – Darwin felt that reading an article in a foreign language was too much for him. In any case the *Proceedings of the Brünn Natural History Society,* as a matter of course, was sent to libraries in universities and learned societies throughout the world, such as the Royal and Linnean Societies of London. The USA received four copies, and Mendel himself had forty offprints, which he would have sent to botanists he knew, such as Nägeli, or people he knew of, such as Darwin. For whatever reasons, his ideas appeared to have fallen on stony ground.[11] He died an obscure scientist, what today we would call a geneticist.

In the light of his later failed attempts to reproduce the results he had obtained with *Pisum,* he was certainly most lucky in the choice of *Pisum* as his research subject. The traits he studied displayed patterns of dominance and recessiveness admirably clearly, being distinct or discontinuous variations. Nor, as it turned out, were they complicated by what geneticists later call linkage, as the genes responsible for each of the traits selected for study were on different chromosomes. Table 3.1 gives a summary of his results.

Mendel's discoveries about heredity, so beautifully and elegantly captured by his experiments, are summed up in what Carl Correns called the 'law of segregation' and the 'law of independent recombination'. These may be illustrated as follows, where two varieties of peas differing in only one character trait are crossed, and the dominant trait is expressed in individuals with either genotype AA or Aa, while the recessive trait is expressed in individuals with the genotype aa:

AA			aa	Parents
	Aa			F_1 hybrid
AA	Aa	Aa	aa	F_2 hybrids

Justice was not done to Mendel until three botanists at the turn of the century simultaneously 'rediscovered' what Mendel had already established.[12] Hugo de Vries (1848–1935), Carl Correns (1864–1935) and Erich von Tschermak (1817–1962) each independently had done work which led

Table 3.1   *Pisum* traits studied by Mendel

Traits studied	Number of plants		Ratio dom./rec.
	Dom.	Rec.	
Length of stem			
Tall vs short	787	2772	84:1
Position of flower:			
Axial vs terminal	651	2073	14:1
Shape of pod			
Inflated vs constricted	882	2992	95:1
Colour of pod:			
Green vs yellow	428	1522	82:1
Shape of seed			
Round vs wrinkled	5474	1850	2.96:1
Colour of cotyledons:			
Yellow vs green	6022	2001	3.01:1
Colour of seed coat:			
Grey vs white	705	224	3.15:1

Source: Magner (1979, p. 418).

them to the 3:1 ratio in the F_2 generation of hybrids.[13] De Vries, who had done the most extensive and conclusive work out of the three, was sore that the laws of heredity were called Mendel's laws, and that Mendel, not himself, was credited with being the founder of genetics. William Bateson (1861–1926), once he got to know Mendel's work, became the 'apostle of Mendelism in England'. He introduced several terms now used in the field, such as 'F_1 and F_2 generations', 'zygote', 'homozygote' and 'heterozygote', and even coined the term 'genetics' itself, borrowing from the Greek word for 'descent', to mark the beginning of the modern era in the understanding of the ancient subject of inheritance. Wilhem L. Johannsen (1857–1927) in 1909 used the word 'gene' to replace older terms such as 'trait', 'character' or 'factor'. In 1911 he also distinguished between the genotype and the phenotype, terms which he had coined. The former denotes the actual genetic inheritance; the latter, the totality of the individual's characteristics, morphological, physiological, behavioural, and so on, which are the result of the interaction between its genotype and the environment. He made it clear that what was inherited, the genotype, was not specific chararcteristics at fertilisation, but certain specific genetic components or potentialities for those characters. That potentiality is passed on to its offspring, but it could also be realised or manifested in a visible form by the organism itself, though not necessarily so. This important clarification served to remove fears about preformationism, which many saw in, and read into, Mendelism.

Even after 1900 there was scepticism about, and resistance to, Mendelism. For instance, the biometricians in Britain opposed it. As they were supporters of Darwin, who emphasised the importance of continuous variations as the basis for natural selection and evolution, they perceived Mendelian theory in terms of 'unit factors' as one of discontinuous variation. It fell to Bateson to defend it against the biometricians' attack. He appeared to have won the argument by 1904. However, that was not the only source of resistance, as we shall see.

As a matter of fact, Mendelian genetics was not consolidated until numerous developments in related disciplines were eventually absorbed and put in place. These, among others, included biochemical, cytological and chromosome studies, as we shall see below.

Mendel's laws provide the basis for the statistical analysis of patterns of inheritance, but they themselves do not give any sound structural/material explanation for why they obtain. A truly proper understanding of genetics has to go beyond statistical laws to cytological as well as biochemical studies. With regard to the former, microscopic research eventually showed that cells have substructures and that they grow and divide. Biochemistry revealed the underlying chemical nature of cellular components. It was the work of August Weismann (1834–1914), a theoretician of biology, which made it in the end possible to unify these three strands, namely, the statistical, the cytological and the biochemical. He introduced two important concepts: (a) the continuity of the germplasm, and (b) his prediction of the reduction division of the chromosome.

Weismann held that the germ or reproductive cells were distinct from the body cells (somatoplasm), and that their rudiments were formed at the earliest stage of an embryo's development. An organism had two distinct parts, the somatoplasm and the germplasm. The former dies with the individual organism, but the latter is handed down from generation to generation during the process of reproduction. As the germplasm was completely isolated from the somatoplasm, whatever characteristics the organism might acquire in its adult life could not affect inheritance. In this view, the inheritance of acquired characteristics was just not possible, contrary to what Larmarck and Darwin believed.[14]

He also said that the transmission of heredity was conducted by the transmission of entities with definite physical and chemical properties. In his essay 'The Continuity of the Germ-plasm as the Foundation for a Theory of Heredity' (1885), he wrote that '"The Continuity of the Germ-plasm" ... is founded upon the idea that heredity is brought about by the transference from one generation to another of a substance with a definite chemical, and above all molecular constitution' (Magner, 1979, p. 431).

In the division of somatoplasmic cells, the chromosome numbers remained constant. But Weismann predicted that in the division of the sex cells in mature ovum and sperm (that is, in meiosis), the number of chromosomes was halved. At fertilisation, the normal number would be restored by the fusion of the male and female nuclei. This prediction he made on purely theoretical grounds, but it was confirmed in 1888 by the experimental work of Boveri and Strasburger.

However, neither Mendel, Weismann nor Darwin initially impressed Thomas Hunt Morgan (1866–1945). Their theories were too broad, too large-scale, like Darwin's, or too fanciful for words, like Weismann's. On the latter, in particular, he poured scorn. He wrote in 1903:

> Weismann has piled up one hypothesis on another as though he could save the integrity of the theory of natural selection by adding new speculative matter to it. The most unfortunate feature is that the new speculation is skillfully removed from the field of verification and invisible germs (particles), whose sole function are those which Weismann's imagination bestows upon them, are brought forward as though they could supply the deficiencies of Darwin's theory. That is, indeed, the old method of the philosophers of nature. An imaginary system has been invented which attempts to explain all difficulties, and if it fails, then new inventions are to be thought of. (Morgan, 1903, pp. 165–6)

His detailed suspicions about Mendel centred on the following legitimate points:

1 Mendel might have demonstrated the validity of his laws in the case of *Pisum* and some other plants. Did they hold only in such cases, but not in others, particularly animals on which no systematic work had been done at all?
2 In the case of sex determination – a problem Morgan was himself interested in – which sex factor was dominant and which recessive?
3 Being tall as a dominant and being short as a recessive factor in pea plants might be clear cut, but in many organisms offspring displayed intermediate conditions.
4 The physical basis for Mendel's 'factors' was missing. His theory of non-blending or particulate inheritance, as far as Morgan was then concerned, was just as fanciful as Weismann's speculations, and Mendelians were objectionable in the way they tried to add or subtract factors in an attempt to explain away results recalcitrant to the theory. In 1909 Morgan wrote:

> In the modern interpretation of Mendelism, facts are being transformed into factors at a rapid rate. If one factor will not explain the facts, then two are invoked; if two prove insufficient, three will sometimes work out. The superior jugglery sometimes necessary to account

for the results are often so excellently explained because the explanation was invented to explain them and then, presto! explain the facts by the very factors that we invented to account for them. (Allen, 1979, pp. 53–4)

Yet a year after that pronouncement, Morgan converted to Mendelism, and became its fervent advocate from the 1920s onwards in the USA. His work on the fruit fly (*Drosophila melanogaster*), which turned out to be as fortunate a choice as *Pisum* had been for Mendel, changed his mind. The fruit fly breeds very quickly, taking ten days to develop from egg to adult within a total life cycle of two weeks. A single pair of parents will produce hundreds of offspring. He was interested in mutations, being a follower of de Vries. He bred the fruit flies to see if de Vriesian mutation could be found in animals. He found a white-eyed male in his breeding population, and crossed it with a normal red-eyed female. All the offspring were red-eyed. When these F_1 red-eyed hybrids were bred with one another the white-eyed characteristic reappeared, but, curiously, always in males and very seldom in females. However, when he crossed a white-eyed male with F_1 females, half of the male and half the female offspring had white eyes. These results, he realised, could be explained in Mendelian terms. This also led him to say that the white-eyed condition is a 'sex-limited character', what today is referred to as 'sex-linked'. He knew that the work done in cell biology (by E. B. Wilson and Nettie M. Stevens) showed that the so-called 'accessory chromosomes' were linked with the inheritance of sex.

This led the way to developing the Mendelian- (or gene-) chromosome theory to become a comprehensive theory of heredity. In 1911 Morgan suggested that the Mendelian factors could be located in a linear fashion on the chromosomes, and that the distances between them could, therefore, be mapped. This, and much else, Morgan's group of researchers at Columbia University were able to produce. In 1915 he and his associates published *The Mechanism of Mendelian Heredity*. This, together with Morgan's two other later books – *The Physical Basis of Heredity* (1919) and *The Theory of the Gene* (1920) – firmly established the following theses. Firstly, Mendel's theory applied to both plant and animal inheritance. Secondly, it could explain breeding results as well as the facts of cytology. Thirdly, Mendel's 'factors' were no mere logical constructs, but were physical units to be found at certain loci on chromosomes, thereby enabling unproblematically the incorporation of Mendelism into the mechanistic–materialistic framework of modern science. Although Morgan's work in turn did not quell all doubts, it put the new science of genetics on a more solid footing than ever before.

The Mendelian-chromosome theory also made it possible for Morgan and others to accept Darwin after all. Mutations of a micro and not a de Vriesian macro kind could be a source of the variability upon which natural selection acted. For instance, micro-mutations could occur in the replication of genetic units. The rate even seemed to be constant – for instance, the white-eye mutation in the fruit fly seemed to appear once in every 10,000 sperm or eggs produced. Spontaneous mutation apart, the existence of modifier genes, chromosonal aberrations such as breakage, deletions, and so on, could produce further variations. Moreover, Morgan realised that there might be a lot more variation in a population than met the eye, as it could be masked – organisms with the same phenotype may not really share the same genotype. However, population genetics was not Morgan's field, and the full integration of Mendelian theory with evolutionary theory was not to take place till the 1930s, when the mathematical theory of natural selection was worked out by Ronald A. Fisher (1890–1962), statistician and geneticist. This synthesis constitutes today's Neo-Darwinian theory of evolution via natural selection.

Mendelian genetics: the technology of hybridisation

When Mendel's work was finally acknowledged in 1900, following the simultaneous discovery on the part of no fewer than three other people, we have seen that, nevertheless, approval of it at first was less than universal on the part of scientists. However, one group of people who became instantaneously enthusiastic had nothing to do with the community of theoretical and pure scientific research as such. It consisted of practical plant and animal breeders, especially those in the USA.[15] Bateson, who took up the cause of Mendelism, was much supported by them. He went to America in 1902 to attend an agricultural conference and found them waving copies of Mendel's paper. The following year they formed the American Breeders Association, whose brief was to enable breeders and scientists to meet and exchange ideas so that 'each may get the point of view of the other and that each appreciate the problem of the other'.

The breeders, whose primary concern was practical, endorsed Mendel for at least two reasons. What he said seemed to make sense in the light of their own experience, and sharpened their focus. Although it was true that, up to then, practical breeders had not looked at the matter of crossing in the way Mendel had done, nevertheless they were most familiar with ratios of offspring in a rough and ready way. Their own rule-of-thumb practices seemed to find validation within the Mendelian framework. Mendel said that an individual with a dominant trait was not necessarily a purebred for that trait. His technique of back-crossing an offspring, exhibiting a dominant trait with its parent, possessing the recessive trait, would enable them to determine whether it was a hybrid or a purebred.

Furthermore, they grasped, too, that Mendelism could be very useful in improving their own breeding practices, even revolutionising them.

Improvement would, of course, lead to economic benefits. As we saw earlier, their euphoria turned out to be one of anticipation rather than instant delivery of new products. But, for the first time, a fundamental biological science was perceived to have radical technological (and therefore also economic) potential and significance.

In the 17th century horse breeders in England imported Arab stallions to rejuvenate the already existing stock of stallions with Arab blood.[16] It was assumed that the transmission of their superior qualities depended on their having been reared in a warmer climate. This, in turn, reflected the thinking current then, that the distinctive features of a breed were the results of adaptation to local conditions. At the same time the breeders also ignored the qualities of the mare, because they thought that the male contribution was the dominant factor in hereditary transmission. But by the 18th century breeders had come to realise that 'degeneration' did not necessarily occur in all cases under changed climatic conditions. Merino sheep, and even Arab horses bred in England, did not degenerate, which led breeders to consider hereditary constitution to be more significant than the environment – see Olby (1990b, p. 525). During the 19th century, it was thought that hereditary transmission had something to do with the traits or characters possessing different 'strengths' in the 'blood', the greater the strength, the longer the trait had been bred. It followed that the older the breed, the more 'potent' it became as breeding stock. Sometimes, a trait not seen in recent generations would suddenly reappear – the problem of distant reversion, as we have seen. At the time of the Mendelian rediscovery in 1900, breeders knew this much, that variability could be achieved through crossing two varieties, and constancy of type through crossing the hybrids themselves. But they lacked any suitable theory which could account for this. In this theoretical vacuum they hailed Mendel as the beacon lighting the way forward.

In 1900 agricultural science, though grounded in biology and field work, did not have all that much to offer the farmer and the stockman. Indeed, in the USA, agricultural successes in the early decades of the 20th century were simply the result of the long-established and well-tried method of plant improvement through the importation of foreign germplasm.[17] For example, from Russia came a group of wheats which eventually transformed the American wheat production scene from producing, instead of only soft wheats, one of three classes of hard wheat for milling and export. Other germplasm imports included Acala and Yuma cottons from southern Mexico and Egypt respectively in 1927, when US cotton cultivation suffered from crown rust. But even more significantly, soya beans were introduced to the USA between 1900 and 1930, with four thousand varieties collected from China, Japan and Korea. The most promising of these varieties were sent out to farmers for local testing and adaptation. By 1914 soya bean production had assumed a prominent role in agricultural production, and in 1924 2.5 million acres were cultivated, worth some $24 million.[18]

At the turn of the century, farmers (in the USA, at least) practised what was called the 'single line selection' method. It consisted of planting in a plot a hundred plants spaced a certain distance apart. From these single plants, seeds were segregated and reproduced, continuously selected from subsequent generations, while the variance revealed in the populations was noted.

Darwinian thinking about selecting for better adapted individuals eventually also influenced the plant breeding programme. To this then was joined the technique of back-crossing reached through an understanding of Mendelian genetics.[19] It consists of the following:[20]

1. Crossbreed two varieties (generating new genetic variability through the combination of their hereditary material).
2. Use single line selection on the offspring of the cross.
3. Then use the 'back-cross' – cross an élite variety (obtained from 2 above) with a so-called exotic variety, say, containing genes for resistance to a disease to which the élite variety is prone.
4. The offspring of this cross is selected for the disease-resistant trait and mated in turn with the élite variety.
5. Repeat the process above until a new variety is obtained possessing all the traits of the élite parent as well as the disease-resistant characteristic of the exotic variety.

One can immediately see that this procedure, unlike single line selection, was much more complicated and difficult to execute. Ordinary farmers would not have the expertise or the time to do so. It included an understanding of genetic knowledge, such as linkage, modifying and multiplying factors, and factor interactions, as well as sophisticated statistical methods in analysing and interpreting experimental data. From being an art or craft, plant breeding became a scientific technology. Farmers could no longer engage in it. Researchers with scientific training attached to agricultural experiment stations (and later to seed companies) took over the task.

This shift to the new division of labour between farmers, on the one hand, and researchers (both in publicly funded institutes and private seed companies) as plant breeders, on the other, was accompanied by a shift in perspective with regard to the plants themselves. Traditional selection was based on the whole plant, but Mendelian thinking was focused on its genetic components. This reductionistic change of emphasis from the whole organism to its parts constituted an increase in the level of artefacticity in the new variety that eventually emerged.[21] Up to then – roughly 1925, when the development of the new technology of hybridisation was substantially completed and in place – in the USA, plant breeders saw it as their task to adapt imported plants from foreign parts to native conditions. But adaptation became supplanted by incorporation of foreign or exotic genes into established native varieties so that improved new varieties would emerge. The exotic plant was no longer regarded as a whole to be superior to existing varieties in the country, but was simply to be appraised and selected for certain specific traits deemed to be desirable or superior to established varieties. These traits, then, were transferred and incorporated into the latter.

Collectors of exotic germplasm were told they were no longer to look out for superior varieties that could adapt well to American conditions, but for plants which possessed a single superior trait. One plant explorer with the United States Department of Agriculture (USDA) summed up the new situation by writing: 'Species and varieties which in themselves have little or no intrinsic value become of first importance if they possess certain desirable characters which may be transmitted through breeding' (Ryerson, 1933, p. 124). This search for useful genes, rather than useful plants, resulted in a much wider range of germ plasm being collected. Varieties that were considered to be too wild before would now be fit material for collection, provided they possessed superior traits of one kind or another.

According to this new technology and strategy of plant breeding, whole plants were not the ultimate units of manipulation and control, but their genes. Gene incorporation gave the breeder much greater control than traditional selection techniques, leaving much less to chance. Bateson, as early as 1902, when he addressed the Second International Conference on Plant Breeding and Hybridization in New York, had already spelt this out. He said that the plant breeder

> *will be able to do what he wants to do instead of merely what happens to turn up.* Hitherto I think it is not too much to say that the results of [craft-based][22] hybridization had given a hopeless entanglement of contradictory results. We crossed two things; we saw the incomprehensible diversity that comes in the second generation; we did not know how to reason about it, how to appreciate it, or what it meant. ... The period of confusion is passing away, and we have at length a basis from which to attack that mystery such as we could scarcely have hoped two years ago would be discovered in our time. (Bateson, 1902, pp. 3–8)

Three years later Bateson's fervent commitment to the new perspective was reinforced by an USDA breeder, who said:

> The plant breeder's new conception of varieties as plastic groups must replace the old idea of fixed forms of chance origin which has long been a bar to progress. ... Since the science of plant breeding has shown that definite qualities may be produced and intensified as required, it is no

longer necessary to wait for nature to supply the deficiency by some chance seedling. (American Breeders Association, 1905, p. 204)

Admittedly, as we have seen, this commitment did not truly bear fruit till much later. But what is crucial to emphasise here is the realisation on the part of Bateson and others that the Mendelian framework made possible an intensification of control over nature. As we shall see in detail later, with regard to hybrid corn, the new improved variety is a product with a much greater degree of artefacticity (relative to the products of craft-based breeding techniques), designed to satisfy certain very specific human ends and purposes and, therefore, a product which incorporated them fully into its being. The degree of control in plant improvement, which the technology of hybridisation provided, far exceeded that given by the technology of selection based on open pollination which, in one form or other, humans had practised from Neolithic times onwards. For the first time in the subject, biological science had been harnessed to produce a very powerful technology. However, for a second time in the 20th century, an even more powerful (and correspondingly, more reductionistic) technology had been generated, but that will be the subject of the next chapter.

For the moment, we turn to the development of hybridisation technology accomplished by experimenting on corn or maize (*Zea mays*).[23] By 1935 hybrid corn had become a commercial success in the USA. One economist concluded that at least '700 percent per year was being earned, as of 1955, on the average dollar invested in hybrid corn research' (Griliches, 1958, p. 419). By 1965 more than 95 per cent of the land under corn used the new seed. Between 1930 and 1965, although 30 million acres were withdrawn from corn cultivation, the increase in volume production was over 2.3 million bushels. Its success has been hailed as epochal.

This success story involves, as earlier mentioned, transforming the plant into an artefact with a far greater degree of control than hitherto possible. In this transformation, what could be the aims and ends designed into the biotic artefact? There are at least three interpenetrating goals: first, to improve yield; second, to ensure that the plant has certain qualities deemed to be desirable, such as 'field uniformity', as well as being amenable to handling and treatment by machines; and third, economic considerations, such as increasing profitability both for the seed companies and the farmers.

The third goal is obviously a general and overarching one in terms of which the other two could be understood and explained. However, on the whole, the account of transformation that follows will not concentrate on it, as to do so would require a far larger analysis than can be afforded by the framework of this book. Moreover, excellent critiques written from the standpoint of the political economy of the seed are available.[24] This book takes it as read that scientific and technological developments do not in any case occur in a social vacuum, as both are social activities per se. Instead, it will focus on the more specific issue of how science and technology are harnessed to achieve certain more seemingly technical ends, such as the first two mentioned above. However, it cannot be denied that in the historical development of hybrid corn (or today, with the products of biotechnology), these are inextricably linked with the larger economic goal of increasing profits on the part of capital. Together they seek to break down the natural barriers which stand in the way of penetrating the germplasm, rendering the latter ultimately a commodity. Admittedly, science and technology on their own provide, at best, only a necessary but not a sufficient condition for the generation of private profitability, but they could be captured by private capital to perform at its behest. And when that happens, how science and technology themselves develop will depend to a large extent on the overriding goal of capital trying ceaselessly to increase profitability.

Genetic variability is celebrated as a good thing in the long run, both in the wild and in domesticated populations. In the case of the former, without it evolution through natural selection would cease. In the latter, without it there would be great difficulty in regenerating agriculture should pest and disease strike and destroy cultivars as they are prone to do, no matter how successful the cultivars might have been up to then. But in the short term and in nearly all contexts, genetic variability is clearly seen as posing a threat to the goal of increasing yield. A cultivar deemed to be successful needs to be 'fixed', which is not helped if it is susceptible to a greater degree of genetic variability than other plants. This appeared to be true of the corn plant, given its sexual morphology. It is not an 'inbreeder' (autogamous), but an 'outbreeder' (allogamous). It does not depend on self-fertilisation but on cross-pollination. In principle, pollen from a different plant may fertilise each and every kernel on an ear of corn. In theory, every corn plant is a unique cross. This means that extreme genetic flux rather than genetic stability is characteristic of a corn variety. When an improved variety has been developed, unless it is isolated from others, there is the danger that it would soon vanish. So to fix 'field uniformity' or phenotypical uniformity in the plant was a clearly desirable goal. However, this uniformity should not be at the expense of a reduction in vigour or in yield. But unfortunately this was precisely what happened in the pre-Mendelian days of corn breeding. Farmers at agricultural shows selected, for seeds, ears of corn which looked good to them; they were guided by aesthetics rather than considerations such as yield. As a result, breeders were encouraged to select continuously, through inbreeding, for aesthetically pleasing ear types, ultimately producing strains with genetic uniformity, and reduced vigour and yield. Between 1900 and 1935 corn yield showed a gradual decline. What was needed was a change, which many hoped would come from the new science of genetics and its technological potentiality. In other words, the agenda must satisfy a testing combination of requirements – uniformity but with no reduction in vigour, and increase in yield – which ultimately led to the 'double-cross' hybrid variety itself.

The first attempt was made by George H. Shull as early as 1908 in his paper 'The Composition of a Field of Maize', and again in 1909, in 'A Pure-Line Method in Corn Breeding', where he argued and laid down a procedure for obtaining 'single-cross' hybrids. He reckoned that although inbreeding reduced vigour and yield, crosses between in-breds sometimes could be more vigorous and higher yielding than the existing variety obtained through selection and the so-called ear-to-row selection procedures then in common use. This was because self-fertilisation brought on deterioration only when there was isolation of homozygous biotypes. But a field of corn would contain individuals that were complex hybrids. A cross of exceptional inbreds might do the trick. He recommended extensive inbreeding to establish homozygous or near-homozygous lines, crossing the selected pure lines, and using the very best crosses for farm production. But his attempt floundered. Few exceptional ones, among the crosses of in-breds, occurred; most fell below 50 per cent of the yield found in open-pollinated populations. Their seeds too were sparse – while not being biologically sterile, they could be said to be economically sterile. Shull's work was dropped, some saying that it was practically flawed, and others, even that it was theoretically flawed.

Then in 1918 D. F. Jones put forward the idea of a 'double-cross' hybrid. This was achieved by crossing two single crosses. The steps are as follows:

1 Take a pair of homozygous inbred lines, A and B. Cross them – A × B – by planting them in alternate rows, having first removed by hand the pollen-shedding tassel from the female parent. This process of de-tasselling ensures that there will be no self-fertilisation.
2 Take another pair of homozygous inbred lines, C and D. And do the same as above.
3 Collect only the seeds from the female parents to ensure that they are not selfed seeds.
4 Grow from these single-cross seeds collected from either pair.
5 Cross these single-cross plants ([A × B] × [C × D]), having also de-tasselled the female plants.
6 The offspring are double-crosses. But collect only the seeds of the female parent. This is the germplasm, which is sold and used for planting on farms.

As the seeds used for farm planting came from the single-cross parents, seed yields per acre were much higher. In Shull's single-cross proposal, they came from the weaker inbred grandparents. However, like Shull's hybrid seeds, the seeds from the double crosses themselves, if saved and replanted, would yield much less, making them, also, economically sterile. This meant that the double-cross hybrid fulfilled the agenda and more. Not only did it satisfy the uniformity, vigour and yield criteria, it also enabled the originator of the hybrid to control it, by allowing him 'to keep the parental types and give out only the crossed seeds, which are less valuable for continued propagation' (East and Jones, 1919, p. 90). This served to sever the grain from the seed, a thread which had been uncut since Neolithic times, as farmers had always been able to reproduce their grain for the next year by holding back some of their harvest as seed corn. But under the technology of hybridisation, this would no longer be so. The farmers would be forever beholden to whoever owned the legal right to the hybrid product if they wanted to keep up the high yield. As things turned out, the legal owners were (are), by and large, seed companies which seized the opportunity for increasing market share and profitability in supplying the highly technologised and engineered seed corn to the farmers. In any case, the elaborate and sophisticated procedures for producing hybrid corn would mean that ordinary farmers could not engage in such operations and, so, would have no choice but to buy from plant breeders/seed companies. The eventual triumph of hybrid corn – beginning in 1924 when a variety called 'copper cross' won a gold medal – is generally considered to be so epochal for precisely the reason that it seems so admirably to fulfil and embody the goals for which the artefact has been designed.

But applied genetics did not stop with increase of yield and hybrid vigour. It also soon lent a hand to increasing productivity and, thereby, profitability, by rendering de-tasselling superfluous. We have seen that de-tasselling of the female plant was required to prevent self-fertilisation through the release of its pollen. Less than thorough de-tasselling would result in some seeds being hybrids and some inbreds. But as inbreds are weak, planting a field with a mixture of pure hybrids and inbreds would lower the yield. However, de-tasselling was accomplished manually. This meant that the hybrid corn industry was labour-intensive in this stage of the production process: for two weeks each year, labour had to be hired, trained and mobilised. In the 1930s, during the depression in the USA, wages were low and labour was readily available. During the Second World War, German and Italian prisoners of war were requisitioned to join women and high-school students to do the job, these having replaced more highly paid males. But after the war, labour costs soared. That, plus the extreme sensitivity of the entire production to any sort of labour problems, made the industry think of alternatives. Using machines appeared not to be feasible. The fields could be wet, and machines get bogged down. Moreover, machines might remove too much, taking not only the tassels but also some leaves away, thereby reducing photosynthesis in the plants, resulting eventually in lower yields.

At this point, biogenetic technology stepped in. The same Jones who devised the double-cross hybrid came up with a neat and elegant genetic solution in 1949, based on swapping certain genetically determined male and female traits. Male corn plants are sterile. Jones proposed that the gene for cytoplasmic male sterility (CMS) be incorporated into the female lines, and in turn that the gene for fertility be incorporated into the male lines. These are called 'restorer' genes to ensure that the eventual seed corn would be fertile. It is obvious that the level of artefacticity in this double-cross hybrid corn, mark II, is greater than that of its predecessor, male sterility having been incorporated into the female, and the latter's fertility into the male.

This manoeuvre enabled the industry to dispense with manual de-tasselling. By 1965 the technique had become standard; in that year, in the USA, 3 billion plants embodying it were being planted, displacing 125,000 labourers. However, its ascendancy was somewhat short-lived. In 1970 an epidemic of southern corn leaf blight attacked about 15 per cent of the crop grown up and down the country. The villain of the piece was traced to the particular type of male-sterile cytoplasm (type T) incorporated into the female lines, which was susceptible to the new variety of corn blight. Seed companies found that they had to discard the technique and return to manual de-tasselling. However, this does not mean that CMS is relegated for good. It is used in the hybrids of other crops, such as onion, sugar beet and sorghum.[25]

One way to increase productivity, and hence profitability, is for an industry to change from being labour-intensive to being capital-intensive. Machines would replace humans. From the 1940s onwards the agricultural industry (soon to be called agribusiness), with the help of the hybridisation technology, was ready to become increasingly mechanised. In 1938 machine harvesting covered only 15 per cent of American corn. But by 1945 in Iowa it had jumped from 15 to 70 per cent. Open-pollinated corn varieties displayed, as we saw, a far greater degree of genetic variability in the field than the double-cross hybrid, which exhibited greater phenotypical uniformity, even though this might not be as great as that in the single-cross. Individual plants in the open-pollination system ripened at different rates and carried different number of ears at different places on the stalk, as well as falling over (called 'lodging'). Mechanical pickers could damage over-ripe cobs, miss some lodged plants, not strip properly stalks with unevenly situated ears. Hybrid varieties had then to be developed which ripened at the same rate, bore their ears at a certain specific level and angle, and were resistant to lodging, qualities designed to make the plant suit the mechanical picker. Moreover, these new hybrids had tougher shanks connecting the ear to the stalk, which made manual harvesting more difficult, thus reinforcing the need for machines. In other words, a successful research project for the successful mechanisation of harvesting is not so much about designing machines to harvest crops – machines being inherently unsuitable for such a purpose – as to design crops to be harvested by machine.

During the Second World War, America's war needs required a tremendous amount of chemicals of one kind or another, especially nitrogen, to be produced. Encouraging farmers, once the war was over, to use more fertilisers was a way to cope with the redundant facilities for nitrogen production. But the hybrids in place in 1944 were not designed for a liberal absorption of fertilisers. Too many applications would make the stalks weak, and end up falling over. New hybrids were engineered which could absorb the generous dosage. A new approach to keep up productivity in a situation in which the market for hybrid corn was reaching saturation point was adopted. This was summed up by what the Funk Seeds research director called the '"high profit trio idea": use special hybrids, plant them thick, and fertilize heavier'. However, this regime, while offering greater plant density and greater luxuriant growth (fuelled by the fertiliser), produced conditions which were ripe for weeds, insects and disease to flourish. These in turn required generous applications of herbicide, insecticide and fungicide.

As just spelt out above, the technology of hybridisation, in its various stages of development and application, constitutes clear evidence that the hybrid plant – in this specific instance, the hybrid corn – is nothing but a 'designer product'. It has been made possible by highly sophisticated scientific procedures, with an excessive degree of artefacticity built into it. Such a product has been created in order to satisfy certain ends, in particular, those of increasing yield and maintaining a high level of phenotypical or field uniformity, which in turn promote the general and overarching economic goal of increasing productivity, thereby maximising profitability.

Of course, it is true that all breeding programmes, whether based on the technology of selection of chance crosses, open pollination and ear-to-row planting (when uninformed by Mendelian genetics) or that of hybridisation, must have clearly defined objectives without which the breeders could not even begin to decide what to do. These objectives would include economic, social and biological considerations. In this sense, breeding programmes are necessarily goal-led and directed, favouring properties which we humans deem to be desirable in one way or another. It follows, too, that their outcomes may be said to be artefacts, reflecting the human purposes for which they have been designed and constructed. But the point emphasised by this book is that they may vary in their level of artefacticity, depending on the degree of control which the basic sciences and their accompanying technologies permit. Here it is claimed that compared to the pre-Mendelian procedures of plant breeding, those for producing double-cross hybrids give the breeders much greater control and precision.

Admittedly, it is not the only technology spawned or improved by Mendelian genetics, but those others when informed and developed by that science have also similarly increased control over their pre-Mendelian counterparts, which had a very long standing in the history of agriculture.[26] But, nevertheless, it is the dominant one, at least up to now, in advanced industrial states, and has been spreading throughout the world. Witness the so-called Green Revolution with regard to 'miracle' wheats and rice in Latin America and Asia from the 1950s onwards, which relied basically on that technology and its package of strategies. The only major difference appears to be the overarching goal between the American programme for hybrid corn and that for the Third World. In the former it was economic consideration, that is, increase of productivity to increase profitability, which inspired it.[27] In the latter it was politics rather than economics that was the basic ideological impulse. Those First World foundations and bodies behind the initiative had intended it as a measure to prevent poor countries from embracing communism, on the assumption that the hungrier the masses, the more likely they would be to turn to such an ideology for salvation. In promising plenty of food, it was promising to save the Third World from communism. It was, in other words, very much part and parcel of Cold War thinking. But a political assessment of that programme is another story altogether. Today, communism is on the retreat, if not totally dead. Moreover, yet another more basic science and more powerful technology are now in place. To these achievements we shall turn in the next chapter.

Glossary

Allele. An alternate form of a gene occupying the same locus in a chromosome.

Apomixis. Asexual reproduction in plants, corresponding to parthenogenesis in animals.

Asexual reproduction. A form of propagation which does not result from zygote formation, that is, by the fusion of two gametes.

Chromosome. A discrete longitudinal body in the nucleus, containing the organised genetic material.

Cytoplasm. Part of a cell outside the nucleus.

Dominant. Describes an allele which in a heterozygote determines the phenotype.

Gamete. A reproductive cell – egg in female, and spermatozoon in male.

Gemmules. Invisibly small particles postulated as carriers of genetic characteristics.

Genotype. The organism's total genetic constitution.

Heterozygote. An individual with different alleles at the same locus in two homologous chromosomes.

Homozygote. An individual with the same allele at the corresponding loci of two homologous chromosomes.

Inheritance, blending. The total fusing of the two parental genetic materials. This is opposed to particulate inheritance, under which there is no fusion of the parental genetic materials during zygote formation.

Linkage. Certain genes being associated, owing to their location on the same chromosome.

Meiosis. The two successive divisions of the nucleus preceding the formation of the gametes.

Mitosis. The division of the nucleus.

Pangenesis. The hypothesis that all parts of the body contribute genetic material to the reproductive cells.

Phenotype. The totality of characteristics of an individual organism, the result of the interaction between its genotype and its environment.

Preformation. The theory that all the structures of an organism are already present in one of the gametes.

Pure line. A genetically uniform (homozygous) population.

Recessive. Describes an allele in a heterozygote which is not expressed in the phenotype.

Reduction division. One of the two meiotic divisions during which the number of chromosomes is halved.

Zygote. The cell which results from the union of two gametes and their nuclei.

Notes

1   The remit of this book specifically excludes a critique of the reductionistic, mechanistic world-view and methodology which have, paradigmatically, produced the science of genetics, Mendelian and molecular – such a critique of reductionistic genetics and its technology as bad or inadequate science may be found, for instance, in Holdrege (1996) or in Ho (1998). A book which celebrates the achievements of reductionistic genetics but which avoids the triumphalism usually associated with them is Jones (1994).

2   There are several views, but no real consensus, as to why the hunting/gathering mode of existence was abandoned in favour of sedentary agriculture, and where the agricultural origin or origins were. See Harlan (1975, pp. 33–60). But see also Jared M. Diamond (1998, pp. 99–103). According to Diamond's account, historically there may have been nine independent centres of domestication and food production, of which the dates of only three are well established: the Fertile Crescent around 8500 BC, the Chinese equally early, and the eastern United States, about 6000 BC. (However, if South China counts as a separate centre from North China, then the number of world centres would go up to ten.) Of the remaining six, their dates are uncertain, and indeed a question mark even hangs over five of them as to whether they are genuine independent centres. (Also, see Diamond's chapter 5 for the dates quoted, which are calibrated radiocarbon dates.)

3   Strictly speaking there is a difference between cultivation and domestication. To quote one writer:

> To cultivate means to conduct those activities involved in caring for a plant, such as tilling the soil, preparing a seedbed, weeding, pruning, protecting, watering, and manuring. Cultivation is concerned with human activities, while domestication deals with the genetic response of the plants or animals being tended or cultivated. It is therefore quite possible to cultivate wild plants, and cultivated plants are not necessarily domesticated. (Harlan, 1975, p. 64)

4   There are two meanings of 'hybrid' and 'hybridisation'. In its original form, it simply means the 'cross-breeding' or sexual combination of two varieties of plant or animal. A hybrid is no more than the product of such a union. However, after

1935, when Mendelian genetics had spawned its own technology, 'hybridisation' acquired a much narrower meaning, referring to the outcome of combining two in-bred lines, as in 'hybrid corn'. When this book talks about Mendelian genetics and its accompanying technology of hybridisation, it is the second sense that is used. But when the context is pre-Mendelian or pre-1935, the word is used in the wider sense. One could conceivably distinguish between them by adding 'pre-Mendelian' or 'Mendelian' in front of 'hybridisation', but this would be cumbersome.

5 Lewis Mumford writes:

> Erich Isaac has pointed out that 'in view of the size and fierceness of the animal, the original domesticators must have had a strong motive for overcoming the difficulties of the task. That this motive was economic is unlikely, since it would not have been possible to foresee the uses to which the animal might be put, and the only obvious use, that of the animal as meat, would not have warranted the effort of capturing the animal, keeping him alive in captivity, and feeding him. … The most sensible explanation remains that of Eduard Hahn, who argued that the *urus* was domesticated for religious, not for economic reasons. Although the reason for the religious significance of the *urus* is not certain, it probably lay in the animals' horns, which were considered to correspond to the horns of the moon, which in turn was identified with the Mother Goddess.' (1967, p. 151)

6 However, this does not necessarily mean that the end product, a new variety or an improved variety, is the result of deliberate selection on the part of the farmer/breeder. There are three distinct possibilities involved:

(a) Farmers/breeders deliberately modified the stock by applying the selective procedures known to them, at any one time, with the objective of achieving such changes.
(b) The changes could be the unintended and even unforeseen consequences of actions taken by farmers/breeders to achieve some other objective.
(c) The changes could even be the consequences of events and processes which were not part of the intentions and actions of any human agents whatsoever.

Possibility (b) would mean that artificial selection and natural selection are not necessarily antagonistic in all contexts. For an emphasis on the contribution of unconscious selection, as opposed to methodical selection as in (a), see Rindos (1984, pp. 1–9).

7 But propagation by cloning is, indeed, also an ancient practice. A few fig clones survive today from the classical Roman period – see Simmonds (1979, p. 127).

Open pollination involves the following: the individual plants in a population (which are genetically diverse) are allowed to breed among themselves. Offspring bearing the most extreme value of the desired trait are selected and planted as the next generation. The process of selection is repeated in each generation, thereby raising the mean value of the desired trait in the population as a whole.

For a historical and theoretical account of pre-Mendelian techniques in plant breeding in Europe, see Roberts (1929). For an account of the rise of botanical gardens in Europe beginning in the 17th century and their contribution to plant improvement, see Brockway (1979). See also Grove (1995); Arnold (1996).

8 For simplicity's sake, the past tense is used with regard to pre-Mendelian agricul-ture. However, as already just commented on, there are parts of the world

(admittedly shrinking) which still practise peasant agriculture using techniques based on craft-technological understanding of the activity rather than modern scientific knowledge and technological breakthroughs.

Furthermore, one should bear in mind that the landraces still in existence in developing countries today are biotic artefacts (but with a much lower degree of artefacticity), just as the hybrids of Mendelian technology and the genetically engineered plants (and animals) of biotechnology are biotic artefacts. Unfortunately, Western transnational biotech companies, in incorporating these landraces in the new varieties they develop, often conveniently perceive them to be the simple products of nature. In such a view, as no capital or labour, economic or intellectual, has been invested in them, they are not regarded as biotic artefacts. (Critics accuse these biotech corporations of 'bio-piracy'.) This, of course, is simply false. The landraces are not raw germplasm. Collectively, over the millennia, these plants have been selected and improved upon during the entire history of their domestication by generations and generations of farmers.

9   For technical terms that follow, see glossary at the end of the chapter.
10 See Keekok Lee (1969).
11 For one account why it did so, see Bowler (1989).
12 The scare quotes around this word reflect the challenge to the orthodox image of Mendel as the founder of genetics – see, for instance, Bowler (1989, pp. 99–109).
13 This may be an oversimplified view of the matter – see Olby (1990b, pp. 528–9); Mayr (1982, pp. 638–807).
14 At least in the case of animals and plants which reproduce sexually.
15 In Britain it appears that the relationship between Mendelism as science and its resultant technology of hybridisation is not as tight as that which obtained in the USA. The relationship differs from the American one in two respects. First, the very successful breeders working at seed firms such as Garton's of Warrington and Carter's Tested Seeds of London used methods which were far more complex, sophisticated and systematic than what Mendelian botanists were prepared to admit in characterising their methods simply as 'mass selection'. Second, in the first two decades following the rediscovery of Mendelian theory, two equally influential academic agricultural scientists and successful breeders – world-renowned for their improved wheat varieties – followed rather different paths. Rowland Biffen, in Cambridge, was a committed Mendelian, while John Percival, at the University College in Reading, challenged the relationship between Mendelian theory and plant breeding. Percival argued that Mendelism was by and large irrelevant, as its principles of independent segregation and random re-assortment of characters were only applicable in the selection of superficial, morphological characters. Farmers and breeders, on the contrary, were interested in those, that were dependent on very complex environmental and physiological interactions, and could not be regarded as independent in the way Mendelian theory required. Percival held that hybridisation would be extremely disruptive of the fine balance between the plant and its environment.

    For details, see Palladino (1993). In another paper Palladino (1994) also pointed out the different fortunes in the careers of people with a minimal education in science but who became very successful plant breeders on either side of the Atlantic. Luther Burbank rejected not only Mendelism but also mutationism of a de Vriesian kind. In turn, the American community of agricultural scientists denied him academic recognition, claiming that his methodology was not acceptable, and that his successes were no more than the result of empirical tinkering. In Britain, Edwin Sloper Beaven had serious reservations about the relevance of Mendelism to plant breeding, as he attached great importance to environmental factors in affecting heredity. Without formally espousing Neo-Lamarckianism, nevertheless, he remained unconvinced that characters varying genetically in response to the environment could not be transmitted. In spite of these differences, he was accepted by Biffen (in Cambridge) as a collaborator. In 1922 the University of Cambridge bestowed on him an honorary degree. Indeed, Cambridge scientists even presented him to the public as a champion of Mendelism in the revolution of established agricultural practices. (The author wishes to thank Jonathan Harwood for drawing attention to the points made by Palladino in his two papers.)

16   See Russell (1986). See also Mayr (1982, pp. 633–38) for a brief account dating back to the ancient Greeks.

17   As early as 1819 William L. Crawford, secretary of the US Treasury, sent a circular to the country's foreign consuls and naval officers, instructing them to collect for the nation any useful new plant, or any superior in quality to those cultivated in the USA, which they might come across in the course of their duties in foreign parts – see Kloppenburg (1990, p. 78). In 1862 the United States Department of Agriculture was established by Congress, which decreed that its main brief was to 'procure, propagate, and distribute among the people new and valuable seeds and plants'. In 1888 the United States Department of Agriculture established the Office of Seed and Plant Introduction to collect seeds and crop varieties.

18   See Kloppenburg (1990, p. 78).

19   Plant breeding itself, being concerned with the crossing (or recombination) and propagation of germplasm with the aim of obtaining a variety possessing certain desirable characteristics, is focused on genetics. But it also draws on many other scientific disciplines: botany, taxonomy, cytology, cell physiology, and so on, although it does exclude ecology, which is concerned, among other things, with the study of the interaction between plants and the environment in terms of soil and nutrient.

20   See Berardi and Geisler (1984, p. 320).

21   Relative to traditional breeding methods, Mendelian breeding technology is reductionistic. Therefore, in this context, the former may be said to be based on selection of the whole organism, and the latter on the selection of only the relevant part of the organism, namely, its genes. In other words, what the breeder looks out for is not necessarily a useful plant but only useful genes. However, as the next chapter will argue, relative to DNA genetics and biotechnology, even Mendelian genetics and its hybridisation technology may be said to be based on the whole organism, as the individual plants or animals, bearing their own respective genetic material, are involved in producing the offspring. It is, in this sense, far less reductionistic in character than the more recent theoretical and technological advances under which some of the genetic material leading to the production of the offspring may have been edited out or edited in, and may include DNA from other organisms across the species or kingdom divide.

22   The words within square brackets have been added by this author.

23   For the sake of simplicity, from now on the term 'corn' will be used simply because the hybrid corn is an American tale of agricultural achievement.

24   See Mooney (1979, 1983); Lewontin (1982); Kloppenburg (1990); Busch et al. (1991); Tiles and Oberdiek (1995).

25 However, hybrid barley also ran into the same difficulty as hybrid corn – the male sterile factor used was susceptible to ergot. See Ramage (1983).

26 For a discussion of other technologies such as inbred lines, open-pollinated populations and clones (these having been incorporated into and developed within the framework of Mendelian genetics), see Simmonds (1979, pp. 122–201).

Here it is fitting to labour a point made earlier, namely, that these advances within the Mendelian framemark are not meant to belittle the impressive achievements in the Neolithic as well as the later periods in the history of plant breeding. Clearly, domesticated forms of a species are very different from their wild relations and/or ancestors. In all parts of the world, except Australia, since Neolithic times, domestication proceeded steadily, particularly in the so-called Vavilov centres, the centres of diversity and origins to which domesticated crops may be traced. It remains true even today that the total genetic change brought about by traditional agriculturists through the millennia is much greater than that caused by systematic modern science-based efforts. There have also been some very spectacular achievements, such as the development of corn from its postulated ancestor, teosinte. Teosinte has only eight kernels to an ear. The pre-Aztec and Inca farmers took advantage of a sexual transmutation in the plant to develop and produce, eventually, the modern ear of corn, with a hundred times more kernels on it. See Iltis (1983).

27 For a systematic account of the development of molecular biology in general within the social framework of industrial capitalism, see Kay (1993). (For the use of the term 'molecular biology', see Chapter 4.)

4

Biotic Artefacts: Molecular Genetics and Biotechnology

Molecular genetics and molecular biology

Molecular genetics is part of a wider approach called molecular biology. The term 'molecular biology' itself was coined in 1938 by Warren Weaver, director of the Natural Sciences Section of the Rockefeller Foundation, to herald a new branch of science, using tools which reached deeper and deeper into the living organism, penetrating the structure and function of minute cellular substances.[1] One of the leading proponents, and exponents, of this broad programme was W. T. Astbury (1898–1951) at Leeds University, who pioneered the study of macromolecules by x-ray crystallography, and had produced the first molecular structures of keratin, the protein found in horn, nail and wool. He said:

> It implies not so much a technique as an approach from the viewpoint of the so-called basic sciences with the leading idea of searching below the large-scale manifestations of classical biology for the corresponding molecular plan. It is concerned particularly with the forms of biological molecules and with the evolution, exploitation and ramification of these forms in the ascent to higher levels of organisations. Molecular biology is predominantly three-dimensional and structural, which does not mean, however, that it is merely a refinement of morphology. It must at the same time inquire into genesis and function. (Astbury, 1950, p. 3)

Through the study of the molecular structure of specific macromolecules, areas as wide-ranging as embryology, heredity and evolution – investigated up to then, respectively, at the level of tissue, cell and population – were shown to have a common foundation.

Biochemical studies clearly also played an important role, as the study of macromolecules, by and large, used the methodology and techniques traditionally employed by biochemists to investigate micromolecules. So important was this role that in the opinion of one writer it was no more than biochemistry practised 'without a license'.

But other disciplines, such as physics, also asserted their claims to provide the framework for the molecular revolution in biology. In particular, some of the more recent practitioners, such as Francis Crick, have expressed a strong reductionism, holding that the aim of molecular biology is to explain '*all* biology in terms of physics and chemistry' (Crick, 1966, p. 14). James Watson, his co-discoverer of the double helix structure of DNA, appears to be of like mind. Crick himself was trained as a physicist, and although Watson was not – he has a degree in phage genetics – he was much influenced by Max Delbrück (originally an atomic physicist), whose biological thinking was shaped by Niels Bohr's lecture in 1932 called 'Life and Light'. In that lecture Bohr (1885–1962) wondered if the new quantum physics, which established indeterminacy in subatomic particles, could be relevant to biological phenomena. The latter also seemed to exhibit an analogous indeterminacy, in that the very attempt to study the chemical components of a living organism effectively could undermine the very conditions which keep the organism whole and alive. The Bohr–Delbrück ideas led another physicist, Erwin Schrödinger (1887–1961), to publish a book entitled *What is Life?* (1945). It was true that classical physics and chemistry could not explain biological phenomena, but might the study of the latter not lead to new understanding which could cause physics and chemistry to revise its own laws? Maybe, biology, like quantum physics, could move to different levels of understanding, using explanatory concepts that transcended the usual mechanistic and reductionist framework. This exciting agenda made some post-war physicists turn their attention to biology instead. But as things turned out, ironically, far from post-war biological investigations at the molecular level forcing a revision in physics and chemistry, Crick, one of these most successful post-war physicists-turned-biologists, as we have seen, became more than ever convinced of the correctness of reductionism.[2]

The account to follow will deal only with matters relevant to the emergence of molecular genetics as part of molecular biology, but not with the broader programme of molecular biology itself. As such, it concentrates on the eventual emergence of DNA as the genetic material: its three-dimensional structure, how it replicates itself, how it contains 'instructions' to form amino acids which make up proteins.

Molecular genetics: the science[3]

According to Garland E. Allen, molecular biology and, in particular, molecular genetics today are the confluence and fusion of three lines of thinking: '1. Structural: concerned with the architecture of biological molecules. 2. Biochemical: concerned with how biological molecules interact in cell metabolism and heredity. 3. Informational: concerned with how information is transferred from one generation of organisms to another, and how that information is translated into unique biological molecules' (Allen, 1979, p. 190).

The revolution in molecular genetics is also called the 'gene revolution'. We saw in the last chapter that Morgan and his school, on the genetics of *Drosophila*, had done a convincing job in putting the study of genes within a materialistic framework by linking seemingly invisible genes with visible chromosomes. All the same, they never really got beyond that to an account of the chemical or physiological functions of the genes. In spite of Herman Joseph Muller (1890–1967) – a member of the Morgan group, who worked on inducing mutation in *Drosophila* by exposing it to x-rays – classical geneticists stuck to what they best understood, namely, the transmission of genetic traits. Molecular genetics grew out of a dissatisfaction with the limitations of the classical programme, attempting to go beyond the still formalistic and abstract Mendelian gene-chromosome framework to tackle how the gene actually worked at the structural, functional and informational levels. This eventual fusion, as we shall see, took a long time coming.

This was partly to be explained by the fact that geneticists and biochemists had not much to do with one another's work. The latter were not interested in their research as a vehicle of genetic transmission. The former ignored the chemistry of the gene, believing that, increasingly, sophisticated genetic analyses would do the job of yielding up the gene's secrets. Indeed, some of them were extremely sceptical about how any particle or molecule could embody the genetic material. For instance, Bateson, in reviewing *The Mechanism of Mendelian Heredity* by Morgan et al., thought

> it is inconceivable that particles of chromatin or of any other substance, however complex, can possess those powers which must be assigned to our factors [i.e. genes]. ... The supposition that particles of chromatin, indistinguishable from each other and indeed almost homogeneous under any known test, can by their material nature confer all the properties of life surpasses the range of even the most convinced materialism. (Bateson, 1916)

Yet others, such as Weismann and de Vries, were convinced that the gene was a special chemical entity. De Vries (1910) wrote that 'Just as physics and chemistry go back to the molecules and atoms, the biological sciences have to penetrate to these units in order to explain, by means of their combinations, the phenomena of the living world' (p. 13).

Is it protein or nucleic acid?

However, yet another reason that could account for the long period of incubation, so to speak, before the actual fusion of the three lines of thinking as elucidated by Allen is, perhaps, the part that proteins played in the saga. As it turned out, they appear to have performed both an obstructive as well as a facilitative role. Obstructive – that is, with hindsight – because it diverted attention from nucleic acids (what today we call DNA as well as RNA) as the relevant genetic material. They were far better known, abundantly available in living tissues, and, to many, the obvious chemical for the physical basis of heredity, as their component parts, the amino acids, could be arranged in numerous ways, thus pointing to their capability for generating immense complexity of information. Furthermore, the colloidal nature of 'protoplasm' as the physical basis of life, postulated by thinkers such as T. H. Huxley, exercised thinking in the field. Proteins were considered then to determine colloidal properties. However, they were also facilitators because the methods used in studying them turn out to be readily transferable to the study of nucleic acids – for instance, one of these indispensable techniques, x-ray crystallography, was first applied to the study of protein structure and only latterly to that of nucleic acids.

The distracting effect of proteins meant that the actual discovery of nuclein – what we call nucleic acids today – which occurred as early as 1869 did not come into its own till well into the 20th century. As far as scientific consensus went, it was not until the publication of the work by Hershey and Chase in 1952 – see below – that DNA was accepted definitively as the physical basis of heredity. Indeed, Crick, up to his meeting with Watson in 1951, appeared not to have thought seriously that DNA could be the relevant molecule to study. As a physicist, influenced by Schrödinger and turning his attention to genetics, he thought that the biologically significant macromolecules to concentrate on were proteins, and that their amino acid sequences had something to do with the arrangement of the hereditary material. He was said to have once remarked in the 1940s to Wilkins, 'What you ought to do is to get yourself a good protein!' (Allen, 1979, p. 212). Wilkins was then studying DNA using x-ray diffraction analysis; his work later played a key role in the Crick and Watson model of DNA.[4]

Johann Friedrich Miescher (1844–1895) was the discoverer of nuclein (nucleic acids) in 1869. His fate, in a way, was harsher than that of Mendel. Mendel was 'rediscovered', and the laws of (classical) genetics were named after him. Miescher is now forgotten except in books on the history of science. However, unlike Mendel, he was not totally ignored when he was alive. As a matter of fact, he was much criticised. One of the critics was Nägeli, the man who was not keen on Mendel either. Some English chemists thought that nuclein was 'nothing but an impure albuminous substance'. A French chemist thought that his results were 'somewhat vague from a chemical point of view' (Magner, 1979, p. 446). In the face of the harsh reception to his work on nuclein, Miescher gave it up after 1874, and did not resume it until just five years before his death. Although he did not publish his views he did speculate that nuclein could be the hereditary material. Its atoms could form 'alternative spatial arrangements' which could account for variations – see Fruton (1972, pp. 193–204). It is indeed true that his nuclein was not pure but, unfortunately, the criticisms made did not spur his contemporaries to produce purer and better specimens.

Miescher, a Swiss studying in the German town of Tübingen and interested in the chemistry of the cell nucleus, worked on the nuclei of white blood cells. He collected pus produced in wounds, which he found in discarded surgical dressings. He separated the nuclei of the white blood cells from their surrounding cytoplasm. He found that they contained an unknown compound made up of large molecules, which was acidic and also rich in phosphorus. This he called 'nuclein'. Richard Altmann, a pupil of his, coined the term 'nucleic acid' in 1889.

Miescher and his pupils succeeded in establishing the chemistry of the nucleic acids. At the turn of the century the three components of nucleic acids were identified and described. First, ribose, a sugar with five carbon atoms in a ring. Second, a phosphate, that is, a phosphorus atom surrounded by four oxygen atoms. The phosphates produced the acidity as well as the phosphorus found in the nucleic acid. They also linked and spaced the sugars in a certain way, alternating sugars with phosphate. Third, a base made up mostly of nitrogen and carbon atoms attached to the sugar in the chain. The sugar, the linking phosphate, and the base made up a nucleotide. The bases were more complex as they were more than one kind. But by the beginning of the century they were identified as five: guanine, adenine, cytosine, thymine and uracil, which are today represented as G, A, C, T and U, respectively. Guanine and adenine are much alike and were called 'purines' because of their chemical relationship to uric acid. The other three were called 'pyrimidines'.

Later, in the 1920s, it was found that there are two kinds of nucleic acids: one found mainly in the cell nucleus, the other around the nucleus in the cytoplasm. The former is deoxyribose nucleic acid (DNA) and the latter, ribonucleic acid (RNA). They were alike in the sense that they both consisted of a long chain of alternating sugar and linking phosphate with a base attached to the sugar. But they differed in the sugar component. DNA lacked an oxygen atom in its sugar, and the base components of DNA contained guanine, adenine, cytosine and thymine, while RNA contained guanine, adenine, cytosine and uracil (uracil and thymine being quite similar). At first it was thought that the bases GACU of RNA were found in plants, and the bases GACT of DNA were found in animals, but by the 1930s overwhelming evidence showed that RNA and DNA were common to plants and animals alike – see Cherfas (1982, p. 5).

However, even with this amount of information available by the 1930s, the fortunes of nucleic acids as the physical basis of heredity did not take off for the better, but rather for the worse. This was partly because the so-called tetranucleotide hypothesis became established as the paradigm in biochemistry. It was associated with the work of Phoebus Aaron Levene

(1869–1940) at the Rockefeller Institute for Medical Research. While distinguishing and clarifying the difference between nucleic acids and proteins, he nevertheless pictured the nucleotides repeating one another in a rigid and fixed order of sets of four bases, each occurring in an equal amount. If so, as repetitious simple linear polymers, they were clearly incapable of generating the variability with which genetic material was known to possess. This 'picture' convinced researchers more than ever before that protein must be the real stuff and not nucleic acids, which, at best, could provide only a kind of structural stiffening for the genetic material.

The tetranucleotide hypothesis was definitively challenged by the studies on nucleic acids, which Erwin Chargaff (1905–2002) undertook between 1946 and 1950. He investigated nucleic acids from a variety of sources – beef thymus, spleen, liver, human sperm, yeast and tubercle bacilli. He proved, in no uncertain terms, that the four bases did not occur in equal amounts. He also overturned the assumption that all DNAs were the same as that of calf thymus DNA. For instance, the four bases of human thymus nuclei were 28 parts of adenine, 19 parts of guanine (totalling 47 parts of purines), and 16 parts of cytosine, 28 parts of thymine (totalling 44 parts of pyrimidines). And very significantly he demonstrated that DNA's composition from different organs of the same species was always constant and characteristic of the species. His correlations showed that the ratios of total purines to total pyrimidines, of adenine to thymine, and of guanine to cytosine, were roughly 1:1. If so, nucleic acids could produce as much variety as proteins. Chargaff's work, then, not only killed off the tetranucleotide hypothesis for good, but also greatly undermined the attractiveness of the protein hypothesis, namely, that proteins were the genetic material.

However, that is only one strand of the complex web which finally led to the ascendancy of DNA over protein. Another strand began with the work, published in 1928, of Frederick Griffith (1877–1941), a doctor doing research at the Pathological Laboratory attached to the Ministry of Health in London. He injected mice with a living but mutant benign strain of the normally disease-causing bacteria *Streptococus pneumoniae,* or pneumococci, as well as the usually virulent, though non-living (killed by heat) strain. He found that the blood of these mice cultured live and virulent pneumococci. No one could make sense of this strange phenomenon, which seemed to go against what was known of genetics and inheritance. Yet it was real enough – laboratories around the world successfully repeated the experiment. It became known as 'bacterial transformation'.

In the 1940s Oswald T. Avery (1877–1955) and his colleagues at the Rockefeller Institute in New York set themselves the task of determining the 'transforming factor' or principle which, they assumed, must have passed from the heat-killed bacteria to the benign strain to render the latter virulent. At first they thought it must be protein, as the bulk of chromosomal material was in fact protein. But after many years of experimentation they came to the conclusion that the transforming factor, of which they eventually collected 25 milligrams, could not be protein, as it did not behave like protein, but was something which, instead, behaved like nucleic acids. Enzymes which attacked protein had no effect on it. Chemical tests for proteins did not work, either. But enzymes known to attack DNA did destroy it, while enzymes which attacked only RNA left it untouched. The evidence was all pointing to DNA as the fundamental unit of the transforming principle. But, nevertheless, Avery and his co-workers were not keen to jump to a general conclusion, namely, that DNA was genes, and genes were really DNA, in all organisms. Instead, they cautiously conceded that the biologically active stuff might not be DNA but some other substance associated with it which could have escaped their detection. In any case, even if this were not so, what they had established was merely that DNA was implicated as the physical basis of heredity for one type of bacteria.

What clinched the argument, finally, for the scientific community in arriving at a consensus was the studies of A. D. Hershey (1908–97) and Martha Chase (b. 1927), at Cold Spring Harbor Laboratory, published in 1952. It is said that Hershey began the experiments in a sceptical frame of mind, treating the possibility of DNA being the hereditary material as somewhat ridiculous and comical – see Magner (1979, p. 454). They worked with phages. Bacteriophages, like all viruses, consist of nucleic acids (usually DNA but in some forms, RNA) surrounded by a coat of protein. Any single one of these viruses can infect a bacterium, which, after half an hour or so, would burst open releasing hundreds of new viruses, each a replica of the original infecting virus or phage. Which then of the two bits of the phage was the real infecting agent, the protein coat or the nucleic acid? They tagged the DNA of the phage with radioactive phosphorus, and the protein coat with radioactive sulphur. When these labelled phages infected the bacteria, it was found that they injected their DNA into the host cells, leaving their protein coats on the outside. Later work showed that only the phage DNA, and not the protein, was biochemically involved with the replication of the new phages.

The rival hypothesis, that protein could be the hereditary substance, was finally eliminated. According to Peter Medawar, this was in spite of the fact that the nucleic acid hypothesis 'aroused much resentment, for many scientists unconsciously deplore the resolution of mysteries they have grown up with and have therefore come to love' (Magner, 1979, p. 455). The resolution of this controversy was obviously very important in the long story of trying to unravel the mystery behind inheritance. But if DNA was indeed the genetic material, its structure remained a mystery; so was the relationship between the chemical composition of the gene and how it acted as the vehicle of inheritance. To the solution of these problems Crick and Watson made their contribution. According to Allen, their achievement involved fusing three strands of thinking or approaches: the structural (the work of x-ray crystallography), the biochemical (the work done on the roles played by biological molecules in cell metabolism and in heredity) and the informational (the work done on bacteriophages).

The contribution of x-ray crystallography

As mentioned earlier, the technique of x-ray crystallography is a central technique first applied to the study of protein structure. Mainly a British invention, pioneered around 1912 by W. H. Bragg (1862–1942), later joined by his son, W. L. Bragg (1890–1971), it became distinctive of what Allen has called the structuralist approach.

Crystals are relatively pure samples of substances, with their molecules all arranged at definite and regular intervals, giving rise to a latticework of constant dimensions, as well as being all oriented in the same direction in space. An x-ray beam directed at the crystal would be deflected by the molecules. The angle and nature of the x-ray diffraction captured and recorded on a photographic plate, which was placed in front of the crystal, while the x-ray source was placed behind it. It turned out that each kind of protein produced a different diffraction pattern. The diffraction pattern, which existed as no more than dots on the screen or photographic plate, was the basis for deducing the molecular structure of the protein molecule – the diffraction patterns of the atomic structure of crystals were used to visualise their three-dimensional structure. First the Braggs did work on small molecules, such as rock salt and diamond, but later, on larger ones, such as hair protein.

By the early 1960s John Kendrew and Max Perutz, at the Cavendish Laboratory in Cambridge, had worked out the detailed structure of two related proteins, haemoglobin and myoglobin. More importantly, they were able to show how knowledge of their three-dimensional structure could cast light on their function. Understanding molecular structure as key to understanding molecular function vitally propelled those researchers who were interested in solving similar problems in nucleic acids. In the meantime, Maurice Wilkins (b. 1916) and Rosalind Franklin (1920–1958), at King's College, London, were applying the techniques of x-ray crystallography to the study of nucleic acids. As we shall see, it was Franklin's x-ray crystallographic data which Crick and Watson relied on in arriving at their double helix model of DNA.

Biochemical genetics

The biochemical geneticists may be said to be interested in determining how genes control metabolic sequences in living cells. But in the early days, between 1905 and 1925, although Muller and others were interested in this issue, they lacked the biochemical tools to attack it. Nevertheless, in 1908 Archibold Garrod (1857–1936) addressed the Royal Society of London in a paper published as 'Inborn Errors of Metabolism', in which he indirectly showed that genes produced effects in metabolic functioning. There were four distinct metabolic disorders that Garrod knew of. One of these was alkaptonuria or phenylkaptonuria. The sufferer could not metabolise tyrosine completely owing to the absence of the enzyme homogentistic acid oxidase. As a result, homogentistic acid collected in the body and was eventually excreted in the urine, making it black. Garrod wondered what caused the metabolic block. He eliminated infection by germs as an explanation, or that it was an effect of some general malfunctioning. He enlisted the help of Bateson to look into the family histories of the sufferers, and found that the condition was inherited, probably the expression of a recessive gene. A large percentage of the sufferers were the children of first cousins; the offspring of such unions were more likely to reveal recessive traits. This made Garrod think that Mendelian genes could affect the production of certain chemicals, namely, enzymes, in the body's biochemical pathways.[5] But Garrod's work was ignored for about thirty years, in spite of the fact that he found evidence that each of the four metabolic disorders (the other three being albinism, cystinuria and pentosuria) was genetic in origin, each causing a specific metabolic block.

The link between genes and enzymes was ultimately established when George Beadle (1903–1989) and Edward L. Tatum (1909–1975) came together in 1928 to work on the red bread mould or bacterium *Neurospora*. Beadle, earlier on, had done work on *Drosophila*. But in deserting the fruit fly for the bacterium at the suggestion of Tatum, he struck upon an experimental organism which turned up trumps for biochemical genetics in the way the fruit fly had done for Morgan in his studies of chromosomal genetics. Neurospora possessed the following advantages: it reproduced quickly with a short life cycle; it grew easily in a synthetic medium containing a carbon source, some inorganic salts and biotin; any metabolic mutants were easily identified; the adult stage had only one set of chromosomes (haploid), such that all mutant genes would be phenotypically expressed, with no danger of recessive genes being masked by dominant ones.

First, they x-rayed the spores to get mutants. Then they grew the irradiated spores on a 'complete medium' (containing all that was required for growth). They harvested these, and next grew them on minimal media to find out which had undergone mutation. Those that failed to grow were assumed to have at least one metabolic block caused by the mutation. In turn the mutated spores were grown on various 'modified media', each lacking some vital ingredient for growth. For instance, if the spores from, say, stock A could grow on all the other modified media except on the one with vitamin B missing, then it could be inferred that stock A spores suffered a metabolic block for synthesising the vitamin in question. These results and further analyses showed that these blocks were directly correlated with genetic mutations – the mutant strains differed from the parental strain by an alteration in a single gene. Genes did regulate development and function after all, as Garrod had found. Furthermore, as it was known then that each step in a metabolic pathway was catalysed by a specific enzyme, Beadle and Tatum were led to conclude that gene mutations produced enzyme changes, and that each gene controlled the synthesis of one particular specific enzyme. In 1945 they enunciated the one-gene–one-enzyme hypothesis.

Later on this was revised somewhat, as it appeared that a gene did not code for a whole enzyme or protein, but for a single polypeptide chain, that is, a long folded chain of amino acids of which proteins were constituted. In 1949 J. V. Neal (b. 1915) showed that sickle-cell anaemia in humans was a Mendelian inheritance, and Linus Pauling (1901–1994) and his colleagues showed that the haemoglobin protein of sufferers was different from that of non-sufferers, which led them to conclude that the difference could be due to a difference in their respective compositions of amino acids. This was verified in 1957 by the work of V. M. Ingram (b. 1924), which established that the two differed by only a single amino acid from among about 300 amino acids in the haemoglobin molecule – the normal haemoglobin had glutamic acid, while the sickle-cell haemoglobin had valine. By the late 1940s and early 1950s it became accepted that genes could control cellular metabolism through controlling the production of specific proteins. This set the stage for the next problem, namely, precisely how DNA directed the synthesis of proteins.

The contribution of the phage group

Allen distinguishes between three phases in the innovation of DNA studies: the romantic, the dogmatic and the academic. But as we shall see, only really the first, strictly, speaking belongs to what Allen calls the informationist approach *simpliciter*. The latter two are in fact the fruit of the fusion between what Allen calls the structuralist, the biochemical and the informationist approaches. For this reason, only the first component will be dealt with under this section.

The chemical nature of the gene was the major concern of the so-called informationists. Allen thinks of them as the romantics because they were, in the main, though not exclusively, physicists who turned their attention to biology, as mentioned earlier. The originator of this trend was Max Delbrück (1906–1981), having been inspired by Bohr's thinking on matters biological. He trained as an atomic physicist, first at Göttingen and then in Copenhagen at Bohr's laboratory. But in the mid-1930s he migrated to the California Institute of Technology to work on biology with Morgan and his group (Morgan having moved to California from Columbia). However, he was not over-impressed by what he found. Research concentrated on the gross chromosomal stages and, moreover, assumed that classical physics and chemistry were adequate in providing a complete and sufficient account of the gene and how it functioned.

Delbrück was convinced otherwise. Genes, admittedly, were molecules. But to him they did not appear to behave in the way physicists and chemists normally conceived of molecules to behave – chemical reactions between these were regarded as uniform processes, and their collision with one another was expected to be random, in accordance with the principles of chemical kinetics. In contrast, chemical reactions, which occurred in cells, were not at all random, but were specific, distinct and separate. Genes appeared to be capable of executing a great variety of reactions over a period of time. So they must themselves be chemically stable and complex, and be able to resist breaking down into simpler forms in order that they be transferred from one generation of cells and organisms to another. In the light of this, Delbrück reasoned that genes must be molecules possessing very special properties, which could not readily be accounted for by the usual way in which physicists and chemists understood other molecules and how they worked.

To be fair to the Morgan group, the significant question of which components exactly of the chromosome carried the hereditary material was never far from the minds of its researchers. But Delbrück realised that *Drosophila* was not suitable as an object of experimental study in order to answer this vital question. It was multi-celled and much too complex for this purpose. It occurred to Delbrück that bacteriophages, viruses which attack and infect bacteria, were more promising as 'ideal objects for the study of self-replication' (Allen, 1979, p. 206). So, in 1943, together with Salvador Luria (1912–1991) and Hershey, he started the so-called 'phage group'.

A virus is a minute infectious agent which can survive but not replicate on its own. For replication it needs to do so inside some other living cell, a host. As mentioned earlier, it is composed of nucleic acid, usually DNA but sometimes RNA, wrapped up in a protein coat. It could be said to be a mobile genetic element. Each bacteriophage particle, a particular type of virus, is said to be shaped rather like a syringe or a tadpole – its smaller end latches onto the outer wall of the bacterial cell, and then proceeds to squirt its DNA into the bacterium, leaving the empty protein coat behind on the outside. Once inside, its DNA requisitions the bacterium's cellular machinery to manufacture not bacteria but viruses, each with a nucleus of its own DNA and a protein coat to protect it. These clump together to form new phages, and then burst out of the bacterial cell walls to go on to infect other bacteria.

The choice of bacteriophages as a research tool was excellently made for the following reasons: their ease of growth, with millions cultivated in a small space; their short life cycle – within 30 minutes or so, a new generation is replicated; their containing only nucleic acids and protein, so that determining their respective roles in the reproductive process is relatively easier. And, as we have seen, the work of the phage workers (the studies of Hershey and Chase published in 1952) finally laid to rest the hypothesis that protein was the genetic material. So phages became celebrated, and it is said that they did for molecular genetics what *Drosophila* had done for chromosomal genetics.

Phage work was also helped by the arrival of the electron microscope, in 1939, in America. With it researchers could see not only their shape for the first time, but also found that each species had a characteristic structure. They could also measure their size.

The ingenious and careful work of the early phage workers had helped to build up a large corpus of knowledge about phages, including the fact that their genetic material could undergo mutation, and that genetic recombination between different strains of the same virus could occur. But the so-called romantic phase, which began with the work of Delbrück and ended with that of Hershey and Chase, did not take seriously the efforts of biochemists in determining how genes could affect metabolic sequences. Indeed, as we have seen, for all their attempts to answer the question about the chemical nature of the gene, on the whole, they remained sceptical that nucleic acids or DNA could be the physical basis of heredity. Instead, they were still putting their money on protein. As mentioned earlier, in the case of Hershey, although he conducted what turned out to be the definitive study which settled the rival claims of protein and nucleic acids, he did so in a deeply sceptical frame of mind regarding the probity of the latter. A fellow researcher recalled a day at Cold Spring Harbor Laboratory discussing with Hershey 'the wildly comical possibility that only the viral DNA finds its way into the host cell, acting there like a transforming principle in altering the synthetic processes of the cell' (Magner, 1979, p. 454).

The work of Hershey and Chase convinced the phage group not merely that DNA was the hereditary material, but also that no new laws of physics or chemistry or biological organisation were required. It became obvious to them that the basic problem of reproduction could be understood in terms of two functions familiar to biochemistry, namely, autocatalysis and heterocatalysis. The former refers to the process whereby a molecule catalyses some of the early steps in its own formation. The latter refers to the process whereby the molecule catalyses the formation or breakdown of other molecules. When phage DNA was used to make several copies of the original virus inside the bacterial cell, this was an instance of autocatalysis at work – today the term used is replication. When phage DNA got the bacterial cellular mechanism to synthesise virus-specific proteins which led to phage growth and replication, this was an instance of heterocatalysis at work – today the term used is translation. Of course, prior to 1953, no one had a clue precisely as to how these two functions were achieved. This, then, constituted the next phase of research. Its success required a fusion of the three strands – the structuralist, the biochemical and the informationist (as identified by Allen) which, up to 1952, was each, more or less, mutually ignored by their respective practitioners.

The unified approach

The unified approach bore fruit in the double helix model of the DNA of Francis Crick (b. 1916) and James D. Watson (b. 1928), first published in *Nature* in 1953. This has been hailed, if not as the greatest, at least as one of the greatest achievements in biology in the 20th century, occupying pride of place comparable to those of Darwin and Mendel in the 19th century. Their work was the more remarkable for the relatively short time within which it came to fruition. They met in Cambridge in 1951, and they constructed the model after an intense flurry of activity in the spring of 1953.

Both Watson and Crick had read Schrödinger's book *What is Life?* But, as earlier mentioned, while Crick was trained as a physicist, Watson was trained as a phage geneticist and was a member of the phage group. Like his mentor, Delbrück, Watson was dismissive of classical geneticists, who were perceived as 'nibbling around the edges of heredity rather than trying for the bull's eye [i.e. to discover the nature of the hereditary molecule and its means of auto- and heterocatalysis]' (Allen, 1979, p. 210). But, unlike Delbrück, he was not dismissive of biochemistry and, like Luria, thought that how genes actually behaved in biochemical terms could be relevant. On the other hand, Crick thought that x-ray crystallography studies on proteins and nucleic acids could be relevant, although he had no interest in or knowledge of biochemistry. He ended up working with Perutz and his group on the x-ray crystallography on haemoglobin. His knowledge of protein crystallography was more or less self-taught. And we have seen, too, that almost right up to his involvement with Watson in the autumn of 1951, he was still backing the protein horse, so to speak. Watson, on the other hand, had trusted Luria's hunch that DNA might turn out to be the winner, in spite of the fact that the work of Avery and his fellow workers was not considered to provide the definitive evidence for it. Both Crick and Watson knew Wilkins (who was working with Franklin at King's College, London, on the x-ray crystallography of nucleic acids, as mentioned earlier). This meant that between them they had overall knowledge of the three fields that were soon to be fused.

They realised that any model devised for the molecular structure of DNA must do justice to at least two things: it must be consonant with the x-ray diffraction data obtained by x-ray crystallography, and it should account for the dual functions of autocatalysis (replication) and heterocatalysis (translation), as thrown up by the work of the phage group.

Franklin's data (which Wilkins passed on to Watson without her knowledge or permission) regarding what she called the B structure of DNA showed that:

1. Its structure was helical, as the stacked layers of its subunits were regularly 3.4 angstroms apart (1 angstrom = one ten-millionth of a millimetre).
2. The helix made one full turn in 34 angstroms, that is, every 10 rungs.

3. Its diameter was constant, about 20 angstroms.
4. The phosphate groups of the molecule appeared to lie on the curve of the helix, which meant that the bases were turned inward.

As mentioned earlier, work by the 1930s had established the chemical composition of DNA – a nucleotide of four bases, attached to sugar and phosphate groups, consisting of the two purines (compounds with two linked rings of carbon and nitrogen), adenine and guanine, on the one hand, and the two pyrimidines (compounds with a single carbon–nitrogen ring), cytosine and thymine, on the other. The sugar groups of one nucleotide were attached to the phosphate groups of another, such that a kind of sugar–phosphate backbone ran down the chain of nucleotides constituting the molecule. But no one knew anything about the exact way in which the bases were ordered and bonded. Would a like base attract another like base, such as adenine and adenine, thymine and thymine? Would a like base type attract another like base type, such as purine and purine, pyrimidine and pyrimidine? Or would an unlike base attract another unlike base, such as a purine and a pyrimidine? Or maybe bases on the same molecule attracted one another? The latter possibility appeared to be uppermost in Crick's mind in 1951.

The possibility of linking a purine to a pyrimidine turned out to be consonant with the experimental work of Chargaff which, we earlier saw, had recently been published, demolishing the tetranucleotide hypothesis. Chargaff had shown that the ratio between total purines and total pyrimidines was more or less 1:1 in the DNA molecules from all the different sources studied. Chargaff had also shown that the ratio between adenine and thymine, on the one hand, and guanine and cytosine, on the other, was also roughly 1:1. Crick had not come across Chargaff's findings at the time he and Watson were furiously agonising about such matters. But during his visit to Cambridge in June 1952 they met Chargaff, who told them about the 1:1 ratios. Actually, the previous year Watson and Crick had asked John Griffith, a mathematician also at Cambridge, to work out for them what the attractive forces would be between like bases in a DNA molecule. Griffith informed them he found from theoretical considerations it appeared more likely that like bases attracted unlike ones and that adenine went with thymine, while guanine went with cytosine – in fact the very pairings that Chargaff had empirically found. But Watson and Crick did not appear to have absorbed the significance of Griffith's calculations until they met Chargaff – see Allen (1979, pp. 216–17).

But curiously it transpired that they did not allow Chargaff's findings and Griffith's calculations to inform and determine their modelling of the DNA structure. Rather, they claimed it was only after they had struck upon the double-stranded model as the correct one that the Chargaff's ratios 'just fell out at the end'. Crick is reported to have said:

Base pairing and complementary replication – you'll recall we had that idea the summer before, when Chargaff came through Cambridge, and I talked to John Griffith, and I realized then that one-to-one ratios could mean complementary replication. So the idea predates the structure. And of course, the paradox of the whole thing is that when we came to build the structure *we did not initially use* that idea. We didn't do it until we were *driven* towards it. (Judson, 1979, p. 172)

With hindsight, perhaps, one could say that if they had taken those findings explicitly on board, they could have got there in less time. But apparently they preferred, according to Watson, 'to use as little data, few assumptions, as possible to solve the structure, and we never knew whether Chargaff's rules had some completely extraneous functional reason, and so we didn't put that in' (ibid., p. 173).

Instead, in their furious model building, Watson, in particular, tried out numerous models, some two-stranded, others three-stranded. He even tried to put the sugar–phosphate backbones on the inside of the molecule, but this solved one problem only to raise another. Finally, they hit upon the double helix with adenine–thymine and guanine–cystosine pairings to be linked by two hydrogen bonds.[6] The A–T pair laid upon the G–C pair comfortably and were congruent. Also, the pairs fitted inside the backbones neatly. This would account for the diameter of the DNA being constant and for Chargaff's 1:1 ratios.

The model, published in *Nature* in April 1953, was in the form of two DNA strands, with the sugar–phosphate backbones forming the twining twin helices, held together by bonds between the two pairs of complementary bases. (See Allen, 1979, p. 220; Cherfas, 1982, p. 15.) Another way of describing it is to say that it was like a winding spiral staircase with the sugar–phosphate backbones as banisters, and the pairs of complementary bases as the steps. As the bases are complementary, the two strands are mirror images of each other. When A occurs on one strand, T occurs on the other opposite to it, and to which it is hydrogen-bonded. A sequence, CACG, on one strand stands opposite to the sequence GTGC on the other. Each strand on its own would be sufficient to produce a complementary strand for pairing. The strand containing CACG would produce GTGC, while the strand containing GTGC would in turn generate CACG. In this way the molecule would have reproduced or replicated itself. This model then accounted beautifully for the major genetic, biochemical and structural characteristics of the hereditary material. On the biochemical and structural levels it explained the x-ray data characteristic of helices, the constant diameter of the fibre, the stacking of the bases at regular intervals, and the 1:1 base ratios. On the biological level it explained both autocatalysis and heterocatalysis, and suggested a mechanism for how DNA stores genetic information. Autocatalysis, or the replication of the DNA molecule, could occur by each strand acting as a template for constructing its partner. Thus, when the strands separated, each formed its own complement, the result being two complete molecules where only one existed before.[7]

But it could be said that 'Watson and Crick arrived at the structure of the double helix by a combination of guessing, model building and the unacknowledged exploitation of Rosalind Franklin's X-ray crystallographic data' (Magner, 1979, p. 459). With regard to the contribution of Franklin, Watson did not do her justice, but Crick was much fairer. He wrote: 'the structure was there waiting to be discovered – Watson and I did not invent it. It seems to me unlikely that either of us would have done it separately, but Rosalind Franklin was pretty close. ... Wilkins, after Franklin left, could well have got there in his own good time' (Olby, 1974, p. vi).

The model, as we have seen, postulated that each strand of the double helix could act as a template for the whole duplex. Experimental confirmation came from the work, in particular, of Messelson and Stahl – see Cherfas (1982, pp. 13–14). But an outstanding theoretical problem remained unsolved relating to the heterocatalytic function of DNA. DNA had been shown to be a good memory bank, but the information it stored and replicated with ease had somehow to be used to make proteins, which ultimately give cells and organisms their characteristic properties of shape, colour, metabolic potential, and so on . Proteins, after all, carry out the chemical reactions which sustain living organisms.

This was cracked in moves, which involved the following main ones:

1. In 1958 Crick formulated what he called the Central Dogma of Molecular Biology, namely, that information went from nucleic acids to proteins, but not the other way round. This principle was accepted, guiding subsequent research in isolating and identifying the components and mechanisms in the cell which 'translate' (the new term for heterocatalyse) genetic information, encoded in DNA, into protein molecules.
2. Proteins, as we have seen, are polypeptides, long folded chains made of between 50 and over 2000 amino acids. But about 20 of them only are used in the synthesis of proteins in living organisms. The proportion of any given amino acid varies from protein to protein. To determine how DNA could ultimately result in the making of proteins, Crick suggested first determining both the amino sequence of a given protein and the base sequence of the bit of nucleic acid that coded for it, and then comparing the two. (This would be consonant with the one-gene–one-enzyme hypothesis of Beadle and Tatum.) This was put to the test by Charles Yanofsky's group at Stanford, and Sidney Brenner at Cambridge, who confirmed that genes and the proteins they coded were collinear – the order of information along the one specified the order of information along the other.

3. Increasing knowledge and clarification about the other type of nucleic acids, RNA (ribonucleic acid), became available in the 1960s. Two sorts of RNA were postulated and then discovered. One was mRNA, short for 'messenger RNA', the other was tRNA, short for 'transfer RNA': mRNA had the job of ferrying genetic information from DNA to the ribosomes, which were small organelles, where the proteins were made; tRNA had the job of reading the coded message and converting (translating) the sequence of bases into the specific amino acid in question. In the light of this, the Central Dogma was amended to read 'DNA makes RNA makes protein'.

4. Crick and Brenner worked out the fundamental properties of the code as follows:
   (a) One amino acid must be represented by three nucleotides in the mRNA. In other words, the code was made up of triplets (called a codon) and was analogous to a three-letter word in English, the smallest word in an alphabet of four letters (in RNA these were U, C, A and G). The reasoning went something like this: given that there were 20 amino acids and 4 bases, single-letter and two-letter words were out of the question, and four-letter words would be wasteful. Hence, three-letter words.
   (b) There would be 64 such codons. But as there were only 20 amino acids, any amino acid could correspond to more than one codon.
   (c) The codons would follow one another in a non-overlapping manner.

Experimental work which followed at the time (by Marshall Nirenberg of the National Institutes of Health at Bethesda, Maryland, and Gobind Khorana at Wisconsin) impressively bore out these speculations to be correct. By 1966 the genetic code was fully deciphered. Every codon was accounted for. It turned out that the code was the same in all organisms, whether the DNA was in bacteria, plants or, indeed, humans. 'No tower of Babel here: the same "words" that instruct the *E. coli* to add another particular amino acid to a protein chain would order up the same amino acid in a honeybee or a man' (Sylvester and Klotz, 1983, p. 28).

In Kuhnian terms, the double helix structure of DNA and the so-called Central Dogma were rapidly accepted as paradigms in molecular genetics. However, work in the 1970s by two independent sets of researchers showed that in the replication of certain tumour cells, called retroviruses, genetic information passed from RNA to DNA. This seemed to be at odds with the Central Dogma. As a consequence, the Dogma was reformulated in the light of this anomaly to read: it is possible for information to pass from nucleic acid to nucleic acid, or from nucleic acid to protein, but it is not possible for information to pass from protein to nucleic acid or from protein to protein. In other words, once information has passed into protein, it cannot get out again; otherwise, this would lead back to Lamarckianism of some kind – see Judson (1979, p. 338).

Impressive as the science of molecular genetics may be, it might be appropriate to end this account of its coming to maturity in such a short span of time by pointing out that molecular genetics could not, and should not, be expected to solve all problems in genetics, never mind in biology. For instance, even nearly fifty years after the appearance of the double helix, scientists still have little understanding of the so-called 'junk DNA', which constitutes a large proportion of the genetic inheritance of an organism, but which seems not to play any role in the process of replication. (Calling it 'junk DNA' simply reflects the ignorance of existing scientific comprehension of the subject.)[8] But even if there were complete knowledge of the molecular structure of DNA, such knowledge would not necessarily lead to knowledge about its function, its self-regulatory processes, its evolution. Just to cite one example – it does not appear to have much to say about how the expression of genetic information is controlled. Only a small amount of the total genetic information in a cell, relevant to the role it plays in the organism, is selectively expressed. So there must be processes controlling the rate of gene expression from DNA via mRNA to protein molecules. Work in the 1970s also showed that the Watson–Crick model could not cope readily with the discovery of split genes; neither was the genetic code universal, as a nucleotide triplet, which codes for a particular amino acid when it is part of a mitochondrial gene, codes for a different amino acid when it is part of a nuclear gene. Of course, as already mentioned, there are even radical critics who maintain that such problems will escape solution, as they fundamentally question the framework of molecular genetics itself.

Molecular genetics: biotechnology

Biotechnology is a method of genetic transformation.[9] If the latter were to be defined extremely broadly as the attempt to affect hereditary transmission with the objective of producing improved varieties of plants and animals (improved, of course, from the standpoint of human purposes), then, historically, it would cover three different strands and periods. As we have seen, the earliest is the ancient art or craft, practised by farmers and breeders, of artificial selection (and in the case of plants, open pollination and chance crossing to procure traditionally produced hybrids). More recent is the incorporation of classical Mendelian genetics to produce, characteristically, the technology of hybridisation, based on double-crossing. The most recent of all is the incorporation of molecular biology and genetics to produce, characteristically, recombinant DNA (rDNA) technology.

The last two, as we know, are science-led and science-induced. Their respective technologies may be subsumed under biogenetic technology.

Biotechnology is then a subset of this, referring to a clutch of new techniques which started to appear from the 1970s onwards, rendered possible by the theoretical advances in basic science at the molecular level with regard to biological phenomena. And within biotechnology itself, one could further distinguish between those techniques springing more directly from molecular genetics and those arising from the wider study of molecular biology itself. The former may be called 'micro-genetic engineering' or rDNA technology; the latter, as in the case of cell biology, has totally transformed the techniques of tissue culture and cloning. Some of the techniques characteristic of each are set out in Figure 4.1.[10]

As one can see from the figure, in contrast to the relatively whole-organism technology based on the classical gene-chromosome theory, the latest, more specifically, should be called molecular biotechnology.[11] From the point of view of the control and manipulation of hereditary material, as we saw in the last chapter, the former is a decided advance upon traditional artificial selection and traditional hybridisation. In the same way, the latter's advance upon the former is equally radical and impressive. Undoubtedly, within the gene-chromosome theory/technology framework, there has been a greatly improved control in the transmission of genetic material from one variety to another, and a greatly improved control in the focusing of desirable genetic characteristics in one variety by creating pure-bred lines. However, all the same, it does not permit the actual transfer of genetic material from an individual of one species to another individual of a different species. Biotechnology is now able to cross this species barrier through techniques such as rDNA transfer (genetic engineering) and protoplast fusion (cell biology), which can produce transgenic organisms, that is, organisms whose DNA has incorporated genetic material from another species.[12] The power of altering what Marx has called 'species being' has arrived. In the words of a botanist from Harvard University at the 1984 USA National Academy of Sciences Convocation on Genetic Engineering of

Figure 4.1   Biogenetic technology

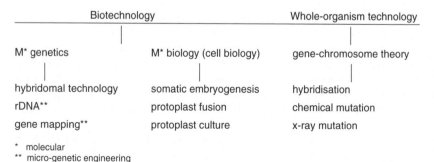

Biotechnology		Whole-organism technology
M* genetics	M* biology (cell biology)	gene-chromosome theory
hybridomal technology	somatic embryogenesis	hybridisation
rDNA**	protoplast fusion	chemical mutation
gene mapping**	protoplast culture	x-ray mutation

*   molecular
** micro-genetic engineering

Plants, that power means: 'We can now operationally have a kind of world gene pool. ... Darwin aside, speciation aside, we can now envision moving any gene, in principle at least, out of any organism and into any organism' (National Research Council, 1984, p. 12).

This is an acknowledgement, if not an outright declaration, that humankind, at least in principle, has the ability to transcend or bypass natural evolution and its processes. A 1975 Nobel prizewinner, the MIT microbiologist David Baltimore, said outright, 'We can outdo evolution' (Cavalieri, 1981, p. 32).[13]

However, it does not mean that the extremely powerful new biotechnology will render obsolete the older biogenetic techniques in the genetic transformation of plants and animals for agricultural and husbandry purposes. For a start, as already hinted at towards the end of the last section in this chapter, not a few theoretical problems remain to be solved. In the first two decades of the revolution in molecular genetics and biology, it is true that strong reductionism was euphorically expressed. But over the years a more sensible reassessment has set in. For instance, as far as its application to plant and animal 'breeding' is concerned, two major difficult issues remain.[14] First, while it may be relatively easy to identify a phenotypic trait considered to be desirable, it is much more difficult to identify the gene(s) correlated with that desirable trait. Second, even if the gene(s) could be found, as we saw earlier, scientists are not clear at all about how the gene complex is controlled and, therefore, expressed in the organism. It is likely that the more recent biogenetic technologies would be conjoined with the older ones. Biotechnology has also rapidly penetrated and radically transformed other fields, such as the pharmaceutical industry – the anti-growth hormone, somatostatin, the growth hormone, somatotropin, and insulin had all been genetically engineered and bacterium-cloned by the late 1970s – the food industry, the chemicals industry, energy, health care, environmental control and resource recovery, indeed, even scientific research itself. It has done so by developing and manufacturing genetically manipulated genes, vectors, enzymes, cells and organisms which produce goods and services for the industries and activities just mentioned.

So far the definitional problem about what constitutes biotechnology has been dealt with. The next task is to complete the outline of the various steps involved in translating the more theoretical disciplines, molecular biology and molecular genetics, into biotechnology. To do this, as it transpired, required further research, which might be more suitably described as theoretical. Without these theoretical breakthroughs, no technology could be spawned. This shows more clearly than ever before that, in contemporary science, theoretical components are integral to basic science-induced technologies.

The early intellectual/theoretical breakthroughs, which themselves constitute a new technological revolution, include at least the following aspects:[15]

1. The development of restriction and other enzymes.
2. The development of vectors and 'vehicles'.
3. The development of gene libraries, particularly, of the higher animals and plants.

Before discussing the development of restriction enzymes, one needs to say something briefly about enzymes themselves. Enzymes are biological catalysts. Catalysts are substances which help a chemical reaction without themselves being used up in the process. They are proteins enabling chemical reactions to take place in the cells at lower temperatures and at a faster rate than might otherwise be possible, and are in general responsible for the biochemistry of the cell. A single enzyme molecule can assist the chemical transformation of many thousands of other molecules. An enzyme acts with a given molecule (a compound), called the substrate, to produce a complex which forms the products of the reaction. Enzymes are very specific to particular reactions.

The emergence of enzymes as a biological force itself, constitutes a revolution, but it was a revolution that long predated the genetic revolution which came in the wake of the Crick and Watson structure of DNA. In the 1850s Louis Pasteur started off a controversy about the agents of fermentation in wine. But in 1897 Eduard Buchner and his helpers showed that the juices inside yeasts would convert sugar to alcohol. He named the enzyme 'zymase'. Subsequent work, however, showed that zymase itself consisted of 14 separate enzymes, each doing a specific job in the conversion of sugar to alcohol. Further understanding of enzymes as large protein molecules led first to their extraction from living organisms, then to their purification into crystals and to their eventual study, as we earlier saw, using x-ray crystallography. But of direct relevance to our concern in this chapter is the discovery that other large biochemicals, like the nucleic acids, are also the substrates for particular enzymes. This meant that enzymes could be used to manipulate nucleic acids. Just to mention one of them, alkaline phosphatase: its job in the cell mechanism is to control the production of phosphate and to recycle phosphorus. But in the hands of the genetic engineer, when used on DNA, it breaks the bond that holds the phosphate to the sugar.

The restriction enzymes are a particular set of enzymes which have proved to be indispensable to the genetic engineer. In the words of Cherfas (1982), they are 'no ordinary enzymes; they are the machine tools of the genetic engineer, the precision cutters that allow the researcher to slice DNA cleanly at any known point' (p. 26). They are bacterial enzymes which cut DNA at specific DNA sequences. They are, therefore, immensely useful in manipulating in vitro genetic recombination, as well as in the analysis of the base sequences of DNA molecules. Matthew Messelson and Robert Yuan were the first to purify the enzymes responsible for restriction in an *E. coli* of strain K (with the code number 1100). They started work on the project in 1966; two years later, they published their findings in *Nature* (1968, pp. 1110–14). But since their pioneering work their techniques have been improved upon; new ones have been discovered, while new understanding of the various types has emerged.

Since the isolation of the first restriction enzyme in 1968, hundreds more have been identified. Each acts as a kind of scissors to cut DNA molecules at a specific site, called the restriction site, which consists of a short sequence of four to ten bases. For instance, the restriction enzyme Eco RI 'recognises' a restriction site with a sequence of six bases – GAATTC – and cuts the DNA with such a sequence between G and Λ, thus:[16]

> the recognition site of Eco RI:
>   -G-A-A-T-T-C-
>   -C-T-T-A-A-G-
> is cut by Eco RI to produce Eco RI fragments:
>   -G-   -A-A-T-T-C-
>   -C-T-T-A-A-   -G-

Enzymes are divided into several classes. The class which is the most serviceable, and which genetic engineers rely on, is class II. These, on the whole, have the virtue of 'recognising' a specific site, and breaking the DNA at a particular place within that site. An example is Hin, discovered by Hamilton Smith, for which he was awarded the Nobel prize in 1978. Unlike Messelson and Yuan, who worked with the bacteria *E. coli* K to produce their restriction enzyme Eco RI, which is now said to fall into class I enzymes, Smith worked with a bacterium called *Haemophilus influenzae* strain RD, and identified a whole new class of restriction enzymes now called Hin.

Enzymes' usefulness to the genetic engineer may be summed up as follows:

> By making a wise choice from the catalogue of known enzymes, the genetic engineer can find one to perform practically any task. Almost any sequence of bases can be located and cut at will. Some enzymes recognize a long sequence, six or seven bases long: they are often useful for opening a circular strand of DNA at just one point. Others have a much smaller site, four or even three bases long: these will produce small fragments that can be used to determine the sequence of bases along the DNA.... Enzymes such as Hin dII...allow some flexibility within a rigid site and are very useful. So cuts can be made anywhere along the DNA, dividing it into many small fragments or a few longer ones. The cuts made by a type II on a given sort of DNA will always be the same. (Cherfas, 1982, pp. 55–6)

Such a technology is clearly inconceivable without the discovery of restriction enzymes. However, another sort of enzyme is also required for in vitro genetic recombination, namely, DNA ligase, which enables two DNA fragments to join together, a ligase being an enzyme which catalyses the joining of two molecules. In other words, while the restriction enzymes work as a pair of scissors, DNA ligase acts as glue or paste. All restriction fragments produced by using the same restriction enzyme will have what are called the same 'sticky ends'. Janet Mertz and Ronald Davis showed that all the ends of restriction fragments made by the restriction enzyme Eco RI are identical and complementary (see above), so that any two fragments produced by Eco RI can join together. They said:

> any two DNAs with RI endonuclease (that is, a restriction enzyme that could break the middle of a chain of nucleic acid molecules, rather than attack at the tips of the molecules) cleavage sites can be 'recombined' at their restriction sites by the sequential action of RI endonuclease and DNA ligase. These hybrid DNAs can be cleaved by RI endonuclease to regenerate the original DNAs. (Cherfas, 1982, p. 80)

As a result, very novel DNA constructs can be designed and manufactured in the laboratory. The hybrid single-stranded DNA fragment could then act as a template to produce the complementary second strand to form the new rDNA molecule.

The above shows, then, that in vitro genetic recombination permits DNA molecules from diverse origins to be put together in a novel manner, thereby enabling so-called 'chimeric' DNA molecules to be produced, such that even the traditional genetic barrier between species can be transcended or circumvented.

Inherent in (in vitro) genetic recombination is the potential genetically to engineer living cells and organisms. So the next step in rDNA technology involves the search for something to perform two functions. First, that something would act as a suitable carrier or vector which can replicate itself and the genetically engineered gene. Second, it would act as a suitable 'vehicle' to transfer the novel genetic material into the living target host cells which will, in turn, not only replicate but also express the rDNA. Two classes of vectors have been developed: plasmids and viruses.

A plasmid is a small circle of double-stranded non-chromosomal DNA, usually found in bacteria, replicating independently of the main bacterial genome. Viruses, as mentioned earlier, consist of a nucleic acid molecule, sometimes RNA but more usually DNA, protected by a protein coat, and can only reproduce when inside a living host cell. The genetic molecule of the plasmid or virus used as a vector is cut or cleaved, and the transfer gene is then inserted or spliced in. This recombinant vector has incorporated the foreign gene into its own genome. These recombinant vectors are allowed to infect the chosen host cells so that, once inside, they start to reproduce or replicate themselves, producing clones embodying the transferred gene.

Stanley Cohen and Annie C. Y. Chang at Stanford University are credited with the breakthrough. In the first of their pioneering experiments in 1973, they used two different plasmids of the bacterium *E. coli* – pSC101, with genes for resistance to the antibiotic tetracycline, and pSC102, with genetic resistance to another antibiotic, kanamycin. (Their antibiotic-resistant genes were meant to play the role of markers to identify the recombinant clones, which were expected to result at the end of the experiment.) They were cleaved by the restriction enzyme Eco RI to produce linear plasmid DNA molecules with sticky ends. These then were incubated together to enable in vitro recombination to take place. The resultant plasmids were, naturally, of three types: pSC101–pSC101, pSC102–pSC102 and the hybrid recombinant pSC101–pSC102. All three types were next incubated with a strain of the bacterium *E. coli* which was sensitive to antibiotics in a solution of calcium chloride, to enable the bacteria to take up the recombinant plasmids. The next step consisted of determining which bacteria had taken up the hybrid recombinant pSC101–pSC102 by using a medium that contained both tetracycline and kanamycin. Those that survived on such a medium would be the ones with the hybrid recombinant plasmids. These bacteria were found to grow into colonies of *E. coli* which turned out, on testing, to be resistant to the two antibiotics. This was clear evidence that *E. coli* genes could be transferred, cloned and expressed in other *E. coli* cells with the help of recombinant plasmids.

But would the same hold if the genes to be transferred were to come from another species? Cohen et al. conducted their next pioneering experiment to test this possibility. This time to produce in vitro genetic recombination they used a plasmid, called p1258, with a gene for resistance to penicillin from the bacteria *Staphylococcus aureus*, recombined with pSC101 plasmids of *E. coli* containing a gene for resistance, as we have seen, to tetracycline. The other steps of the first experiment were repeated. It was found that *E. coli* colonies grew on a medium that contained both tetracycline and penicillin. This provided clear evidence that genes from one species of bacteria can be transferred, cloned and expressed in another species of bacteria using rDNA techniques. Cohen wrote that these experiments had produced 'a breach in the barriers that normally separate biological species. The bulk of the genetic information expressed in the transformed bacteria defined it as *E. coli*, but the transformed cells also carried replication DNA molecules that had molecular and biological characteristics derived from a different species, *S. aureus*' (Cherfas, 1982, pp. 88–9).[17]

The next question to be tackled was this: would the same techniques work with genes from eukaryote organisms, such as animal genes? To test this possibility, Cohen *et al.* in 1974 recombined a gene from the African clawed toad, *Xenopus laevis*, which coded for a cellular component called a ribosome, with the *E. coli* plasmid pSC101 (with a gene for resistance to tetracycline). These hybrid recombinant plasmids survived on a medium of tetracycline and grew into colonies of *E. coli*, which, upon testing, were found to contain the toad component. This then was clear evidence that rDNA techniques were successful in transferring a gene from a eukaryote organism to a prokaryote organism, a bacterium, which replicated and expressed it. In 1977 Cohen and Shing Chang exposed plasmids in *E. coli*, in the presence of specific enzymes, to cleaved fragments of mouse DNA and found that the plasmids had taken up the mouse DNA.

These pioneering experiments relied on making the host cells 'leaky' in order to take up the recombinant plasmids. The method worked, but could not be said to be efficient if rDNA technology were to have large-scale industrial application. The problem of finding a more efficient 'vehicle' for transferring the recombinant molecules to the host cells remained. A solution lay in the development of cosmids, the first of which was produced in 1978 by John Collins and Barbara Hohn. This consisted of inserting only a particular part of the DNA of a phage called lambda into a plasmid with an antibiotic resistance marker. This, in turn, was incubated with Eco RI fragments (containing the DNA to be replicated and expressed in the host cells) and DNA ligase (to produce recombinants). These recombinants, then, would be injected into the host cells as if they were lambda DNA. Once inside, the lambda DNA component would set about replicating the rDNA only. Cosmids, then, are pseudo-virus vectors which combine two properties considered by genetic engineers to be very important, the superiority of the phage as a vector, and that of the plasmid as a cloning device.

The experiments mentioned so far used antibiotic resistance genes in the plasmids as markers, to identify accurately and to select the hybrid rDNA. Later, other methods were developed for such identification and selection – see Cherfas (1982, pp. 95–103).

Stanley Cohen, one of the pioneers of the several experiments mentioned above, succinctly identified the essential elements of a successful rDNA technology:

> There are four essential elements: a method of breaking and joining DNA molecules derived from different sources; a suitable gene carrier that can replicate both itself and a foreign DNA segment linked to it; a means of introducing the composite DNA molecule, or chimera, into a functional bacterial cell, and a method of selecting from a large population of cells a clone of recipient cells that has acquired the molecular chimera. (Cohen, 1978, p. 113)

By the late 1970s, these elements were in place, as we have seen. This meant that the biotechnology industry itself also could begin to take off towards the end of that decade. In the USA companies sprouted up with names such as Biogen, Genentech, Calgene. On 14 October 1980 Genentech sold shares to the public. It had succeeded in 1977 in expressing in bacteria the first human gene for the anti-growth hormone, somato-statin; in 1978, in synthesising the hormone insulin in microbes; and, in 1979, in synthesing the growth hormone, somatotropin. In 1980 Biogen succeeded in engineering microbes to synthesise human alpha-interferon.

But to complete the account of rDNA technology attaining its predomi-nant status today (at the very dawn of the 21st century), other fundamen-tal breakthroughs in technique must also be mentioned. Most research in this field so far mentioned has been done on lower organisms, such as the bacteria species, especially *E. coli* and the bacteriophage. These are prokary-otes, that is to say, organisms with no distinct nucleus. But what needed urgent tackling was the eukaryotes, organisms considered to be more highly organised than the prokaryotes, with a well-defined nucleus con-taining the DNA. The so-called 'shotgun' technique was developed, as a result of which fragments of DNA belonging to eukaryotes can be isolated and cloned, and genetic maps of these organisms can be produced. The entire genome of the organism is cut up into random fragments. Each frag-ment is inserted into a vector, which is then used to transform a host cell so that it can be cloned. The clones from these numerous recombinant vectors constitute a library containing all the information about the genome of that organism. The shotgun technique is acknowledged to be crude but effective.[18]

Nevertheless, its crudeness was a distinct drawback. The cloning process was relatively slow, taking weeks of intensive scientific work. At the same time, the amount of DNA for cloning, though relatively small, nevertheless involved material involving thousands of cells. But these shortcomings were transcended in the 1980s by the invention of the polymerase chain reaction, which enables rDNA technology to be thousands of times more powerful than it was before.[19] PCR is an in vitro process for generating in a short space of time extremely large amounts of a specific DNA sequence. The term itself is a deliberate analogue of the nuclear chain reaction. In a chain reaction, whether nuclear or DNA, an initial small event, in the case of the former, or a bit of matter, in the latter, is amplified at each step in the chain – one generates two, two generate four, four sixteen, and so on. In other words, its growth rate is an exponential one. In the case of PCR, in addition to its speed, it also requires only very small starting amounts of the DNA sequence to be copied and amplified; nor does it require any prior detailed knowledge of such a sequence regarding the specific arrangement of the nucleotide bases in the sequence itself. Its impact, hence, on genetics and microbiology is immense, but suffice it to name only three areas as illustration: the forensic use of genetic fingerprints, paternity testing and determining the genetic predisposition to certain diseases in people.

Recombinant DNA technology is, so to speak, the child of molecular genetics based on an understanding of the structure of the DNA molecule. It constitutes a key component of biotechnology. But at least one other no less important component of genetic engineering is hybridoma technology. (However, only the briefest passing account of it is possible here.)[20] Its origins can be traced to tissue culture methods used in studying the genetic basis of different kinds of antibodies. An antibody is a protein molecule produced by the immune system of an organism in response to an invasion by a foreign protein, an antigen. Its function is to destroy its antigen. Hybridoma technology enables any one specific antibody to be cloned; hence, it is also called monoclonal antibody technology. It involves a kind of cell fusion in which two or more cells are fused into a single cell to produce new cell types, as well as new types of organisms. Cell fusion is a technique in hybridisation developed in the 1960s.

To investigate the workings of the immune system properly, researchers would need large amounts of single, pure antibodies, which destroy a single known antigen. But this requirement could not be readily met. The single cell responsible for the manufacture of a single antibody is not easy to identify and locate; moreover, even if found, it could not be cultured indefinitely. But in 1975 Georges Kohler and Cesar Milstein at Cambridge University fused for the first time a single spleen cell to a cancer cell. The spleen cell was designed to produce a single antibody which the cancer cell would then multiply indefinitely. The colony of cells produced would be identical clones, all descended from the fused hybrid cell. First, they immunised mice with a particular antigen which produced a specific antibody to destroy that antigen. They then used the spleen cells from such antibody-producing mice to fuse with mouse myeloma (bone marrow cancer) cells. These cell hybrids of antibody-producing cells and myeloma cells are called hybridomas. When cultured, they replicate indefinitely like cancer cells, producing a clone of the specific antibody in question.

Monoclonal antibodies have a range of applications, actual and potential: in medical diagnostics, in the treatment of cancer, in genetic screening, in the treatment and prevention of AIDS (acquired immune deficiency syndrome), in the production of novel enzymes called abzymes.[21]

Glossary

Adenine. A purine nucleic acid base. It pairs with thymine in DNA and uracil in RNA.

Amino acids. The fundamental building blocks of protein structure. There are many types but only 20 are commonly found in living organisms. These are linked by their shared 'backbones', so to speak, while their respective uinque 'residue' defines their individual properties – for instance, some attract water molecules, others repel them, some possess electric charge, negative or positive, while others are neutral.

Antibiotic. A substance that can kill or prevent the growth of a microorganism. It can now be produced by another microorganism or synthetically.

Antibody. A protein produced by the immune system of an organism in response to the presence of an antigen (a foreign chemical substance or organism). Each antibody is shaped to fit precisely to its antigen, thereby helping to destroy it.

Antigen. A substance, usually foreign to the organism, which causes its immune system to produce specific antibodies to destroy it.

Bacteria. The simplest organisms that can reproduce unaided; a major class of prokaryotes. *Escherichia coli* (*E. coli*) is the species most commonly used as a host cell in rDNA technology.

Bacteriophages. Viruses which infect bacteria. They are also called phages and are used as vectors in rDNA technology.

Base. Part of the building blocks of nucleic acids, of which there are two types: purines and pyrimidines.

Biochemistry. The study of the chemistry of living things.

Biopolymers. Long chain-like molecules which organisms make. Proteins are polymers of amino acid monomers.

Biotechnology. That type of biogenetic technology which uses techniques induced by and based on molecular biology, in particular molecular genetics.

Catalyst. A substance which helps a chemical reaction without itself being affected in the process. Enzymes are catalysts.

Cell. Generally described as a mass of cytoplasm within a semipermeable membrane containing a spherical body called the nucleus.

Cell fusion. The fusing together of two or more cells to produce a single hybrid cell.

Chimera. An organism, a cell or a bit of DNA constructed from two different individuals or species. A stricter definition: embryos and animals formed by combining cells from different fertilised eggs.

Chromosomes. Structures bearing the genetic material for transmission, composed of DNA and protein found in the nucleus of eukaryotic cells but free in prokaryotic ones.

Clones. The genetically identical, asexually produced descendants of a single organism, cell or molecule. The process involved is called cloning.

Cloning vector. Used to put DNA into a cell.

Coding sequence. That region of a gene that is expressed, translated into protein.

Codon. The genetic code of three-letter words. Each codon has three successive nucleotides or bases which specify a particular amino acid.

Colony of microorganisms. A mass of microorganisms asexually produced from an individual microorganism.

Cosmid. A cloning vehicle with foreign DNA attached to the packaging (cos) sites of a virus, thus inserting the foreign DNA into an infective virus particle.

Crystallography. A technique for studying the structure of crystals by bombarding them with x-rays. The pictures thus produced are interpreted to show the internal arrangement of the molecules of the crystal.

Cytoplasm. The living contents of a cell minus the nucleus.

Cytosine. A pyrimidine nucleic acid base, pairing with guanine, a purine.

Deoxyribose. The sugar of DNA.

DNA. Deoxyribonucleic acid, the molecule which carries the hereditary message in all organisms except RNA viruses. It encodes information for the replication of the DNA molecule itself and for the reproduction and functioning of cells.

DNA base pair. A pair of DNA nucleotide bases, one of which is on one chain of the duplex DNA molecule and the other on the complementary chain. They pair in the following way: adenine (A) pairs only with thymine (T), cytosine (C) only with guanine (G). This ensures accurate replication of the chromosomes and preserves the constancy of the genetic material.

DNA sequence. The order of base pairs in the DNA molecule encoding genetic information.

Double helix. The structure of the DNA molecule, with two complementary strands twining round each other, joined by the base pairing of A with T and C with G.

Electrophoresis. A technique for separating molecules. In travelling along an electric current, usually in gel as the medium, the molecules do so at different rates depending on their size and charge.

Endonuclease. A restriction enzyme which acts within a double helix of DNA to break it, rather than attacking the ends of the helix.

Enzymes. Biological catalysts produced by living cells. They are proteins which assist chemical reactions to take place at lower temperatures without themselves being altered or destroyed. They are also responsible for the biochemistry of the cell.

***Escherichia coli* (*E. coli*)**. A bacterial species much favoured as host cells for rDNA.

Eukaryotes. Organisms or cells whose DNA is contained in a well-defined nucleus surrounded by protein. Except for viruses, bacteria and blue-green algae, all organisms are eukaryotes, which are more highly organised than prokaryotes.

Exons. DNA sequences which code for genes. See **Introns**.

Gene. In molecular biology, a section of nucleic acid that codes for a specific protein. But one can also speak of a gene for a particular trait which may not correspond to a particular section of nucleic acid.

Genetic code. The relationship between the sequence of bases in the nucleic acids of genes and the sequence of amino acids in the proteins they code for.

Genetic engineering. Techniques pioneered mainly in the 20th century to manipulate hereditary material. They cover two broad types – artificial mutagenesis and hybridisation underpinned by the classical gene-chromosome theory, on the one hand, and, on the other, rDNA, hybridoma technologies, protoplast fusion, and so on. underpinned by molecular genetics in particular, and molecular biology in general. But more commonly, the term is used only with regard to the latter broad category of techniques; this book, however, reserves the term 'biotechnology' for it. (See also **micro-genetic engineering**.)

Genetic expression. The decoding of the genetic information in a cell which usually results in the production of a protein.

Genome. The entire genetic information carried by an organism, although not all portions of a genome are genes as it includes non-coding DNA.

Hormone. A chemical messenger secreted by a gland in the organism, carried in the bloodstream to a target organ which it regulates.

Host. A cell, whether microbial, plant or animal, whose metabolism is used to replicate a virus, a plasmid or forms of foreign DNA.

Hybridoma technology. Involves fusing antibody-producing cells with tumour cells to produce endlessly proliferating cells which produce monoclonal antibodies.

Immune system. The organism's system of defence against invasions by foreign bodies or certain chemicals.

Introns. DNA sequences which do not code for any gene; sometimes referred to as 'junk' DNA. See **Exons**.

In vitro. Biological processes conducted outside the living organism.

In vitro genetic recombination. The cleaving and joining of DNA fragments to produce rDNA in the laboratory.

Library. The entire genome of an organism stored in a collection of hosts.

Ligase. An enzyme that catalyses the joining together of two molecules. DNA ligase joins two strands of DNA together.

Messenger RNA (mRNA). Carries the genetic code for a protein from the DNA to the ribosomes where the code is deciphered and the protein then synthesized.

Molecules of mRNA are single-stranded, relatively short-lived, and formed (by the process of transcription) from the template strand of genomic DNA.

Micro-genetic engineering. A form of genetic engineering using techniques which decode, compare, excise, join, transfer and/or clone specific sequences of DNA, or techniques such as cell fusion.

Microorganisms (or microbes). Organisms which are viruses, bacteria, algae or protozoa.

Mitochondria. These transfer chemical energy from foods to energy-rich storage compounds which are then used to power chemical reactions elsewhere in the cell. They are thus the powerhouses of the cell.

Molecule. A complex of two or more atoms held together by chemical bonds in a specific way.

Monoclonal antibody. An antibody descending from a single clone of antibody-producing cells in hybridoma technology.

Monomers. The units that combine to form a polymer.

Mutation. Any change in the genetic material.

Nucleic acids. Either RNA or DNA. They consist of a chain of alternating sugars and phosphates with a base, a letter of the genetic code, attached to each sugar.

Nucleotides. The building blocks of nucleic acids. They are made up of a sugar with a base, a letter of the genetic code, attached to one atom and a phosphate group attached to another. The phosphate group of one nucleotide bond with the sugar of another nucleotide to form a chain.

Nucleus. That region of the cell in eukaryotes containing the DNA.

Plasmid. A small circle of DNA, found in prokaryotes, which can replicate independently of the main chromosomes. It transfers from one cell to another, even crossing species boundaries. It is used as a vector for cloning rDNA in bacterial hosts.

Polymerase chain reaction (PCR). A set of techniques for copying and amplifying DNA sequences which has three virtues – it is simple and immensely rapid, and uses very small amounts of starting material.

Polymers. See **Biopolymers**.

Polypeptides. Long folded chains of amino acids (usually more than 100) – a short chain if a peptide – which form proteins.

Prokaryotes. Organisms whose genetic material is not contained within a distinct nucleus, such as bacteria, algae.

Proteins. Polypeptides occuring as hormones, enzymes, connecting and contractile structures, giving cells and organisms their characteristic shape, metabolic potential, colour and other physical capacities.

Protoplast culture. Protoplasts growing in a culture medium to produce plantlets which can be grown up into mature plants.

Protoplast fusion. Protoplasts from different varieties/species fused to form hybrids.

Protoplasts. Plant and other cells from which the outer cell walls have been stripped.

Purine. A type of base of nucleic acids. There are two purines: adenine and guanine.

Pyrimidine. A type of base of nucleic acids. There are three pyrimidines: uracil, thymine and cystosine.

Recombinant bacterium/cell/plasmid/vector/virus. These contain rDNA.

Recombinant DNA (rDNA). A hybrid DNA molecule containing DNA from two distinct sources.

Recombinant DNA technology. Ensemble of techniques of in vitro genetic recombination together with those for the insertion, replication and expression of rDNA inside living cells.

Restriction enzymes. Bacterial enzymes which recognise a base sequence on DNA and cut it into fragments. Some cut the DNA at a particular point, others at random.

Reverse transcriptase. A DNA polymerase which uses an RNA template.

Ribonucleic acid (RNA). A molecule similar in structure to DNA that helps in the mediation and execution of the genetic instructions encoded in DNA. Some viruses (retroviruses) store their genetic information as RNA, not as DNA.

Ribose. The sugar of RNA.

Ribosome. A small body made of RNA and proteins which synthesises proteins.

Shotgun technique. Used to cut up the entire genome of an organism into fragments which can then be inserted into hosts for cloning to form a gene library for the organism.

Somatic embryogenesis. The use of tissue from a seed embryo induced **in vitro** to form millions of individual embryos which are identical copies of the plant from which the original embryonic tissue has been taken.

Species. A group of individual organisms not able to breed with those of another group – the biological species concept.

Thymine. A pyrimidine nucleic acid base, pairing with adenine.

Transcription. The synthesis of RNA from a DNA template.

Transfer RNA (tRNA). The molecule that carries the amino acids to the ribosomes.

Transformation. The process when a segment of foreign DNA is taken up by a cell, giving the host its properties.

Transgenic organism. A genetically engineered organism whose genome contains genetic material derived from a different species/kingdom. It is a type of so-called 'chimeric' organism.

Translation. The conversion of the genetic information carried by mRNA into a protein.

Vectors. Self-replicating entities used as vehicles to transfer foreign DNA into living cells so that they can replicate and express the foreign DNA. Plasmids and viruses are types of vectors.

Virus. The smallest type of organism which is composed of nucleic acid (either DNA or RNA) wrapped in a protein coat. It can survive but cannot replicate on its own and so has to infect a living cell to do so by requisitioning its mechanism.

Notes

1 For a further discussion on the use of the term 'molecular biology', see Kay (1993, pp. 5–6).

2 The critics of such a grossly reductionist science and the technology of genetic engineering induced by it argue that each of the four assumptions behind the science/technology can be challenged theoretically and empirically. The four assumptions are: 1. 'Genes determine characters in linear causal chains; one gene gives one function.' 2. 'Genes and genomes are not subject to environmental influence.' 3. 'Genes and genomes are stable and unchanging.' 4. 'Genes stay where they are put' – see Ho (1998, pp. 51–4). The challenge to 1 and 2 has been strengthened in the light of the downward revised estimate (since February 2001) that there are only just under 40,000 genes in the human genome.

3 For technical terms in what follows, see glossary at the end of the chapter.

4 However, the facts of the case are not quite as straightforward as presented at the moment; the complexities will be mentioned later in the chapter.

5　Finally, in 1995, molecular geneticists found that the gene which codes for the protein homogentisate dioxygenase is found on the long arm of chromosome 3 in the human genome, and that people with alkaptonuria have one 'letter' different from those without, either the 690th or the 901st – see Ridley (1999, p. 52).

6　But later, the second pair was shown by Linus Pauling to have a third hydrogen bond – see Judson (1979, p. 174).

7　See Allen (1979, pp. 210–20).

8　The technical term for it is 'introns' – those DNA sequences that do not code for any gene. 'Exons', on the other hand, refer to those that do.

9　In this book the definition of this term follows, by and large, the usage found in Kloppenburg (1990). An account of the disparate meanings of the term, and their history, may be found in Bud (1993).

10　This is an adaptation of Kloppenburg (1990, p. 203).

11　In the last chapter, traditional methods of selective breeding were characterised as 'whole-organism' technology, while Mendelian techniques were said to be reductionistic, based on the gene and the chromosome. But in this chapter, relative to the techniques induced by molecular genetics and biology, Mendelian ones may, themselves, be said to constitute 'whole-organism' technology. If the relative factor is borne in mind there is no contradiction between what the two chapters say.

12　Two comments are called for here:

(a)　It is not intended to deny that what exactly counts as a species is uncontroversial in biological literature today. However, for the purpose of biotechnology, what is crucial is that, in absolutely clear cases, where the organisms are recognised to belong to two distinct species, such as humans and mice, it is possible to insert genetic material belonging to the former into the latter, and vice versa – a phenomenon which does not occur naturally but only as a consequence of this particular form of advanced technological intervention.

(b)　This is about a matter of terminology – in this book 'transgenic organism' is always used to refer to an organism into which genetic material from another organism belonging to a totally different species/kingdom has been inserted. The term 'chimera' or 'chimeric' is normally used to refer to very different kinds of genetically engineered entities: it is not favoured by this author throughout the book, although there may be quotations cited from the works of other authors who use the term. The author also puts the term within quotation marks to indicate general usage rather than her own. Some writers appear to have used the terms 'transgenic organisms' and 'chimera' interchangeably; other writers use the latter to refer only to embryos and animals of the same species which are formed simply by combining cells from different fertilised eggs. In the case of human 'chimeras' (in this latter sense), since the 1950s more than a hundred natural-born 'chimeric' humans have been identified. Each is the result of the fusion of two embryos which themselves resulted from the fertilisation of two eggs simultaneously ovulated by the mother – see Silver (1998, p. 180); Ridley (1999, p. 214).

13　For a more detailed discussion on this point, see the section in Chapter 6 entitled 'The humanisation of biotic nature: the supersession of natural evolution' (pp. 189 ff.).

14   The word 'breeding' itself refers to processes which involve the transmission of genetic material through sexual union. The word has been put within quotes in the text precisely to draw attention to this fact, and that, perhaps, a different word should be coined to refer to this new type of human intervention, such as 'plant or animal genetic engineering', as has been suggested.

15   For a quick summary of the historical development of this technology, and of its techniques, in greater detail, see Judson (1992). See also Thomas F. Lee (1991). Any summary can at best be partial given the rapidity of development in this field. As such, it is not the aim of this book to provide up to the minute innovations, but just to give the reader some idea of the basic techniques which lie at the foundation of this technology.

16   Quotation marks have been used to indicate that, in this kind of context, 'recognises' is not used in the normal sense, which implies consciousness and awareness.

17   Cohen appeared to have changed his mind by 1977 – see Krimsky (1982, pp. 84, 165–7, 197–8, 272–3, 335–6).

18   For an account of the battery of techniques now used in the Human Genome Project, see Hood (1992) and Judson (1992); Kevles and Hood (1992) contains other chapters dealing with both the scientific as well as the social issues raised by the Human Genome Project. Another account may be found in Thomas F. Lee (1991).

19   For an ethnographic, historical account of the development of PCR technology, see Rabinow (1996). For a technical but nevertheless accessible account, see Thomas F. Lee (1991, pp. 140–6).

20   For a readily accessible account, see Wheale and McNally (1988, pp. 23–5).

21   Abzymes are a cross between enzymes and antibodies; these are most useful in speeding up reactions by a factor of 15,000, thereby making it possible to replace high-pressure, high-temperature chemical processes by biological ones.

5
Biotechnology and Patentability

Biotechnology has now enabled us to create transgenic organisms as well as to isolate, in principle, the raw DNA sequences of which any genome, whether human or non-human, is constituted. The biotechnological industry naturally has a keen vested interest in urging that both transgenic organisms and raw DNA sequences are patentable products. This chapter explores the philosophical dimension, especially from the ontological standpoint, to the issue of their patentability.[1] It would argue for an asymmetry between the two – while bestowing the status of patentability upon transgenic organisms may be justifiable on ontological grounds, a similar case, however, could not be made regarding raw DNA sequences.

Modern patent law: a brief account

Patent law itself as it exists today, at least within the tradition of English (common) law, is said to date from the Patent Law Amendment Act of 1852, although prior to it, the monarch had granted patent monopolies of one kind or another for over five hundred years.[2] The first patent act in the USA was drawn up by Thomas Jefferson and passed by Congress in 1790.[3] Outside the modern Anglo-American tradition, much earlier instances include a grant of monopoly made by Sybaris to encourage artistic activities around the fifth century BC. In Venice, in 1443, one Antonius Marini received a patent, lasting twenty years, for a flour mill which did not use water in its operation.[4]

Patents are about inventions and the legal rights over their financial exploitation (for a limited period). To obtain a patent, the item for which application has been filed must, first of all, crucially constitute an invention; furthermore, at least three other conditions must obtain: the invention must be novel, it must not be something obvious to an expert in the field and it should have industrial application.[5] In other words, modern patent law appears to recognise a fundamental distinction between an invention on the one hand and a discovery on the other; while the former is patentable, the latter is not.[6] For example, it is obvious that the steam engine is an invention and, therefore, patentable, but that the second law of thermodynamics is a discovery (of theoretical science), said to be a law of nature and, therefore, not patentable. However, not all cases are as clear cut. The concern of this chapter is to investigate whether transgenic organisms, on the one hand, and raw DNA sequences, on the other, count as inventions or whether only the former do, although both have come to light only in the wake of the discovery of the molecular structure of DNA by Crick and Watson, roughly half a century ago.

The fundamental distinction between invention and discovery apart, modern patent law also distinguishes between product patent, on the one hand, and process patent, on the other.[7] The discussion in this chapter will bear out the importance of this second distinction, as the end result of applying a technological procedure, which itself may qualify for a process patent, may not necessarily be eligible as a product patent.

Classical product patents, such as the spinning jenny, are not biotic but abiotic or ex-biotic in character. However, since the fourth quarter of the last century, the modern legal system in general, and patent law in particular, has had to cope with some startlingly radical scientific and technological developments. Up to 1980, no one could be sure in any country with a Western-type legal system whether patents could be granted to any living organism which claimed to have been made by humans. Up to then, animal varieties and any biological processes which underpinned the production of animals and plants were assumed to fall outside the ambit of patenting. Indeed, the 1790 patent act in the USA deliberately excluded life forms as something which could be patented.[8] There is also legislation to protect plant varieties – in the USA the 1930 Plant Patent Act (PPA) covers asexually reproducing plants, and the 1970 Plant Variety Protection Act (PVPA) covers sexually reproducing ones, while in the UK the 1983 Plant Varieties Act came under the aegis of the Ministry of Agriculture, Fisheries and Food, not the Patenting Office, and covers the reproductive materials of plants. There is also the 1968 International Union for the Protection of Plant Varieties.

However, in June 1980, the situation appeared to have altered with the decision of the US Supreme Court in the case of *Diamond* v. *Chakrabarty*. Chakrabarty, a scientist who worked for General Electric, submitted an application to the US Patent Office in 1972 for a new strain of the bacterium *Pseudomonas*. The novel bacteria were intended to clean up oil spills in water by degrading the crude oil then ingesting the degraded material, with the bacteria themselves in turn forming part of the normal food chain. Chakrabarty did not use rDNA techniques in producing the new strain. He relied on other techniques. Plasmids from separate organisms – each able to degrade one of the important hydrocarbons which constitute crude oil – were bred into a single bacterium, thus combining all their superior properties in a single strain of super bacteria. The Patent Office rejected the application for a patent on the organism itself on the grounds that the 1930 PPA and 1970 PVPA showed that Congress had not meant living organisms in general to be patentable, and was simply making special arrangements in providing protection for plants. However, the Court of Customs and Patent Appeals (CCPA) rejected this interpretation, arguing that 'the fact that micro-organisms, as distinguished from chemical compounds, are alive, is a distinction without legal significance'. The US government itself in 1979 lodged an appeal against the CCPA's decision. The crucial issue before the Supreme Court was whether 'a living organism which otherwise complies with legal requirements for patentability nevertheless [is] disqualified because it is alive'. A five to four majority upheld the line argued by the CCPA, deciding in favour of patentability.

That USA Supreme Court decision radically breached the traditional stance of the Patent Office with regard to the usual domesticated varieties of plants and animals. For the first time in human thought, living organisms per se were no longer regarded as bar to patentability. The floodgates are said to have opened, making way for the first wave of the new biotechnological products which were already waiting in the wings for endorsement. One of the most radical of such products is the transgenic organism, to which we now turn our attention.

Transgenic organisms

It is necessary to clarify a point of terminology before proceeding to the exploration of the issue itself. The term 'transgenic organism' (at least as used in this book) is not identical either with the term 'chimera'/'chimeric' or the term 'genetically modified organism'.[9] The latter is a much broader category, involving either the excision of genetic material from an individual organism, or the insertion of genetic material from other organisms, whether belonging to the same species or a different species. 'Transgenic organism' is used in the context of inserting into an individual organism genetic material belonging to a different species – the inserted material may cross species and/or kingdom barriers. However, the term 'transgenomic' to characterise the insertion of genetic material from an organism belonging to the same species has been suggested by Richard Jefferson, a molecular biologist who heads a non-profit plant biotechnology research centre in Canberra.[10]

From the preceding chapter, it is obvious that the maturity of a new basic scientific discipline, that is, molecular biology, and in particular its sub-branch molecular genetics, has engendered a technology, namely, biotechnology, which permits a quantum leap, so to speak, in the kind and degree of control of biotic nature over its predecessor technology based on the classical gene-chromosome theory. For the first time ever, we humans are able to create novel organisms and new species.[11] Biotechnology makes it possible for us to make biotic nature over to our will and design. To quote one writer:

> Many of the things that were discussed as science fiction five years ago have already happened. This is not just a change of technique, it is a new way of seeing. . . . The limitations of species can be transcended by splicing organisms, combining functions, dovetailing abilities and linking together chains of properties. The living world can now be viewed as a vast organic Lego kit inviting combination, hybridization, and continual rebuilding. Life is manipulability. (Yoxen, 1983, p. 15)

How transgenic organisms differ from Mendelian hybrids

The plants and animals produced by the biogenetic technology of hybridis-ation may be said to embody a lower level of artefacticity than those pro-duced by rDNA or hybridoma technology. In the case of the latter, their greater degree of artefacticity is due to the fact that their mode of produc-tion involves the manipulation, and indeed the exchange, of genetic mate-rial at the molecular level across kingdoms. This then locates them at the pole which is directly opposite to that occupied by organisms regarded as naturally occurring. In this respect, they are distinctly human artefacts in the same way as houses or paintings are paradigmatically human artefacts, which ex hypothesi could not be naturally occurring entities. Transgenic organisms are biotic, while houses and paintings are abiotic artefacts. However, unlike houses and paintings, some transgenic organisms are capable of biological reproduction or replication and could, under certain conditions, eventually escape from the human-controlled environment to lead an independent existence outside it. It is precisely because of this pos-sibility that so much angst and discussion have been generated about the environmental risks which could be involved in rDNA technology.[12]

The so-called quantum leap in the level of artefacticity between the hybrids produced by biogenetic whole-organism technology and those by molecular DNA technology lies in the fact that, though the selection in the former is artificial, it is, nevertheless, more closely aligned with the processes of natural evolution. The hybrids are between varieties of the same species and, though they are highly unlikely to occur in nature, that is, without deliberate human intervention, nevertheless, they could be said in principle to be conceivable. But recombinant hybrids involve artificial selection (if one still cares to use that term), which radically defies the processes of natural evolution, as they cross the species barrier not merely within the respective contexts of animal and plant species, but also between animal and plant species themselves, between the eukaryotes and the prokaryotes. Transgenic organisms ex hypothesi cannot be naturally occurring entities in the sense that they cannot be the results of the processes of natural evolution. They are the paradigmatic biotic artefact.[13]

Patenting and transgenic organisms

Even before the Chakrabarty decision, following the work done by the research teams of Stanley Cohen at Stanford University and Herbert Boyer of the University of California in San Francisco in 1973 and 1974, Stanford University in 1974 filed an application to patent rDNA techniques for transforming cells with recombinant plasmids, using antibiotic-resistant genes on plasmids as genetic markers, in vitro genetic recombination techniques for producing recombinant plasmids, as well as for the recombinant plasmids themselves. In 1978 the submission was divided into two applications, one for a process patent and the other for a product patent. The process patent was granted in December 1980, following the Chakrabarty decision; the product patent was issued in 1984, covering as well products made by bacterial plasmids in bacterial hosts.[14]

The first Cohen–Boyer patent is registered as no. 4,237,224 and issued for the 'Process for producing biologically functional molecular chimeras'. The Patent Office spelt out the novelty of the procedure leading to the production of novel biotic artefacts very clearly indeed: 'The ability of genes derived from totally different biological classes to replicate and be expressed in a particular microorganism permits the attainment of interspecies genetic recombination. Thus, it becomes practical to introduce into a particular microorganism . . . functions which are indigenous to other classes of organisms' (United States Patent Office, 1980, p. 1). In other words, the patenting of transgenic organisms recognises that paradigmatically they are biotic artefacts. Whether one disapproves of it or has reservations on other grounds is another matter, but the successful patenting is the logical conclusion from the fundamental premises that they are undoubtedly artefacts, and that they are novel artefacts.

However, it was not till 1984 that a transgenic vertebrate was submitted to the US Patent and Trademark Office by Harvard University. This was to patent its 'oncomouse', a strain of laboratory mouse in which a gene involved with the onset of breast cancer in humans has been inserted. In 1988 the oncomouse was granted patent; a year earlier the US PTO had already granted patent on a transgenic oyster. In 1993 the European Patent Office granted patent on the oncomouse.[15] The status of the oncomouse as patentable artefact is further confirmed by its display in a leading science museum. In 1989 Harvard Medical School presented the London Science Museum with the gift of two male oncomice preserved by freeze-drying. This has prompted one commentator to write:

> The Science Museum collects artefacts, not organisms. This rule has applied in the Museum since its foundation. But in 1989 the rule was apparently broken when two mice were acquired for its permanent collection. . . . The interest in these mice reflects the revolution in the biological sciences that has accompanied the development of what is often

termed genetic engineering. . . . The Harvard oncomice . . . represent an important phase in the development of molecular genetics. With the advent of biotechnology and transgenic animals, it seems that organisms can also be artefacts. (Durant, 1992, p. 214)

As already observed, to qualify successfully as a patent, the item must crucially constitute an invention which satisfies the requirements of being novel and non-obvious to an expert in the field, as well as having industrial application.[16] The discussion so far appears to have established that transgenic organisms are indeed inventions – artefacts – within the meaning of modern patent law. The discussion to follow will consider them under the novelty requirement. However, the condition of non-obviousness will not be explicitly touched upon, and the discussion will simply assume that transgenic organisms have, on the whole, been fabricated with industrial application in mind.[17]

Depth of manipulation vs extensiveness of manipulation

The novelty of transgenic organisms may become a matter of contention, particularly when the biotic artefacts involved are not mere microorganisms, such as bacteria, but animals and plants, which are relatively much more complex organisms.[18] Here the counter-arguments against patentability of transgenic animals and plants may lie not so much in refusing to accept that they are biotic artefacts, but in holding that in spite of the 'depth' at which they have been created, nevertheless, depth alone is not sufficient. Another dimension must be taken into account – extensiveness of change may be relevant and may, indeed, be said to override depth if depth is not accompanied by extensiveness.[19] However, it may immediately be in order to enter a caveat. As far as this author can ascertain, the argument just mentioned against patentability has not played a role, to date, in legal patent debate, but it is explored here for the sake of theoretical completeness, as it could in principle be articulated and enter such discourse, and it could do so via the requirement of novelty. So far this paper has interpreted novelty to refer to 'depth' manipulation at the molecular level. However, according to the line of reasoning under examination, novelty may also be understood to refer to extensiveness of phenotypical change (whether involving extensive or limited genotypical change). Judged by this alternative interpretation of novelty, existing transgenic organisms may be said not to be truly novel, thereby excluding themselves from qualification under current patent law. In other words, the argument points to a potential ambiguity in the concept of novelty in the context of transgenic organisms.

In one interpretation of novelty, the transgenic cow with the human DNA sequence which makes it manufacture a human protein in its milk may be taken as a typical product of certain deep biotechnological techniques and procedures at work.[20] However, it could be argued that the alteration perpetrated by biotechnology is, according to the second interpretaion, not very impressive as the phenotypical change is so minimal as to be hardly observable. This indeed is true today.

However, ironically, in 1985 when the first transgenic piglet was created, the situation was quite different. Scientists succeeded in inserting the piece of DNA encoding the production of human somatotropin into the nucleus of the fertilised pig eggs. These embryos were then transplanted into the sow's uterus. Nineteen – the Beltsville pigs – were born with the human gene in their genome. These pigs unfortunately suffered from 'deleterious pleiotropic effects', that is to say, their development was abnormal, their bodies and skulls being deformed. Some had crossed eyes; others had swollen legs. They suffered from renal disease or arthritis, as well as decreased immune functions, and were susceptible to pneumonia. And they were all sterile.[21] These animals did suffer. However, genetic engineers have since refined their techniques, and transgenic animals fabricated today no longer display 'deleterious pleiotropic effects'; nor do they suffer from unintended side-effects.[22] What this shows is that as biotechnological procedures advance and are refined, greater precision in manipulating genetic material in general becomes possible; unwanted effects like those just mentioned could be eliminated such that only phenotypical/behavioural changes of the limited intended kind manifest themselves. One could say that it was the early lack of sophistication in genetic manipulation which produced a whole suite of undesirable phenotypical characteristics, rendering it obvious that DNA genetic manipulation could produce spectacular changes in the transgenic organism. Today, improvements in techniques and procedures mean DNA engineering is less likely to induce a large suite of phenotypical changes to the organism.

So from the point of view of patentability, one might then be tempted to argue that the transgenic organism is not a suitable candidate for patentability, as its extent of artefacticity is really quite minor or limited. Before rushing to this plausible conclusion, perhaps one should ponder other aspects which may be relevant to the debate. First, does the point above involve nothing more than a purely empirical issue? True, transgenic organisms today seem to involve only a specific limited change, such as the ability to produce a human protein in their milk or whatever. However, in principle, are biotechnological methods and procedures thus restricted? As far as one can ascertain, the answer seems to be no. One day, provided they can get away with it, genetic engineers in the agribusiness industries could well produce a non-sentient, wingless, featherless, beakless organism with avocado-coloured flesh tasting like strawberries. Such a transgenic organism, given the extensive range of its unique characteristics has a sui generis identity which, nevertheless, relies on the mechanisms possessed by the original bird to carry out its various biological functions, such as digestion, respiration, defecation, etc. The degree of artefacticity of such a product of genetic engineering would then be both deep and extensive.

In other words, what should be a condition *sine qua non* for patentability? Should one rely (a) solely on extensiveness of change to the organism in question? (b) solely on depth at which genetic material is manipulated? or (c) on both extensiveness and depth? In invoking extensiveness alone, then, on the whole, domesticated organisms produced by the less radical breeding technologies would be covered. (This scenario, however, has been included in this discussion solely for completeness and for the purpose of clarification, as it can have no policy implication – modern patent law, by and large, has left domesticated organisms of such kinds outside the domain of patentability.) It would then exclude those transgenic organisms with one alien DNA sequence inserted into its genome and displaying only a specific and limited change in its phenotype – let us call this the type A transgenic organism. Vice versa, in invoking depth alone, domesticated organisms bred in relatively traditional ways would then be excluded. However, if both depth and extensiveness were invoked, then transgenic organisms in principle would certainly qualify.

If organisms could, indeed, be manipulated at the deeper and more radical level of their genetic material, crossing both species and kingdom barriers and in such a way as to display a suite of phenotypical changes attendant upon genotypical ones – let us call this the type B transgenic organism – then it is merely academic to confine discussion only to the majority of existing transgenic organisms. In any case, as a matter of fact, some transgenic organisms have already been produced, such as the 'liger' (or the 'tiglon'), whose genome shares the genetic components of both the lion and the tiger and which correspondingly exhibits extensive phenotypical changes from its respective parents.[23] The same holds true of the 'geep' or 'shoat', which incorporates the genetic material from the sheep and the goat.[24]

To date, type B transgenic organisms are not so common simply because, for the moment, the climate and the market are not quite ready for them. Surely agribusiness industries would not be averse to opting for this kind of manipulation should the circumstances turn out to be propitious. Furthermore, ponder what might be the response of such industries should type A transgenic organisms be denied patentability on the grounds that they are not sufficiently novel. This would immediately prompt these industries to change tack: their genetic engineers would be instructed to design and manufacture type B transgenic organisms only.[25] Just to take one hypothetical example: the cow with the alien DNA sequence to produce a human protein in her milk could then be the recipient of other transgenic DNA sequences which might make her glow green under blue light, or render the animal luminescent in the dark, etc., so long as these other sequences do not interfere with the capability of the transgenic cow to produce the human protein in question, or to cause it suffering in the way that the Beltsville pigs suffered.[26] The obstacle to patentability encountered by type A transgenic organisms could in practice be overcome by simply pursuing the strategy of manufacturing only type B transgenic organisms. The ability of biotechnology to confine itself to effecting only one limited specific change in type A transgenic organisms may, as we have seen, be testimony to its powers of precise control and not, necessarily, to an inability on its part to bring about more extensive changes, should those wielding the technology so wish to do.

Depth of manipulation is critical

However, although in principle there may be no incompatibility between depth and extensiveness, it remains the case that most existing transgenic organisms are type A rather than type B. So the question remains whether the former ought to be considered patentable. The inclination to answer it affirmatively remains strong in spite of the fact that, as they stand, they fail the test of extensiveness. The principal reason rests on the simple consideration that they are, indeed, transgenic organisms. Such organisms are au fond artefacts – ex hypothesi, without direct human manipulation at the molecular level of their genome they could not, and would not, have come into existence. As already observed, non-transgenic organisms bred via the less radical technologies have in their genomes genetic material which comes from related varieties; transgenic organisms have in their genomes genetic material which has crossed species and kingdom barriers. No strawberry or tomato plant could have come to possess a gene from the flounder, a fish, either as a result of the processes of natural evolution, on the one hand, or from craft-based breeding technology, or Mendelian hybridisation technology, on the other. In other words, their very identity is defined in terms of their being transgenic in character and essence. This deep ontological dimension is of fundamental significance.

However, one must not allow this realisation to obscure the fact that a transgenic organism, though an artefact, nevertheless remains undoubtedly an organism. As such, it functions as one with its various metabolic and other mechanisms intact. From the point of view of its biological functioning, it appears no different from a naturally occurring organism or from domesticated animals and plants. The transgenic animal in which a DNA sequence encoding for a human protein has been inserted into its genome would eat, digest, defecate and mate in much the same way as its non-transgenic counterpart. However, one should not be over-impressed by such similarities, as these biological mechanisms simply define its identity as an organism of a certain kind. However, they do not define its identity as the transgenic organism it now is. That identity is given to it by the fact that its genome now contains DNA which is alien to the organism it was before it lost that identity. Some of its biological mechanisms, as an organism *simpliciter*, have been hijacked, as it were, by the foreign DNA, such that the transgenic animal, which it now is, expresses a human protein in its milk.

In other words, direct human manipulation at the molecular genetic level has ensured that its naturally evolved biological mechanisms are used to fulfil a human purpose, and not the end that those naturally evolved mechanisms normally serve, namely, the animal's own end, which is to produce milk containing proteins peculiar to the natural kind that it is.[27]

This constitutes the essential subversive character of biotechnology from the ontological viewpoint. To argue that depth of manipulation without extensiveness does not yield a sufficient degree of artefacticity to satisfy the condition of novelty for patentability is precisely to fail to grasp this profoundly significant feature about the new technology. Earlier breeding technologies can only eliminate undesirable (undesirable only, of course, from the human point of view) traits from an organism's genome, or enhance existing or introduce new traits deemed desirable. Changes to the genetic constitution are made through mating or, of late, in the case of animals, via in vitro fertilisation, or in the case of plants, via hand pollination, a technique of long standing. The traits chosen for reproductive manipulation are simply traits of different organisms belonging to the same variety or species, that is to say, the same natural kind. However, as biotechnology is able to bypass such constraints, transgenic organisms ex hypothesi are beings whose genomes permit them to exhibit modes of behaviour or traits which their naturally occurring counterparts do not and cannot possess.

Identity of transgenic organisms

On the surface, it appears that the animal is carrying out its own *telos* as its biological mechanisms remain intact; but if the implications of being a transgenic organism are fully teased out, the appearance of normality vanishes.[28] This can be brought out by posing the question, as already observed, about its identity. There are two possible ways of answering the question 'what is it?'. One way is simply to say that it is still a cow, a tomato plant or whatever, which happens to produce a human protein in her milk or which happens to be able to withstand frost. The other is to say that it differs so fundamentally from a normal non-transgenic cow or tomato plant that it would be misleading to say *simpliciter* that it is a common or garden variety cow or tomato plant. One could perhaps call it a *Tg*cow (short for 'transgenic') or a *Tg*tomato plant.

To adopt the first approach is to go for appearances only while ignoring the underlying reality. It is to say that the animal looks every bit like a cow; it behaves like a cow as it still eats grass (or whatever substitutes modern cows eat), it moos, it lactates, etc. Its milk looks like ordinary cow's milk and probably tastes like ordinary cow's milk, too. It is only when its milk is subjected to laboratory analysis that human protein would be found in its make-up. The presence of the human protein, therefore, seems to be the single 'odd' fact about the animal compared with the very long list of 'normal' facts which one can draw up about it. However, such an approach fails to recognise the profound alteration to the genome of the ordinary 'normal' cow, which has enabled its transgenic counterpart to produce that so-called single 'odd' fact about its milk. However, when that single 'odd' fact is properly placed and understood within the context of the kind of radical genetic manipulation which biotechnology permits, then its singularity and its oddness should lead one to conclude that the degree of artefacticity, via depth of genetic manipulation, inherent in a transgenic organism is sufficient to qualify for patentability. The transgenic organism is the paradigm of a biotic artefact where the deep level at which genetic manipulation takes place and the ensuing degree of artefacticity are inextricably interwined. The manipulation of genetic material at the molecular level leads to a degree of artefacticity which is the antithesis of the processes of natural evolution and of the products of such evolutionary processes.

Technological procedures and their products

Another related point which should be borne in mind is that there are laboratory products and laboratory products.[29] Consider the technique of in vitro fertilisation in the following two contexts. The semen from a prize bull is used to fertilise the egg from a cow deemed in turn to possess a desirable trait, such as being an abundant milk producer. In theory, and in many cases even in practice, the farmer does not need to resort to in vitro fertilisation but does so primarily for reasons of economic efficiency – the semen of one prize bull can serve numerous cows without the bother of transporting any of the animals to meet for the purpose of mating. This short cut to nature's way of producing calves is, however, still within the framework of possible mating in order to produce offspring. Both the resulting embryo and the calf which eventually ensues from it may be said to be laboratory products. However, this is not the 'deep' sense in which something is a laboratory product when in vitro fertilisation is used to produce the tiglon or the liger. Here, the procedure occurs, in principle, outside the framework of the processes of mating, or even of cloning (which is the mode of replication in the case of some plants). While the prize bull and the prize cow could have mated, while the prize plant could have been propagated by cloning, ex hypothesi, the cow and the human could not have mated; nor could the flounder impart its genetic material to the tomato plant. The use of in vitro fertilisation or other genetic engineering techniques in this second context is not a mere short cut to the natural processes of reproduction; it is a full-frontal, 'in your face' bypassing of such processes.

Genes as raw DNA sequences: are these patentable?

As the 20th century drew to a close it became obvious that the radical decisions of the USA Supreme Court in the 1980s to bestow patentability on living organisms that had come into existence via biotechnological procedures would not automatically cover the even more innovative developments in biotechnology on the horizon. The issue goes beyond the patenting of an entire organism, such as the transgenic organism or bacterium. The Human Genome Project (HGP) has prompted a controversy whether patents should be granted to raw DNA sequences either as partial gene fragments or, indeed, even as complete gene sequences (with their known associated proteins).

Genome projects

The Human Genome Project is not the only genome project; it is merely one of several ongoing studies on the so-called genome of entire organisms. It has naturally generated a great deal of attention in the media as it concerns the human organism. Other successfully completed analogous undertakings, for example, include that of the nematode *Caenorhabditis elegans* and the fruit fly, *Drosophila melanogaster*.[30] The genome of the former is only about 100 million base pairs, compared with the 3 billion in the human genome. In December 2000, scientists celebrated the completion of the entire DNA sequence of a plant, *Arabidopsis thaliana*, a member of the mustard and cabbage family, also called the thale cress. The excitement concerned the discovery of a gene called *Frigida*, which stops the plant from flowering until after the winter. Genetic engineers see great commercial possibilities in this gene for plant breeding.[31] Another landmark was reported in January/February 2001 – the genome of rice was unravelled by the European agribusiness Syngenta and an American company, Myriad Genetics of Salt Lake City. Rice has the smallest genome of all the cereals, with 50,000 genes on just 12 chromosomes.[32]

With regard to the study of the human genome, there appears to have been a race to uncover all its genes. Two bodies have been and are involved in this race (but now denied by one of the parties to have been a race at all). One is supported by public/government funding in universities and research centres in several countries throughout the world, including the USA, the UK and France, co-operating under the umbrella of the HGP. The other is a private company called Celera Genomics, part owned and controlled by a scientist whose name is Craig Venter. The former was/is dedicated to the quickest possible public access to the fruit of their research. The latter had argued that a period of five years should lapse before it is made available and free of charge to all. In other words, while Celera Genomics appeared to favour patentability for raw DNA sequences, the HGP has appeared to argue against it. As the first draft of the HGP (decoding around 90 per cent of the genetic material) neared completion, Bill Clinton, the then US President, put great pressure upon Craig Venter as well as Francis Collins of the HGP to agree at least to a simultaneous, if not joint, announcement of their findings. This was achieved at the end of June 2000.

The scope of the exploration

One should immediately point out that the question about the patentability or otherwise of raw DNA sequences ought to cover all DNA sequences in all organisms which could in principle be isolated. The discussion is not, therefore, confined simply to human DNA sequences. It just happens to be the case that people get more worked up about human genome research than that of other genomes. If human DNA sequences are not patentable, then ipso facto the arguments supporting that view would also apply to the DNA sequences in other genomes, whether of the nematode or the fruit fly.

Note also that the discussion is primarily about raw DNA sequences which constitute the genes in any particular genome. The operative word here is 'raw'.[33] Hence, it rules out rDNA – that is to say, recombinant DNA – which ex hypothesi is not raw, and therefore, eminently suitable as a candidate for patentability.

It must also be borne in mind that this discussion explores the patentability or otherwise of complete gene sequences and their protein functions, as well as fragments or portions of such sequences whose functions are as yet unknown. The thrust of the argument pursued here leads to the conclusion that the former falls outside the patents domain, not merely that the latter is not patent-eligible as it stands today. In other words, the philosophical strategy pursued here, in the main, is to argue that even complete gene sequences with known protein functions do not qualify for patentability; if those arguments are successful, then ipso facto the case will also have been made that partial gene sequences with no known protein functions to date are similarly not eligible for patentability. In other words, the ontological focus on raw DNA in any form as a naturally occurring item, not as an invention/artefact, is fundamental; whether it exists as whole gene sequences with known protein functions or only as partial gene sequences is an irrelevant contingency according to this ontological perspective.

As a matter of fact, up to now, the bulk of the applications before the US Patent and Trademark Office has consisted of partial gene sequences with as yet no known functions; these are referred to as expressed sequence tags (ESTs).[34] This is for the simple reason that scientists, by and large, remain ignorant about the relation between gene sequences and the specific proteins they may express. ESTs exploit the fact that only a small portion of the DNA in a genome actually codes for proteins; the genes themselves are not continuous base sequences but are broken up into exons, that is, those parts carrying the instructions, and introns, which appear to carry no significant information, and are sometimes referred to as 'junk' DNA. The techniques for producing cDNA – that is, 'junk-free' complementary DNA, have been pioneered by Craig Venter.[35] Random sequences of the coding DNA are separated out, often without any knowledge of what the DNA in them codes. It is true that ESTs could be useful as probes in locating particular genes, but they themselves do not identify the function of the gene or any protein associated with the gene.

Although this exploration focuses on raw DNA sequences in general, however, if the arguments to be mounted against their patentability are successful, then they can equally be mounted against the patentability of single nucleotide polymorphisms (SNPs/Snips). A SNP represents a DNA sequence variation among individuals of a population. SNPs promise to be a money-spinner as they can be used to identify individuals who could be vulnerable to diseases such as cancer.[36]

Raw DNA sequences and their patenting so far

USA

In February 1997 the US PTO announced that ESTs are patentable, provided they go beyond their mere utility as probes, such as their utility for forensic identification, tissue type or origin, chromosome mapping, etc. This announcement, together with the ruling in 1995 by the US Court of Appeal for the Federal Circuit in the case of In re Deuel, encouraged a spate of patent applications regarding ESTs.[37] In February 1999 the PTO claimed that there were approximately 600 applications pending: these were 'huge sequences' applications, each containing hundreds of very short nucleic acid gene fragments or ESTs. Human Genome Sciences Inc., in its 1997 report, stated that it had filed more than 200,000 US Patent applications for partial human gene sequences.[38] (The European Patent Office in Munich was reported in December 2000 as saying that it faced a mountain of 7600 applications. The World Intellectual Property Organization in Geneva was reported in December 2000 as saying that it would soon be receiving two enormous biotech applications, each over 40,000 pages long.)[39]

ESTs will probably remain at the centre of the current debate about patent eligibility for some time to come, in spite of the emergence of a new trend to move the focus to complete gene sequences with known protein function.[40] However, it looks unlikely that they will be superseded till scientific knowledge has advanced much further regarding the relation between gene sequences and their protein functions, a quest which has just begun with the completion of the first draft of the HGP. In the USA the National Institutes of Health (one of the sponsoring bodies of the HGP) first filed patent applications in 1991 and 1992, thereby precipitating a rush to patent ESTs. However, they later withdrew them on the grounds that such patenting is not in the public interest. Other organisations in the USA, such as the Human Genome Organization, have urged the PTO to rescind its decision that ESTs are patentable.[41]

Europe

However, the situation in Europe today regarding the patentability of life forms, in general, and raw DNA sequences, whether as whole sequences or as ESTs, in particular, is much less clear cut. The biotech lobby both in the USA and in Europe has put tremendous pressure on the European Union (EU) to fall in line with the position taken by the US Patent and Trademark Office. As a result, the EU in 1998 passed a directive allowing the patenting of complete gene sequences as well as partial gene sequences (ESTs) – Directive 98/44/EC of the European Parliament and of the Council, 6 July 1998, on the legal protection of biotechnological inventions. However, it is important to grasp that the European Patent Office (EPO) based in Munich is not a part of the EU. It gets its powers from a treaty called the European Patent Convention; its jurisdiction covers twenty European countries, not just the EU. It can issue Europe-wide patents, as well as allow patents issued by national patent offices of the signatories to the European Patent Convention to extend throughout Europe. However, the Convention itself has not to date specifically allowed for gene patenting; it has also issued contradictory decisions on bio-patents in general.

However, in response to the EU 1998 directive, the head of the EPO, a German called Ingo Kober, asked his administrative council, made up of the representatives of the national patent offices, to allow him to implement it. But many legal experts, as well as bodies such as German Greenpeace, maintained that this move violated the terms of the original patent convention. Only four EU states had incorporated the directive into their domestic legislation when the deadline for doing so expired at the end of July 2000. Furthermore, some other EU states, such as the Netherlands, France and Italy, are actively against gene patenting and are challenging the legitimacy of the EU directive. In 2001 the European Court of Justice heard the case for its annulment, filed primarily by the Dutch government in October 1998 against the European Parliament and the Council of the European Union; but the Court rejected all six pleas.[42] However, at the same time, these very same governments of the EU agreed to remove the issue of bio-patents from the agenda of the meeting of the European Patent Office which took place in Munich on 20–29 November 2000.[43]

Raw complete DNA sequences and ESTs are not patentable

The conclusion of the philosophical exploration to follow comes down on the side of those who are not in favour of DNA patenting either as complete or partial gene sequences, but it seeks to show that the arguments mounted by either side of the divide concerning gene fragments or ESTs, as well as the compromise stance between these contesting views (as advanced by John Sulston, among others, holding that while gene fragments are not eligible, complete genes ought to be), are flawed and leave much to be desired. Vitiating them are inappropriate and misleading analogies, and failure to distinguish between (certain parts of) the *raison d'être* of modern patent law and the (ontological) requirements determining patentability. Indeed, there is even constant confusion between the very notions of discovery and invention, with scientists and commentators using these interchangeably when talking about matters raised by research on the human genome.[44] This exploration will argue that the only secure philosophical route to resolving the controversy is the ontological one. This involves recognising that modern patent law itself, as was mentioned at the beginning of the chapter, presupposes that an intelligible distinction can be made between what naturally occurs and can be discovered/found, on the one hand, and what is invented/fabricated through human ingenuity, on the other. It is to say that one ought to distinguish between natural kinds, which occur without human intervention and manipulation, and artefactual kinds, which are deliberately designed and fabricated by humans. Patentability can only be bestowed on the latter, not on the former. However, this discussion also argues the need to distinguish between 'products of nature', on the one hand, and the techniques/procedures devised through human ingenuity to appropriate them, on the other; the techniques and procedures are, of course, patentable, but the 'products of nature' themselves are not so. It seeks to show that raw DNA sequences are precisely such 'products of nature' which are, therefore, not patentable, although techniques/procedures now standardly deployed by biotechnology, such as the use of restriction and other enzymes, gel electrophoresis or PCR, have been successfully patented. Furthermore, this account advocates that the criteria for determining the patentability or otherwise of any application should be lexically ordered.[45]

Distinctions: discovery vs invention, process vs procedure

One needs straightaway to consider four major sets of distinctions:

A (a) the natural (or naturally occurring)	A (b) the artefactual[46]
B (a) discovery	B (b) invention[47]
C (a) (i) 'product of nature'	C (b) (i) process
(a) (ii) 'product of nature'	(b) (ii) procedure[48]
(a) (iii) human products	(b) (iii) procedure
D (a) biotic	D (b) abiotic

The distinction between A(a) and A(b) is to be understood as an ontological one, whereas that between B(a) and B(b) may be construed in epistemological terms – humans discover naturally occurring items and come to know that they exist, but we know what is artefactual by inventing and creating them ourselves. What exist as naturally occurring items ('products of nature') exist necessarily independent of us. In ontological contrast, artefacts (human products) would not exist but for the fact that we have deliberately invented and created them. Artefacts (human products as inventions) may be either biotic or abiotic.[49] Minimally, patentability is bestowed on items which fall under A(b), B(b), C(a)(iii) and C(b)(iii).

One may argue that transgenic organisms and rDNA fall under A(b), B(b), C(a)(iii), C(b)(iii) and D(a). However, one needs to get to grips with some of the other categories introduced above before one is able to answer definitively the question about the ontological status of raw DNA sequences. The debate centres on the issue whether they constitute scientific discoveries (of naturally occurring items) or whether they are artefacts, the outcome of technological innovations and procedures. As set out above, C is not a straightforward category. As a result, one needs to consider the matter at hand under three distinct possibilities: C(a)(i) and C(b)(i); C(a)(ii) and C(b)(ii); C(a)(iii) and C(b)(iii). The rest of this paper will argue that it is neither the first nor the last, but, more intriguingly, the second, which is relevant to this discussion, namely, that although raw DNA sequences can only be appropriated via certain procedures/techniques/protocols, they are, nevertheless, a 'product of nature'.

Product of nature and procedures?

In other words, this account argues that (A(a), C(a)(ii), C(b)(ii), D(a)) is not an empty class. It follows that one can meaningfully claim that something is naturally occurring, and therefore, not an invention but a 'product of nature' in spite of the fact that the procedures themselves involved in accessing it constitute inventions which are entirely devised and manipulated by humans. And if this class is intelligible and has members, then might not raw DNA sequences and the procedures involved in getting at them satisfy the requirements of membership?

A priori there seem to be no good reasons for rejecting the possibility just outlined. Let us consider a plausible instance which has nothing to do with raw DNA. Take so-called artificial pearls. Are they artefactual in the way that transgenic organisms can be said to be artefactual? No, because the pearl is actually formed in the oyster and by the oyster. In that sense, the pearl may be said to be a 'product of nature', primarily the outcome of natural processes which have been initiated by the oyster itself. However, unlike the 'natural pearls' which the oyster has also made, in the case of 'the artificial pearl', humans are involved in certain stages of its production.[50] Humans have deliberately inserted the grit into the oysters, and confined the oysters in certain ways in the sea waters for easy harvest. It requires human ingenuity to prise open the oysters (without killing them) for insertion and to devise ways and means of anchoring oysters in concentrated space which can withstand the natural forces at work, such as the waves and the winds.

Modern patent law accepts the distinction between product and procedures (or in its terminology, 'processes'). One could allow patenting the latter, but not the former in any one case. In the example just cited, the inventor of inserting grit into oysters and of constructing pens or stands for secure containment of the oysters at sea should be allowed his patents, provided that these are indeed novel methods, and not simply an application of what in patent law is called 'prior art'.[51] However, the pearl itself cannot be patented, as it itself does not amount to an invention; it is a misnomer to call it an 'artificial pearl'. If this line of reasoning is plausible, then there is nothing suspect in principle to grant that something may remain a 'product of nature' in spite of the fact that some human ingenuity may have been at work in its ultimate appearance.[52]

The case of raw DNA sequences may be said to be analogous to that of the so-called artificial pearl. With the latter, we have seen that the human ingenuity expressed itself in a relatively low-tech way. Not so with the former – the conditions under which raw DNA are uncovered are extremely high-tech, as DNA sequences are state-of-the-art laboratory products. In other words, one does not find a DNA sequence constituting a gene in the way that one finds a butterfly belonging to a rare or new species. As a substance, DNA in test tubes is a highly technologised product.[53] It would be silly to deny this aspect.[54]

One may re-pose the original question in the following way: given the highly technologised nature of the operation under which DNA is obtained, are raw DNA sequences artefacts, and therefore, fit candidates for patentability? An affirmative answer may, however, be unjustified, notwithstanding its initial plausibility. There may be good reasons for resisting it.

Misleading analogies and metaphors

First of all, one should not be mesmerised by misleading analogies and metaphors. As we shall see, both sides of the controversy concerning raw DNA sequences appear to have fallen into such a trap. Indeed, 'finding' DNA sequences in organisms is not analogous to finding pieces of gold in a treasure chest. The analogy actually fails to obtain because the phrase 'in a treasure chest' may turn out to be a red herring. The natural home of gold, so to speak, as a natural kind, is not a treasure chest, but the earth, either at its surface or deep underneath it. Gold in the ground or in river sediments exists in an impure form, that is to say, it is often mixed up with other natural kinds. To get pure nuggets of gold, one has to purify and refine the ore. To do that, one needs technology, either relatively sophisticated or primitive. This is equally true of other natural kinds such as diamonds (for example the Koh-i-noor which exists today in the British royal treasure chest). Just as pure samples of these natural kinds can only be obtained via technological means of one kind or another, so pure samples of DNA sequences can only be obtained via technological methods. However, the mere use of technological procedures in either type of context does not turn gold or diamond, on the one hand, and DNA sequences, on the other, into artefactual kinds. They remain natural kinds. The molecular composition and structure of gold remains identical whether the gold exists as a nugget in Fort Knox, a ring on someone's finger, or as part of a large lump of ore just dug up in some gold mine. Similarly, the molecular structure of DNA, whether it exists embedded in a cell in an organism, or in a purified form in a test tube in some laboratory, remains identical. That molecular structure itself is not an artefact, in spite of the fact that in order to get at it in its raw form one has to use a very sophisticated technology applying a set of very complicated techniques.

From this perspective, it is not justified that patent authorities, so far, have granted patents to complete DNA gene sequences on the grounds that sophisticated technological procedures in obtaining the item and its industrial applicability are jointly necessary and sufficient for determining patentability. For instance, a spokesperson of the UK Patent Office has been cited as saying: 'If you find something in nature, then finding some way to separate it and to make it into something useful can be an invention.'[55] It is also instructive to note that the European Union Directive 98/44/EC takes a similar stance. Article 3(2) of the directive reads: 'Biological material which is isolated from its natural environment or produced by means of a technical process may be the subject of an invention even if it previously occurred in nature.' Article 5(2) says: 'An element isolated from the human body or otherwise produced by means of a technical process, including the sequence or partial sequence of a gene, may constitute a patentable invention, even if the structure of that element is identical to that of a natural element.'[56]

To labour a crucial point, the complex technological procedures at work are simply dictated by the goal of obtaining raw DNA sequences; the manipulation and intervention on the part of the scientists have not been used with the aim of altering or modifying the DNA sequences themselves, unlike the case of rDNA.[57]

It is, therefore, crucial to grasp that one should distinguish between the substance itself and the technological procedures involved in obtaining the substance in a pure form.[58] Admittedly, the technological procedures themselves involve artefacts, but the substance that is the outcome of applying them is not necessarily an artefact. In the case of DNA, this means that, in ontological terms, while the transgenic organism or rDNA is an invention/artefact, the raw DNA sequence itself which has been inserted into the organism to turn it into a transgenic organism is not artefactual in character or status. We humans have designed and created the transgenic organism or rDNA – ex hypothesi, it would not have existed but for our fabrication of it. But we have not designed and created the raw DNA sequences themselves. In one clear sense, we have 'found' and 'discovered' them, as they exist independently of our fabrication of them, although it remains true that attempts to obtain raw samples of them involve procedures which rely on artefacts, from the humble test tube to the current most expensive, sophisticated state-of-the-art instruments.

Philosophically, the point above may be brought out further by comparing the transgenic organism with raw DNA sequences in three different ways, in terms of (a) Aristotle's four causes; (b) the distinction between the thesis of intrinsic/immanent teleology, on the one hand, and that of extrinsic/imposed teleology, on the other; (c) the distinction between 'for itself' and 'by itself'. The earlier chapters of the book have already set these out in some detail. One may briefly mention here that the four causes of the transgenic organism may all be assigned to human agencies. Take, for example, the cow that has been genetically engineered to produce a human protein in its milk. Such a cow would not, and could not, have come into existence if humans (the efficient cause) had not designed it as such in accordance with a human blueprint (the formal cause), with the explicit aim that it should produce a human protein in its milk (final cause), by inserting a human DNA sequence into its genome (the material cause). Human manipulation has thereby displaced intrinsic/immanent teleology by extrinsic/imposed teleology – the non-transgenic ordinary domesticated cow, in accordance with its own *telos*, produces milk which contains no human protein, whereas the transgenic cow, in accordance with human intentionality, produces milk containing an alien protein. As the transgenic organism ex hypothesi would not, and could not, have come into existence in the absence of deliberate human design and manipulation, it can be said that it no longer exists 'by itself'; furthermore this has also compromised its efforts to live 'for itself' because, as we have seen, its own *telos* has been distorted to serve the human end of producing milk containing a human protein. On the other hand, the raw DNA sequences (but, not of course, rDNA) have come into existence independently of human intention; as such they may be said to exist 'by themselves'. They also exist 'for themselves' as they have a specific biological function when embedded in the cells of the (naturally occurring) organism of which they are a part, that is, to ensure that the necessary proteins for which they code will ultimately be made. Their material, formal, final and efficient causes have nothing to do with human intentionality or manipulation. They, therefore, instantiate intrinsic/immanent teleology, not extrinsic/imposed teleology.

Discovery and invention

Next, one needs to look briefly at a fundamental presupposition of patent law, namely, that a distinction between the concept of discovery and that of invention can intelligibly be made. However, in general, these two concepts are not properly grasped and understood; nor is the exact boundary between the two in practice easy to determine in many cases of application. Conceptually, the distinction is easy enough to formulate: 'to discover' or 'to find' something implies that the object exists prior to, as well as independently of, the act of discovering or finding it. In contrast, 'to invent' something implies that the object of invention (be it a technique, a procedure or an artefact) cannot and does not exist prior to the act of creation or invention; nor does it exist independently of the act of invention itself.[59]

For many, the paradigm of a discovery is given either by geography, such as the discovery of an island or the source of a river, or by astronomy, such as the discovery of a star with the help of a telescope. As we have seen, this may not exhaust the notion of discovery in the natural sciences.[60] Some discoveries may require the assistance of relatively more complex instrumentation than a boat or a telescope, a fact which has sometimes given rise to the argument that what the instruments reveal is not really there but is the mere effect of the instruments themselves.[61] Others require complicated procedures of isolation before the substance in its raw state can emerge, as we have seen.

However, none of the points just mentioned touches the core of the matter, namely, that while discoveries are of naturally occurring phenomena – be these a star, a nugget of pure gold, raw DNA sequences or electromagnetic forces – inventions are the products of deliberate human design and fabrication. Naturally occurring phenomena and matter are not created by humans but are found by them, no matter how arduous the labour or complicated the technological procedures involved in uncovering them; they exist/occur independently of human intentions and manipulation.[62] The electromagnetic forces, the gold and the DNA (at least in non-human organisms) exist whether humans exist or not. Of course, in the absence of humans, ex hypothesi, there can be no knowledge about their existence.[63] In contrast, inventions are the ontological foil of naturally occurring matter/phenomena; they would not and could not exist in the absence of deliberate human design in creating them.[64] To labour an extremely important point: a world without humans is a world without transgenic organisms, the Taj Mahal, the Great Wall of China, but such a world would still contain DNA sequences (as part of cells in non-human organisms), the spider's web, the Grand Canyon.[65]

Ontological status: structure and function

To sum up the arguments so far at this stage of the discussion we have already proposed one criterion for testing the ontological character of raw DNA sequences as natural kinds, namely, that the procedures and protocols for obtaining them, such as gel electrophoresis, gene mapping or the 'shotgun' technique, have not altered in any way their molecular structure.[66] However, another related criterion consists of posing the question whether these methods and procedures have altered functions in essential ways. Indeed, the answer to this question must be in the negative and has already been touched on earlier en passant; otherwise, the raw DNA sequence would have lost its original power or potentiality via mRNA to instruct the cell to produce the protein for which the gene encodes.

However, one should be careful in this context to distinguish between two kinds of function: some commentators have, for instance, understood function to refer to the use of ESTs as probes or as gene markers.[67] But for others, this interpretation of 'function' is too wide.[68] However, the kind of function one is emphasising here has nothing to do with the suitability of raw DNA sequences to perform as probes or gene markers, or whatever; it has to do with their capability to code for certain proteins given their molecular structure. Any medical/industrial application to which the sequence can eventually be put depends on its retention of such a power.[69] As such, this indicates that the ontological character of the DNA sequences as naturally occurring items has not been affected. In contrast, the methods and procedures involved in getting plastic out of oil or petroleum have altered the oil, in terms of both its structure and its properties, in essential ways. Plastic is derived from oil; it itself is not oil. As pointed out in an earlier chapter, oil is a naturally occurring entity or natural kind, but plastic is an artefactual kind (in terms of second, though not first, matter).

It may be appropriate here to remind the reader of another associated issue mentioned at the beginning of this discussion, namely, how the word 'raw' is to be understood in the expression 'raw DNA sequences' (as is the section title on p. 155). We have seen that the two closely related criteria of the naturally occurring structure of the DNA sequences and their function go hand in hand; these two jointly determine whether a DNA sequence remains 'raw' in spite of the fact that complicated technological procedures are, undoubtedly, involved in its sequencing. Relying on these criteria also means that complementary DNA (cDNA) on which ESTs are based is itself raw in the sense just defined, unlike recombinant DNA (rDNA), which involves equally complex technological procedures.

Sulston, ESTs and complete DNA sequences

So far we have looked at some arguments in favour of the patentability of raw DNA as complete sequences and concluded that they are flawed, primarily because they have failed to take into account certain crucial distinctions, especially the ontological one between what is naturally occurring and what is artefactual. We now need to look at another stance in the debate, which is most closely linked to John Sulston – molecular biologist at the Sangar Laboratory in Cambridge and UK director of the joint US and UK Human Genome Project. Sulston's strategy is to argue against the patentability of most of the raw DNA sequences as they stand today, until such time as their protein functions become known. It will be argued here that such a strategy is also basically flawed. However, it should be noted that Sulston's position (or at least one which approximates to his) appears to have acquired a wider following, even including the present government headed by Tony Blair in the UK.[70] In the wake of the simultaneous announcement of the first draft of the HGP in June 2000, Venter was reported as saying that he has 'no plans to patent the genome. There's no value in that.'[71] Instead, he said that Celera Genomics would make money selling gene maps to drug companies and renting data to researchers, as well as doing its own gene research in human and related species. However, this does not mean that Venter has given up patenting raw DNA; he has simply changed tack. Indeed, both Venter and Collins are said now to see eye to eye on a significant point, namely, 'that patents are appropriate only at the point where a gene's function is understood'.[72] In practice, this might mean that the pressure to file patent applications on behalf of ESTs would ease. However, it might simply add weight to the view that while ESTs are a premature and, therefore, unsuitable candidate for patentability, complete DNA sequences with known gene functions would be eminently worthy candidates. Such a line of reasoning would undoubtedly become the dominant view, even if it were not the only view aired, given the near consensus now apparently emerging among extremely powerful players. However, it runs counter to the arguments advanced here that not even complete DNA sequences with known gene functions are suitable candidates for patentability. And in any case, national patent offices (in the USA or elsewhere) have yet to pronounce definitively on the EST patent applications still pending.

Sulston's account has been singled out here for close attention for the simple reason that he has elaborated and defended his position in some detail, much more than any of the other scientists whose utterances have entered into the debate.[73] A reconstruction of Sulston's thoughts begins with an analogy and the following distinctions which he makes: between (a) the letters of the alphabet, (b) the application of the letters to write a novel, on the one hand, and (c) the DNA sequences themselves, (d) the application of the DNA sequences, say, to create a transgenic organism, which produces a particular protein for which the inserted DNA sequence codes, on the other.[74] In his view the DNA sequences themselves are analogous to the letters of the alphabet; using them to create a transgenic organism, which in turn produces a protein, is analogous to writing a novel using the letters of the alphabet. Furthermore, while the novel and the transgenic organism are patentable, the letters of the alphabet and the raw DNA sequences are not. However, this line of reasoning, too, appears to be based on misleading analogies.

The conclusion, namely, that raw DNA sequences are not patentable is sound. However, Sulston's arguments supporting it are not. For a start, recall that not all human inventions involve artefacts; some inventions are techniques which are not embodied in material forms. This would be true of the invention of an alphabet – strictly speaking, an alphabet is a technique of recording speech and thought. It may or may not involve the use of arte-facts. Clearly, today one writes with pen and paper or increasingly, one does so in an electronic form using a computer – pen, paper, computer are indeed all artefacts. But one could just simply write with one's finger on sand; this still happens in some very poor parts of the world where educational resources, by way of classrooms, board and chalk, pens and books, are virtu-ally non-existent. Finger and sand are not artefacts, but they can be used to apply the technique of writing, using an alphabet or some other script.

The analogy Sulston has proposed between the alphabet and the raw DNA sequences is highly misleading for the simply reason that raw DNA sequences are not a human invention in the way that the letters of an alphabet are a pure human invention. It is important to grasp this point; otherwise, one could be accused of having scored a mere pedantic point against Sulston – after all, he is only invoking an analogy, the point of which for Sulston is that just as a novelist cannot patent the letters used in writing a novel because the letters are not that author's invention but rather are 'public property', similarly the biotechnologist cannot patent raw DNA because it, too, is not his invention but is 'public property'. If this indeed is Sulston's claim, it is, nevertheless, ill-conceived; as raw DNA is *tout court* not a human invention whatsoever, it is ex hypothesi not anybody's invention. Sulston seems to imply that raw DNA and the letters of the alphabet are 'public property' in an identical sense. However, the argument against Sulston is that they are not. The latter is not patentable because it is not the novelist's own invention, but the invention of some other humans in the dim and distant past; the former is not patentable because it fails to satisfy the more fundamental ontological requirement of patent law that only inventions, not discoveries, are patentable. As already argued, a crucial condition of patentability is that the item proposed for that status be a human invention (be it a technique/procedure or a material object).[75] Ironically, if Sulston's analogical reasoning were accepted as valid and taken seriously, then raw DNA sequences, whether as whole genes or as gene fragments/ESTs, far from being non-patentable, would be emi-nently fit candidates for patentability, as they would themselves be inven-tions, in just the way that the letters of an alphabet are, in principle, inventions. Of course, nobody has proposed to patent the latter, but only for the contingent reason that the invention of alphabets – whether Latin, Greek or whatever – has been lost in the mists of time. In any case, we cannot determine today how they were invented, although it seems unlikely that they were consciously designed and devised by the ingenuity of a single individual, or indeed a committee.[76] Furthermore, when they first appeared, modern patent law itself had not been invented, anyway.[77]

Sulston appears to be confused when he further argues that patentability does not, and should not arise, unless the item can be (industrially) applied in a particular way to gain a certain result. In spite of the rapid strides in knowledge in this field, we still do not know as much as we would like about how genes as DNA sequences function or 'express' themselves in an organism as complex as the human one. Nearly all of them, as they stand today, would have no application in the crucial sense, namely, in biotechnological terms.[78] Potentially they may have application, but according to Sulston's line of reasoning, until that were to happen, those DNA sequences should not be patentable. However, by the same reasoning, this would also imply that the moment a (biological) use or (industrial) application is found for a raw DNA sequence, that sequence would become an invention and, hence, be patentable. Is the issue of patentability dependent crucially upon novel use and application, whether actual or potential? Surely not.[79]

Use and application, actual or potential, is totally irrelevant to the issue about the ontological status of raw DNA sequences as a natural kind. Of course, biotechnology may enable one to insert a certain DNA sequence into another animal; this has already happened in experimental cases, which have potential xenotransplantation in view.[80] The animal becomes a transgenic organism, which clearly is an artefact, and therefore is itself eminently patentable, like the Harvard oncomouse or the Hsiao mouse. However, the foreign DNA sequence spliced into the mouse's genome belongs not to an artefactual but a natural kind, as has already been argued. One should not confuse the ontological character of an entity with its use and application, whether actual or potential.

A red herring: Locke's labour theory of value

Another source of confusion behind the controversy of the patentability of raw DNA sequences (either as ESTs or as complete genes) may be detected; it appears to be a matter connected with Locke's labour theory of value.[81] This seems to underpin the view of those in favour of patentability. Locke has proposed a theory of the ownership and distribution of property based on the expenditure of labour in its appropriation. To Locke, the peat out there in the bog belongs to no one; but if I were to cut out a chunk and bring it back to my cottage, then I become (morally/legally) entitled to it; it has become my property, because I have expended labour in appropriating it. Labour has costs, in economic terms, as it involves not only effort but also time. Labour, too, is not normally done with a pair of bare hands. Even peat digging and cutting require tools of some kind; tools have cost in economic terms, as they, too, involve effort, time and capital in their production.[82]

Obviously, as raw DNA sequences are laboratory products, a lot of expertise, effort, time and capital have been invested in them. Following Locke, it is only fair that those who have made the investment ought to be entitled to the fruit of their labour. And what better way to ensure that the rightful owners should get the proceeds from the fruit of their labour than permitting them to patent the DNA sequences? Craig Venter, as share-holder of Celera Genomics, as venture capitalist, is no different from other entrepreneurs in the marketplace.

This line of argument seems to confuse two things, namely, the economic *raison d'être* of patent law with the qualifying requirements which govern the patentability of particular items. It is undoubtedly true that patent law exists for the purpose of rewarding inventors, that is, to say, those who have expended effort, time and resources on something novel, which could have industrial application and could command a market. However, as far as this point is concerned, the HGP is publicly funded. The scientists, and indeed, the governments which fund it, have specifically abjured any direct monetary benefits which could come from being granted patents for the human DNA sequences its laboratories have isolated and identified. Their discoveries, the moment they occur, are immediately posted up on the internet to ensure immediate access, in order to facilitate further research and advancement in knowledge and human well-being. The scientists involved are rewarded for their labour, materially by their salaries, and non-materially by other status symbols, such as chairs at universities, and prestigious awards, such as the Nobel prize.

The issue whether investment capital should be rewarded financially, like investment in normal economic enterprises, ought to be considered in its own right. It ought not be confused with the different issue whether certain items are patentable because they are inventions, either as procedures of production or as artefacts which go beyond 'prior art'. At best, there is only a contingent relationship between these two issues – for instance, one could argue that in the absence of financial reward guaranteed under patent law for a limited period of time, the number of inventions would diminish, as would-be inventors and their backers would not wish to engage in activities which, even if successful, offer no guarantee of financial return.[83] While it is true that patent law is underwritten by the *raison d'être* of financial reward, we have also seen that granting patents with no further constraints would simply dispense with the fundamental issue, namely, which items are suitable candidates for patentability.

Lexical ordering of criteria

According to the line pursued here, it would not do to argue that at best only three criteria are relevant in considering a patent application, namely, that the item should be novel, non-obvious and useful. This set of determinants is too narrow, as well as too crudely understood.

A fuller and less misleading list of criteria would include the following, which should be lexically ordered. In this context, a lexical ordering amounts to the requirement that the first criterion be satisfied before moving on to apply the second. If the item does not pass the first test, then the operation should be aborted. The same holds for the second test, and so on.[84] An item is eligible for patentability if and only if the answers to the following questions turn out to be appropriate in the way set out below:

1. Is direct human manipulation of the DNA confined merely to the procedures of getting at a raw or pure sample of the naturally occurring item?[85] (The answer must be negative.)
2. Does direct manipulation alter the item so that it no longer possesses properties (both in terms of structure and function) essential to its identity as a naturally occurring item?[86] (The answer must be affirmative.)
3. Is the item entirely or sufficiently novel and non-obvious?[87] (The answer must be affirmative.)
4. Does the item have novel industrial/medical application?[88] (The answer must be affirmative.)
5. Is such an item against *ordre public* and morality? (The answer must be negative.)[89]

According to the above schema, raw DNA sequences (as complete genes and as ESTs or gene fragments) answer the first question affirmatively and the second negatively. However, unless the answer to the first question is in the negative, there would be no necessity to raise the second question, in any case. Furthermore, it would be equally superfluous to pose question 3 unless the answer to 1 is negative and that to 2 is affirmative. Question 4, in turn, should not be posed independently of questions 1 and 2 – invoking it would only be relevant if each of the three preceding questions has respectively been answered in the appropriate manner. A patent may yet be withheld should it fail to produce a negative answer to question 5 (even if the item were to satisfy the foregoing four questions in the appropriate manner).

Note that questions 1 and 2 attempt to assess the ontological status of the item filed for patenting. If the item turns out to be a discovery and not an invention (artefact or artefact embodying a technological procedure), it fails to qualify to be considered for patentability. Questions 3 and 4 come into play only after the item has been ascertained to be an invention. It is a mistake to think that 3 and 4 are the only relevant issues for determination in considering a patent application.[90] In other words, questions 1 and 2 raise a totally different category of issues from that of questions 3 and 4 (and question 5, for different reasons). Questions 1 and 2 pertain to matters ontological, questions 3 and 4 to practical considerations, and question 5 raises ethical issues. Question 5, although last in the lexical ordering, could well be regarded as the trump card – even should an item answer the preceding questions respectively in the appropriate way as indicated, it might yet fail the last hurdle and thus be rejected for patentability. In view of such a possibility, some critics of gene patenting could well be tempted to advocate its sole use in determining patentability as a short cut. However, that would be a 'cop-out', a failure of intellectual nerves, unhelpful at best and confusing at worst.[91]

To sum up, if the arguments presented above are plausible, then raw DNA sequences (either complete genes or as ESTs/gene fragments) are not patentable, as they are members of a natural kind, unlike rDNA or transgenic organisms, which do appear to qualify for patentability. However, the arguments commonly put forward to reach this conclusion are at worst not cogent, and at best, tangential. A sound foundation for the claim of non-patentability, it has been argued, lies crucially in the ontological distinction between natural kinds, on the one hand, and artefactual kinds, on the other – raw DNA sequences belong to the former domain, but rDNA and transgenic organisms fall into the latter. The research into the genomes of humans and non-humans alike yields discoveries, not inventions, about their genes and their appropriate protein functions. In addition, one must distinguish between 'product of nature', on the one hand, and the technological procedures for appropriating such naturally occurring items, on the other. At the same time, one must grasp that the question of the ontological status of raw DNA sequences is lexically prior to the question about whether they are novel/non-obvious in character, or have industrial applications – the utilitarian cart, so to speak, cannot move if it is hitched to the wrong ontological horse.

Notes

1 The exploration is specifically confined to this dimension alone, and is not concerned about related issues such as the ethical problems raised by biotechnology, whether in terms of safety to human health or the environment, of its consequences for social justice in global terms, of the nature of transnational capitalism and corporations and their exploitation of the rich genetic material found in many developing countries, of animal welfare, whether patenting biological products would be morally acceptable as it involves the commercialisation of living organisms and/or of their parts, etc. For the view that patents and the patent system are not a desirable mechanism for controlling biotechnology and its products from the social, ethical and political standpoints, see Draper (1996) and Tokar (2001, part III).
2 See Philip and Firth (1995, chapter 4).
3 See Manfield (1990).
4 See Philip and Firth (1995, chapter 4).
5 Its specification must satisfy the following three requirements: the written description requirement, the utility requirement, the non-obviousness requirement – see Ben-Ami et al. (1999).
6 For an account of the difficulties surrounding the application of the distinction in the history of patent law, see Stephen A. Ben et al. (1991, chapter 2). This chapter will pursue the matter in some detail in its discussion regarding raw DNA sequences.
7 The standard legal term is 'process patent', but this author prefers the term 'procedure patent'. The reason for this will become clear in the part of this chapter which deals with the patentability or otherwise of raw DNA sequences.

8 See Manfield (1990).
9 See Chapter 4 for comments on the use of 'chimera'.
10 See 'Seeds of Discontent', *New Scientist*, 21 October 2000, pp. 66–8.
11 In the 1977 experiments, the investigators, Shing Chang and Stanley N. Cohen, said in their paper that 'Although methods for cleaving and joining DNA segments in cell-free systems have enabled construction of a wide variety of recombinant DNA molecules that have not been observed in nature, there is reason to suspect that restriction endonuclease-promoted genetic combination may also occur intracellularly as a natural biological process' (Chang and Cohen, 1977). They claimed that enzymes similar to the ones they used in their experiments are found in many bacterial species and that the enzymes, which join DNA fragments (ligases), are also commonly found in nature. They thereby implied that their laboratory findings could have counterparts in nature, albeit at a low frequency, as the chemicals used in their experiments exist also in nature. In particular, Cohen appeared to have changed from an earlier position to the one just mentioned, which held that rDNA technology introduces no quantum leap in the crossing of 'natural barrier' or 'species barrier' (or between eukaryotes and prokaryotes), because genetic intercourse could occur between certain species, for all we know, at a low frequency in nature. But for a countervailing opinion, see Ho (1998), who argues 'that the *raison d'être* and aspiration of genetic engineering *is* to increase the facility of horizontal gene transfer, so as to create ever more exotic transgenic organisms', p. 162).
    To clarify the issues behind the controversy between those who hold and those who deny that there are species barriers in nature, and whether rDNA technology has breached them, Krimsky (1982) distinguishes between three forms of 'natural genetic barriers': ecological, absolute and statistical:

> Two organisms are separated by an ecological genetic barrier if the exchange of DNA between them is not observed under conditions resembling those considered as natural for the species in question. Two organisms are separated by an absolute genetic barrier if the exchange of DNA between them is not observed under natural or artificially engineered environments limited to non-rDNA techniques. Two organisms are separated by a statistical genetic barrier if the exchange of DNA is observed with low but not necessarily zero frequency under natural or artificially engineered environments limited to non-rDNA techniques. (p. 271)

    Transgenic organisms via rDNA technology could be said to breach the first two barriers identified. (In spite of the fact that the second is labelled 'absolute genetic barrier', rDNA technology may, nevertheless, be said to breach it, given the way Krimsky has defined the term in the quotation cited above.) And even if they could not be said to breach the third kind of barrier, it remains true, as the plasmid biologist Richard P. Novick has said: 'Just because an organism can be coaxed to take up foreign DNA in the lab, one has no right to assume that it does so regularly, if at all, in the wild; and further, even if uptake occurs, experimental evidence now available suggests that incorporation of foreign DNA into the cell's genome is a very special and unusual event' (Krimsky, 1982, p. 276).
12 See, for example, Cherfas (1982, pp. 126–41); Krimsky (1982); Wheale and McNally (1988); Ho (1998).
13 The procedure for fabricating biotic artefacts based on DNA manipulation in the laboratory is immensely complex, in spite of the fact that today one could train

science undergraduates to carry it out. Take as an illustration the result of the experiment published in *Nature*, May 1991 (by P. Koopman et al.) which reported success in turning a female mouse into a male one. A summary of it may be found in Holdrege (1996, p. 110).

Note, too, that the successful genetically altered mouse whose picture appeared on *Nature*'s cover had XX chromosomes, and therefore, was female in her body cell, but male in anatomy and behaviour, presumably because of the Sry DNA – his testicles were very small, and although he was sterile, he displayed normal male mating behaviour. In the experiment, altogether ninety three mice were born, of which only five, however, were identified as transgenic, that is, having taken up the Sry (sex-determining region) DNA. Of the five, sex reversal only occurred in the one case, as just described.

14 The success caused a good deal of ill will within the scientific community as it credited Cohen and Boyer as the inventors. Patent law assumes co-authors to be co-inventors; yet co-authors were left out. The two patents together were esti- mated to be worth more than a 1000 million dollars, but as the earnings in the end, in the main, went to the two universities for research purposes rather than the two individuals named as the inventors, the acrimony eventually subsided.

15 However, 16 legal oppositions were lodged with the EPO against it and hearings were scheduled – see Wheale and McNally (1995, p. 152). By 1997 over 300 European patent applications on animals had been filed, but only three had been granted. The objections, on the whole, have come from animal welfare and animal rights groups. Their main argument appears to be based on the suffering and, there- fore, its immorality, caused to such transgenic animals – see Stevenson (1995); Emmott (2001). (This chapter later on will raise further details about the EPO.)

16 The main section in this chapter dealing with raw DNA will examine in greater detail and more precisely the relationship between these and other relevant conditions.

17 In general, up to now, research laboratories (both privately and publicly funded) engage in producing transgenic organisms with medical/agricultural/husbandry purposes in mind.

18 Current biology, apart from the eukaryote/prokaryote distinction, recognises five kingdoms: Animals and Plants (multi-cellular eukaryotic organisms), Monera (prokaryotic organisms, such as bacteria), Protista (unicellular eukaryotic organ- isms, such as protozoa), Fungi (multi-cellular eukaryotic organisms). Some biolo- gists even talk of a sixth, Archaea.

19 The author owes this point of view to Ned Hettinger, especially in personal com- munication with him. However, he might not have formulated it in quite the way set out here. See also Hettinger (1995).

20 Another example is a small herd of transgenic brown Nigerian goats whose milk is expected to contain a 'spider-fibre'. Their creator is a team of Canadian scien- tists at Nexia Biotechnologies of Quebec. These researchers first bred two male goats whose genome had been altered to include the silk-making genes of a spider. When the transgenic males reached sexual maturity, they mated with 50 female goats, thereby producing numerous 'spider-fibre' females among their offspring. Spider silk is exceptionally strong and light. As it is difficult to farm spiders for their silk, which one could do in the case of silk worms, biotechnol- ogy has now stepped in to provide a solution through developing the new science of bio-mimicry, which permits pharmaceutical and other materials to be harvested from genetically engineered domestic animals. In this case, the spider

silk molecules from the goats' milk could be used to make anything from sutures to components of air/space craft. (See Burke and McKie, 2000.)

21 See Gary Comstock (2000, chapter 3).

22 See Comstock (2000, chapter 3).

23 The liger has a lion as father and tiger as mother, the tiglon is the other way round.

24 The main technological procedure used in these examples of genetic manipulation is in vitro fertilisation, rather than the insertion of specific alien DNA
sequences into the genome of either the lion or the tiger. (However, note that
under the terminology used in this book, the term 'biotechnology' covers more
than just DNA engineering and encompasses the techniques and procedures
derived from a general understanding of molecular biology itself, including cell
biology. In vitro fertilisation is a technique in biotechnology.)

25 For examples which already exist of this move, see Bent et al. (1991).

26 As for fluorescence, the technique has been in place since about 1993 – the gene
for GFP, which codes for a green fluorescent protein, was isolated from the phos-
phorescent perimeter of a jellyfish. GFP has turned out to be tremendously
useful, given its fluorescent property, its small size and its lack of any adverse
effects on the host organism when introduced into it. It is now routinely used as
a marker to tell scientists whether genes are switched 'on' or 'off' in living cells
or organisms. When GFP is fused to a protein under study, scientists can
monitor the protein as it traverses the living cell.

In 2000, a Chicago-based artist, Eduardo Kac, with the help of genetic engineers
in a French laboratory produced a transgenic rabbit, named Alba, which glows
green when exposed to blue light, the GFP gene having been inserted into its
genome. Kac maintains that Alba is a new form of art whereas the director of the
French laboratory holds that it is no more and no less than a transgenic rabbit,
which the laboratory intends to keep. (See *New Scientist*, 6 January 2001, pp. 34–7.)

On 12 January 2001 newspapers reported the publication in *Science* that at the
Oregon Primate Research Centre in the USA, scientists had inserted the same
gene into a recently born rhesus monkey, called ANDi (acronym for 'inserted
DNA' spelt backwards) – see Meek (12 January 2001). The experiment shows that
primates, too, can be successfully manipulated in this fashion. The team used
224 monkey eggs and a retrovirus as vector to carry the jellyfish gene inside each
of the eggs. When the eggs were fertilised with monkey sperm, just over half
developed into properly functioning embryos, of which 40 were implanted in
surrogate monkey mothers. There were five births of which two, however, were
still-born. Of the remaining three, the gene failed to show up in two; only one
possessed the jellyfish gene. However, so far, ANDi has failed to glow; its hair
roots and toe nails do not glow under flourescent light, although the other two
still-born ones did. ANDi may yet glow when he matures. If he does, will he also
be able to pass on the gene to his offspring, which will then express it? Is the use
of retroviruses as vectors really reliable and efficient? Maybe not, as ANDi has
failed to glow so far. (See Coghlan and Young, 2001.)

27 Chapter 3 has pointed out that the mechanisms responsible for producing milk in
the domesticated cow, too, have been hijacked by craft-based or Mendelian hybridisation technologies to serve a human end. The milk produced is not destined for the
cow's calves but for us humans. However, there remains a crucial difference between
the two situations. The dairy cow, nevertheless, produces cow's milk; the transgenic
cow produces not cow's milk as such, with proteins in it peculiar to cows, but
instead milk which also contains a human protein. The (transgenic) cow's milk-

producing capability has been captured and diverted by biotechnology in a fundamentally more radical fashion than is the case of the dairy cow. The dairy cow may have a DNA sequence inserted into her genome from another variety of cow noted for abundance in milk production; but such a genetically modified dairy cow still produces milk containing only proteins peculiar to cows.

28 The *telos* and its related theses will be looked at in greater detail later in the next main section of this chapter, dealing with raw DNA.

29 This distinction will be explored in the next main section on raw DNA sequences.

30 The former was completed primarily by the British team working under the aegis of the HGP; the latter, a little earlier, by a rival body, Celera Genomics, which has recently announced that it would be starting the mouse genome project.

31 See Radford (2000); Coghlan (2000); see also *Nature*, vol. 408 (2000), pp. 796, 816, 820, 823.

32 See Coghlan (2001).

33 The word 'raw' in the expression 'raw DNA sequences' is used here in a very specific way which should become obvious as the discussion progresses; suffice it for now to say that its 'rawness' is constituted by its naturally occurring structure and function, and not merely that no technological procedures are involved in its sequencing.

34 One definition of an EST may be given as follows: a partial sequence of a clone picked at random from a cDNA library and used in the identification of genes being expressed in a particular tissue. The technique exploits recent advances in automated DNA sequencing and sequence data handling, and a remarkably high number of ESTs turn out to represent previously unknown genes. These are identified by the predicted primary structure of the proteins that would be expressed and their relation to proteins of known structure. ESTs have proved extremely valuable in mapping the human genome. (*Oxford Dictionary of Biochemistry and Molecular Biology*, 1997, p. 223.) (For an account of cDNA, see note which follows.)

35 Complementary DNA (cDNA) is unlike genomic DNA (found in cells and tissues of an organism) only in one respect, that it contains no introns (as already mentioned), as it is derived from messenger RNA (mRNA). It is 'a single-stranded DNA molecule that has a complementary base sequence to a molecule of a messenger RNA, from which it is produced by the action of reverse transcriptase, and is used in molecular cloning, or as a molecular probe in hybridization tests for a specific sequence in cellular DNA' (*Oxford Dictionary of Biochemistry and Molecular Biology*, 1997, p. 129).

36 See Marchant (2000, pp. 46–50).

37 The first true EST patent granted is the so-called '479 patent entitled 'Human kinase homologs'.

38 See Ben-Ami et al. (1999).

39 See Fox and Coghlan (2000).

40 This point will be addressed in a later subsection – Raw complete DNA sequences and ESTs are not patentable.

41 For an account of the objections to the PTO's stance, see Dastgheib-Vinarov (2000), in which she also argues that a more stringent standard be adopted in order to discourage and stop the irresponsible stockpiling of partial DNA sequences with no known functions by biotech companies and organisations, thus hindering the progress of research. In one part of the article, she urges that

'The applicant must sequence a complete gene, or at least enough of a gene necessary to determine its function and preliminary diagnostic application'; in another part, she calls for a complete gene sequence and solid understanding of the gene's functions. As we shall see later, the scientist John Sulston (UK) seems to advocate a similar stance.

42 See Case C-377/98, *Official Journal of the European Union*, 5 December 1998, p. 13, and the European Court Reports (2001).

43 See Meek and Brown (2000). For details, in general, on the respective positions of the European Union and the European Patent Office, see van de Graaf (1997, chapter 3); Baggot (1998); Nott (1998); Schatz (1998).

44 Craig Venter is an example of such a scientist who has referred to the research on the human genome in terms of 'making ... discoveries' – see Golden and Lemonick (2000). As for commentators, see Dastgheib-Vinarov (2000). Indeed, even the US Constitution itself is not beyond such confusion: 'to promote the Progress of the Useful Arts, by securing for limited Times to . . . Inventors the exclusive Right to their Discoveries' (art. 1, sec. 8, cl. 8; cited by Dastgheib-Vinarov).

45 Lexical ordering is discussed on pp. 170–2.

46 For details about this distinction, see Keekok Lee (1999).

47 Although all artefacts are inventions, not all inventions are or involve artefacts; for instance, some techniques are inventions although they are not necessarily materially embodied as artefacts are. But this point will be further clarified later.

48 In this discussion, the distinction between 'process' and 'procedure' is used as follows: the former is always invoked in connection with naturally occurring phenomena whereas the latter is always invoked in the context of human manipulation and fabrication. Thus, one talks about the volcano and the processes which have created as well as sustained it, namely, C(a)(i) and C(b)(i); but one talks about the hydroelectric dam and the procedures/techniques/protocols which have been used and followed in building it, namely, C(a)(iii) and C(b)(iii).

49 Each may display varying degrees as well as levels of artefacticity. For details, refer back to Chapter 1 on this and related points.

50 The truly artificial pearl would be one made of plastic, but coloured and polished to look like the natural pearl.

51 Of course what constitutes 'prior art', in many instances, may not be obvious and could give rise to dispute and contention. The UK Patents Act 1949, ss. 14 (I) (c) and 32 (I) (f), says that the invention must not be 'obvious'; its successor Act of 1977, s. 3, stipulates more precisely that it be 'not obvious to a person skilled in the art'.

52 It is instructive, at this point, to consider the case of artificial diamonds as opposed to natural diamonds. The latter are said to be natural and 'real', not because no technological means or procedures are involved in isolating the pure diamond from the diamond ore, but because their very existence and the geological processes which had brought about their existence are totally independent of human ingenuity and manipulation. In contrast, so-called artificial diamonds are brought into existence entirely through human ingenuity and manipulation. It follows from this that, on the one hand, both the artificial diamonds and the technological procedures (if novel and non-obvious) of their production are patentable; but on the other hand, the natural diamond itself is not patentable, being a 'product of nature'.

The approach urged here is clearly at odds with the decisions reached by some recent cases in patent law, particularly regarding pure cultures of microorganisms – see Bent et al. (1991, pp. 34–8 and pp. 262–3). Any given soil or water sample would contain many different kinds of microorganisms found in that particular ecology from which the sample has been taken. Only one of these kinds of microorganisms might have industrial application. The laboratory would have to isolate this from the rest and culture it on its own, producing a colony of such individual organisms. The isolated microorganisms themselves are clearly naturally occurring biotic entities whose existence and functioning have nothing to do with human ingenuity and manipulation. But a complex set of biochemical procedures are involved, first in the isolation, and then, in the propagation of the selected organisms themselves. The procedures are patentable but, however, not the organisms, according to the line of argument pursued here.

53 To labour an extremely important point. It is a highly technologised product only in the limited sense that the technology used in extracting it from the cells (tissues or organs) uses highly sophisticated technological means. This fact should not be allowed to undermine the status of the raw DNA sequences thus extracted as belonging to natural, not artefactual, kinds.

54 To appreciate the processes involved in isolating DNA, let us turn to one account of its production:

> Here, for example, is how DNA can be isolated out of a mouse. The mouse is killed and its thymus is immediately frozen (to prevent decomposition). The frozen tissue in a salt solution is homgenized in a mixer for three minutes. The homogenized pulp is centrifuged at three thousand revolutions per minute for ten minutes. A separation takes place, and the more solid precipitate is saved; the more fluid portion is discarded. Centrifugation is usually repeated one or two times. Then a salt solution and alcohol are added, and a milky white precipitate begins to form in the solution. This is 'unrefined' DNA, which can be further purified in additional steps by adding specific enzymes or other substances. When alcohol is added again, white threads form, which can be rolled up on a glass rod. One now has DNA in hand! . . .
>
> This description of DNA isolation shows that, in order to obtain the final substance, a specific set of actions utilizing physical, chemical, and electrical forces is required. At each step the previous state is altered and a particular result of the analysis is isolated. At the end (which is always a matter of stopping: there is no absolute end of anyalysis) the obtained result bears no similarity to the origin. (Holdrege, 1996, pp. 101–2)

55 See Clark and Meek (2000).

56 These points are reinforced by Recitals 20 and 21 to the directive. Recital 20 reads:

> Whereas, therefore, it should be made clear that an invention based on an element isolated from the human body or otherwise produced by means of a technical process, which is susceptible of industrial application, is not excluded from patentability, even where the structure of that element is identical to that of a natural element, given that the rights conferred by the patent do not extend to the human body and its elements in their natural environment[.]

Recital 21 reads:

> Whereas such an element isolated from the human body or otherwise produced is not excluded from patentability since it is, for example, the result of

technical processes used to identify, purify and classify it and to reproduce it outside the human body, techniques which human beings alone are capable of putting into practice and which nature is incapable of accomplishing by itself[.]

Admittedly, Article 5(1) states that 'The human body, at the various stages of its formation and development, and the simple discovery of one of its elements, including the sequences or partial sequence of a gene, cannot constitute patentable inventions.' However, this read in conjunction with Article 5(2) and Recitals 20 and 21 – already cited above – shows that, in the view of the directive, what transforms the ontological status of sequences (or partial sequence of a gene) from being a discovery to being a patentable invention is the mere use of technical processes (procedures, as favoured by this book), in spite of the fact that the structure of the DNA sequence remains unchanged.

57 Or if the language of information is preferred, one could make the same point by saying that the scientists, in their efforts to isolate raw DNA sequences, have not introduced any new, but only extracted existing, information.

58 It has been reported that Celera Genomics would use the 'shotgun' method in its mouse genome project. If so, the company could be relying only on 'prior art' – see *New Scientist* (22 April 2000, p. 5). Should it introduce distinctly novel techniques, then these could be patented. But in neither case does it follow that the DNA sequences of the mouse genome themselves be patentable. Their status as 'products of nature' is not affected one way or the other by the actual technological means used to extract them, whether these are within or beyond 'prior art'.

(The 'shotgun' sequencing technique chops up the entire genome into little pieces. These random bits are sorted out by computers searching for overlapping fragments. In contrast, the HGP sequences adjacent segments of chromosomes. A short piece of chromosome is taken and thousands of incomplete copies are made from it, all starting from the same end. At the other end, a fluorescent label is attached, using different colours for different letters of the four-letter code. Then the fragments are separated out according to size from which the sequence can be read. When strung together, they give the entire sequence of the chromosome. Today, sequencing machines exist to hasten the procedure.)

59 Reinventing the wheel is not a proper counter-example to the claim just made.

The distinction as set out does not take into account the postmodernist critique of it, as this would be beyond its remit. This book, throughout, adopts the standpoint of what may be called critical realism – refer to earlier comments in Chapter 2, section entitled 'The philosophy of technology and the philosophy of science' (pp. 63ff.).

60 Pure mathematics is not a natural science in the way that physics and biology, undisputedly, are natural sciences.

61 When Galileo claimed that he saw craters on the moon's surface through his telescope, some of his critics reprimanded him for mistaking an optical phenomenon for something real out there on the moon.

62 In this context the matter that one is interested in is what Aristotle calls second matter or natural kinds.

63 But this merely shows that ontology – that branch of philosophy which deals with what exists – is prior to epistemology – that branch of philosophy which deals with what we can know. Epistemology is necessarily anthropogenic, as far as its source is concerned, though the implications of all knowledge claims are not wholly anthropogenic – while 'I know that my tooth aches' is wholly anthro-

pogenic, 'I know that the earth goes round the sun' is not wholly anthropogenic, as the assertion, if true, presupposes that the earth does go round the sun, a state of affairs which obtains irrespective of human awareness of it. Nor is the whole of ontology necessarily non-anthropogenic – while naturally occurring entities, such as the geological forms we call the Himalayas are/were necessarily non-anthropogenic, fictitious entities, such as Pegasus, are necessarily anthropogenic.

64 For a detailed exploration of these philosophical points, see Keekok Lee (1999).

65 According to (some versions of) postmodernism, the natural sciences do not study naturally occurring phenomena. Its point baldly put is that the object of scientific study is not nature; nature, essentially a social construct, does not exist per se independently of human thought. See Keekok Lee (1999, appendix 2).

66 Refer to the European Union Directive 98/44/EC, cited earlier.

67 See Oser (1999).

68 See Dastgheib-Vinarov (2000).

69 It bears reminding the reader that science today does not really understand the mechanisms in terms of which proteins are formed by instructions from DNA and RNA. However, it knows enough to be confident of the importance of the respective roles of DNA and RNA in protein formation.

Now that the first draft of the HGP is completed, scientists are turning to this very problem of how amino acids, which proteins consist of, are formed atom by atom according to the genetic instructions, and how these fold to form the protein that they do. Computers are expected to play a key role – IBM is reported to be committing over $100 million, primarily to building a computer, already nicknamed Blue Gene, capable of tackling a quadrillion operations a second. There is talk of a 'human proteome project', analogous to the HGP, to isolate and characterise every protein in the human body. (See Meek and Ellison, 2000).

70 Sulston's reasoning appears to reflect closely the line adopted by the British Government regarding this issue, for some time. While the French are against patenting all human genes, the British 'as usual, tried to compromise. Their position was that gene sequences "of no known utility" (i.e. the random sequences which the Americans were trying to patent) should not be covered by patents and no one should seek patent protection for them. On the other hand, sequences whose function was known (the mutant cystic fibrosis gene for example) could be patented' (Wilkie, 1994, pp. 93–4). However, which is the chicken and which is the egg? Has the British government co-opted Sulston's view as its official policy or has Sulston adopted government policy as his own? This author would not know.

71 See Greising (2000).

72 See Golden and Lemonick (3 July 2000).

73 For an exponent on the part of academic lawyers, see Dastgheib-Vinarov (2000).

74 See Sulston (2000).

75 In precisely what way it is crucial will be made clear in a later section – see Lexical ordering of criteria.

76 Although this is the case with most scripts, it is not true, at least, in one exceptional instance. The distinctive Korean script was indeed invented by a Korean king in the first half of the 15th century. He did it to advance Korean culture – patenting, even if it had been available in his country at the time, would not have been relevant, although such a hypothetical application would satisfy the conditions for patentability, as modern patent law is predicated upon the clear identification of a single individual or a group of individuals as the inventor of the item.

77 Patent law cannot address more complicated conditions under which invention takes place, for instance, when it is the product of the accumulation of the consequences of individual actions (even if intended) over a long period of time, and in which the individuals involved are anonymous. Hence, it cannot really cope with landraces which have (culturally) evolved in traditional societies over the millennia. They fall outside the remit of modern patent law. In the same way, as already observed, so would the letters of the Latin, Greek, Arabic alphabets or any other scripts which have evolved from time immemorial as collective inventions.

78 For a start, introns, the non-coding parts of the gene, so-called 'junk' DNA because they appear not to be fulfilling any obvious biological purpose, far exceed exons, the coding regions of the gene. For instance, the gene containing the instructions for adenosine deaminase (ADA) covers 32,000 base pairs; yet the bits which actually code for ADA are only about 1500 base pairs long, interrupted, however, by 11 introns. Indeed, introns constitute 90 per cent of the human genome. We cannot preclude the possibility that one day we might discover their biological function, and even turn that function into industrial application; however, such a discovery would not undermine their status as naturally occurring entities, then or now.

79 An example of filing for patents of a complete DNA sequence with a known function (both named Hpa2), after June 2000, is that of Oxford GlycoSciences, whose scientists claimed to have identified a gene and a protein which could be crucial in controlling the supply of blood to cancer tumours. Oxford GlycoSciences is paying Medarex, a US pharmaceuticals company, to develop antibodies to counteract the heparanase enzymes produced by the gene and protein. In anticipation of profits following the patent applications, the shares of Oxford GlycoSciences leapt from 89p to £22.54. (See Clark, 2000.)

80 For instance, a certain DNA sequence which codes for a human protein has been inserted into experimental pigs, whose hearts, upon transplantation, would then be less likely to be rejected by the human immune system.

81 For a more detailed discussion, see Keekok Lee (1996a).

82 Karl Marx, following Locke, regarded capital as no more than congealed labour.

83 The grounds and evidence for this claim, historically, are not all that strong – see Eric Schiff (1971); Phillips and Firth (1995, chapter 9). However, the arrival of biotechnology may alter the situation; see Monbiot (2002) for a different opinion.

84 In his arguments Sulston fails to recognise the lexical ordering of the criteria involved. But to be fair, he is not the only one; the concept of lexical ordering of criteria appears so far not to have been raised in the literature concerning patentability of DNA or, indeed, in patent law in general.

85 Techniques and procedures such as PCR, etc., indeed, are indispensable in enabling molecular biologists to obtain raw DNA sequences. However, rDNA is a case in which the techniques/procedures involved, such as the use of restriction enzymes for fragmenting the DNA sequence and other enzymes, such as ligase, to 'glue' the fragments together, have led to a product which is no longer a naturally occurring item.

86 Such manipulation, via gel electrophoresis and PCR, has not altered either the molecular structure of DNA or of the ability of DNA sequences (in principle) to code for certain proteins. With rDNA, similar direct manipulation alters the property of the original sequence for gene expression. So while raw DNA sequences remain naturally occurring items, rDNA sequences are artefactual in character.

87 Raw DNA sequences, ex hypothesi, are not novel items as they are not inventions.
88 As already observed, the majority of the DNA in the human genome appears at the moment to have no (known) biological functions, never mind industrial/medical application.
89 For instance, as we will see in Chapter 6, such an objection has been made against the patenting of transgenic animals which incorporate human genetic material as well as against the cloning of humans.
90 Questions 3 and 4 between them cover the criteria of being novel, useful and non-obvious, covering the three requirements: the utility, non-obviousness and written description requirements.
91 It cannot be assumed a priori that every application involving the DNA sequences of genes would be against '*ordre public* and morality'. On the contrary, certain applications leading to the elimination of incurable medical conditions via somatic therapy are clearly beneficial. The Roslin Institute in Edinburgh announced, in December 2000, a joint project with Viragen (a US company) to begin a programme, using the techniques successful in creating Dolly, which could obtain proteins from the egg white of transgenic chickens to fight skin and lung cancer. (See Scott, 7 December 2000.) On the other hand, if gene patenting is considered to be immoral a priori and in principle, what constitutes its immorality? As answer, in part if not wholly, is the fact that genes are held to be naturally occurring or God-given (for the theologically minded) and not human inventions. In other words, it would involve question-begging as it simply assumes the critical point at issue, namely, whether there are good reasons for holding either that they are or that they are not naturally occurring.

6
Homo Faber: The Humanisation of Biotic Nature and the Naturalisation of Humans

Homo faber: the fundamental category of human agency in modernity[1]

Modernity is often associated with the celebration of abstract reason. Its elevation of 'the rational' as the epistemological authority toppled traditional authority in the form of the theological and the ecclesiastical. Although this is undoubtedly correct historically speaking, it should also be pointed out that the celebration of abstract reason is not new in the history of Western philosophy. Plato stands out as an uncompromising champion in classical Greek philosophy. Modern European thought revived and reconstrued that ancient Greek notion, developing it in radically new directions to serve very different ideological goals from those of the classical age.

The ideology of materialism and scientific naturalism

As we saw in Chapter 2, the ancient Greeks regarded *episteme*, achieved through the exercise of reason, to be both intellectually and morally superior to *techne*. For Plato, the material world upon which *techne* operates belongs to Appearance, not Reality. The pursuit of wisdom and virtue through grasping the forms of the Good, Justice and Beauty is the ultimate philosophical goal. Anything else is a distraction. The highest intellectual/moral life is that of the contemplation and the love of such forms. The desire to dominate the material/natural world through *techne* is no part of this ideal. The role played by *techne* in such a conception of the good life and the good society is a very limited one. The highest human fulfilment and flourishing is not to be found in the mastery of the sensory world nor in the comforts that such control may bring.

The ancient Greeks held material affluence to be a form of corruption, and according to Socrates, a society addicted to it was a 'feverish state'. In Plato's *Republic*, Socrates, in reply to Glaucon's criticism about his characterisation of the good state, says:

The true state I believe to be the one we have described – the healthy state, as it were. But if it is your pleasure that we contemplate also a fevered state, there is nothing to hinder. For there are some, it appears, who will not be contented with this sort of fare or with this way of life; but couches will have to be added thereto and tables and other furniture, yes, and relishes and myrrh and incense and girls and cakes – all sorts of all of them. And the requirements we first mentioned, houses and garments and shoes, will no longer be confined to necessities, but we must set painting to work and embroidery and procure gold and ivory and similar adornments, must we not? 'Yes,' he said. 'Then shall we not have to enlarge the city again? For that healthy state is no longer sufficient, but we must proceed to swell out its bulk and fill it up with a multitude of things that exceed the requirements of necessity in states'. (Plato, 1982, Republic 372D–373B)

For Socrates, human flourishing is not predicated upon 'the realm of necessity' which is taken care of by *techne* (technology). On the contrary, the love of the soul for the Good will be diverted, beyond a certain point, by technological deliverance from 'necessity'. For moderns such as Marx, intellectual and artistic flourishing is only meaningful and possible if structured upon a material base of abundance, if not superabundance. The Socratic life, however, is predicated upon sufficiency, not abundance or superabundance, and must necessarily exclude material affluence, as the latter nourishes the weaker, less perfect side of human nature, undermining any genuine pursuit of the soul's desire for perfection, for the Good.[2]

Aristotle, too, shares Plato's attitude to *techne*. In *Metaphysics*, he distinguishes between the theoretical, the practical and the productive sciences. The first type, like physics, mathematics and metaphysics, is concerned with principles of being which cannot be other than what they are, and whose investigation primarily satisfies the intellectual faculty for understanding and making sense of the cosmos. The second includes ethics and politics. The goal of ethics is to attain *eudaimonia* (happiness is not, however, understood in the utilitarian sense of pleasure as a sensation, but as well-being, issuing from an integrated life of fulfilling pursuits). The goal of politics is the realisation of the common good, which includes the ethical goal of the pursuit of *eudaimonia*. We try to do things well in the practical sciences. But in the productive sciences, we make things instead. For Aristotle as for Plato, the *bios theoretikos* (the life of contemplation) constitutes the highest plane of activity, as it addresses the divine element in human beings.[3] *Bios praktikos* occupies the level below. But productive activities as fabrication, or making things, constitute the lowest form of life. It has no intrinsic value. It is not worth doing for its own sake. It has only instrumental value as it supplies the basic necessities without which life, and ex hypothesi the good life, is not possible. In other words, for Aristotle in particular and the ancient Greeks in general, the life of fabrication may be a necessary subsidiary preoccupation but cannot itself constitute a focal point in human life, metaphysically, spiritually or morally.[4]

Modernity may also celebrate abstract reason but does so in an entirely different ideological context. Here, abstract reason, as manifested in scientific methodology in particular, is harnessed to the goal of controlling nature. While there is some emphasis on the pursuit of scientific knowledge out of pure intellectual curiosity, the predominant motivation, as we saw in Chapter 2, is to translate that knowledge into technological terms to serve the overwhelming goal of improving the material well-being of humans. The life of fabrication, far from being a subordinate, subsidiary, though necessary human activity, has become a central preoccupation, so central that fabrication becomes the very essence and constitution of human nature. In a word, the notion homo faber captures the spirit of modernity itself.[5]

Locke, via has labour theory of value, reinforced the stance endorsed by modern science and technology towards nature.[6] For Locke, nature is virtually valueless until humans impart value to it by appropriating it through their labour, as the quotation below bears out:[7]

> Nor is it strange, as perhaps before consideration it may appear, that *the Property of labour* should be able to over-ballance the Community of Land. For 'tis *Labour* indeed that *puts the difference of value* on everything; and let any one consider, what the difference is between an Acre of Land planted with Tobacco, or Sugar, sown with Wheat or Barley; and an Acre of the same Land lying in common, without any Husbandry upon it, and he will find that the improvement of *labour makes* the far greater part of *the value*. I think it will be but a very modest Computation to say, that of the *Products* of the Earth useful to the Life of Man, 9/10 are the *effects of labour*: nay, if we will rightly estimate things as they come to our use, and cast up the several Expences about them, what in them is purely owing to *Nature*, and what to *Labour*, we shall find, that in most of them, 99/100 are wholly to be put on the account of *labour*. (Locke, 1988 *Second Treatise*, p. 296)

The ideology of idealism

So far we have shown that the ideology of Scientific Naturalism, whose metaphysics is materialistic, sees the control of nature as central to the Modern Project. However, one should also point out that materialism is not the only metaphysics in modern Western philosophy, though admittedly, a very powerful one as it is the dominant tradition. For there is another influential current at work, namely, idealism. Could it be that this rival metaphysics does (did) not subscribe to the ideology of control of nature, which is an integral part, therefore, only of Scientific Naturalism and materialism? The answer to this is 'no'. Take Fichte, a prominent exponent of the philosophy of idealism. Fichte expresses the idealist conception of the relationship between humankind and nature most forcefully and succinctly, as the following quotation bears out:

> Nature must gradually be resolved into a condition in which her regular action may be calculated and safely relied upon, and her power bear a fixed and definite relation to that which is destined to govern it, – that of man. In so far as this relation already exists, and the cultivation of Nature has obtained a firm footing, the works of man, by their mere existence, and by an influence altogether beyond the original intent of their authors, shall again react upon Nature, and become to her a new vivifying principle. Cultivation shall quicken and ameliorate the sluggish and baleful atmosphere of primeval forests, deserts and marshes; more regular and varied cultivation shall diffuse through the air new impulses to life and fertility; and the sun shall pour his most animating rays into an atmosphere breathed by healthy, industrious, and civilized nations. Science, first called into existence by the pressure of necessity, shall afterwards calmly and carefully investigate the unchangeable laws of Nature, review its powers at large, and learn to calculate their possible manifestations; and while closely following the footsteps of Nature in the living and actual world, form for itself in thought a new ideal one. Every discovery which Reason has extorted from Nature shall be maintained throughout the ages, and become the ground of new knowledge, for the common possession of our race. Thus shall Nature ever become more and more intelligible and transparent even in her most secret depths; human power, enlightened and armed by human invention, shall rule over her without difficulty, and the conquest, once made, be peacefully maintained. This dominion of man over Nature shall gradually be extended, until, at length, no farther expenditure of mechanical labour shall be necessary than what the human body requires for its development, cultivation and health. (Fichte, 1848, pp. 136–8.)

It is clear that, for Fichte, nature has no being, or value except for what we humans choose to create out of it, to endow it with, and to transform it into by means of our labour, our science and our technology.

Hegel, the intellectual giant of this tradition, has written: 'A person has as his substantive end the right of putting his will into any and every thing and thereby making it his, because it has no such end in itself and derives its destiny and soul from his will. This is the absolute right of appropriation which man has over all "things".'[8]

In other words, the concept of homo faber in defining 'species being' or human essence embodies two interrelated themes, which give in turn the key notion of the humanisation of nature. These are: (a) that humans realise themselves through fabrication, that is, through imposing their ends and values on nature via their labour and their tools/technology; (b) that nature, even biotic nature, itself is bereft of being or of value until humans work upon such a blank canvas to endow it with being and with value. This means that the two related concepts – homo faber and the humanisation of nature – constitute the most extreme form of anthropocentrism possible. They go beyond the more usual Humean/Cartesian theses, that human consciousness is the source of all values as well as the sole locus of intrinsic value, and that nature is only of instrumental value to humans. To these, another two are added – nature is not only morally but also ontologically latent or void, with the potential to be, and to be valuable, only when acted upon and transformed by human labour; humans themselves achieve their true being via the continuous creative procedure of fabricating artefacts out of the morally and ontologically latent non-human nature.

Thus understood, the law of progress will reach its ultimate, highest level when the whole of nature has become humanised. This, then, shows that the metaphysics of idealism is not at odds with the materialist metaphysics of Scientific Naturalism in underpinning the humanisation of nature project. We saw that modern science at its very beginning in the 17th century granted extremely limited ontological space to nature – as *res extensa*, nature exists, and is real, only as atoms and molecules, and in terms of so-called primary qualities. In this view, natural entities and kinds, in the forms of individual organisms and species, are not as real as the atoms and their arrangements to which natural entities and kinds may be reduced. The respective metaphysics of idealism and of Scientific Naturalism are, then, not that dissimilar after all in their implications for the Modern Project, except in a few respects.

Firstly, while idealism regards nature to be bereft of being and reality altogether in the absence of human fabrication, Scientific Naturalism grants nature a limited reality and being in the form of atoms and their molecules. But from the standpoint of the humanisation of nature project, this philosophical theoretical difference does not appear to be critical. Of course, as far as *praxis* is concerned, only science and technology undertaken within the metaphysical framework of Scientific Naturalism could make the humanisation of nature project actually come to pass.

Secondly, while the ideology of Scientific Naturalism celebrates the control of nature in order to promote the overarching goal of improving human material well-being, idealism celebrates such control in order to promote the non-material goals of advancing human freedom and self-realisation. Before physics, astronomy and other sciences provided humans with the relevant understanding to enable them to devise spaceships, humans could only dream of going to outer space through myths initially and science fiction latterly. But since space technology has been developed, humankind collectively, though not yet individually as a matter of routine, has enjoyed the freedom to travel beyond earth's gravitational field and to realise itself through this particular project. While materialism emphasises the open-ended quest to fill the belly and to stimulate the other senses in ever more diverse ways, as well as in overcoming disease through ever more sophisticated means, idealism emphasises the soaring of the human spirit in its open-ended quest for the new goals of self-realisation and expression. But together, they put humankind on the same road which marches inexorably towards progress.

It is fitting to end this section with two quotations from Bergson, who has captured so perfectly the spirit of modernity, which construes homo faber as constituting the essence of human nature. In the first, he says:

> If we could rid ourselves of all pride, if, to define our species, we kept strictly to what the historic and the prehistoric periods show us to be the constant characteristic of man and of intelligence, we should say perhaps not *Homo sapiens*, but *Homo faber*. In short, intelligence, considered in what seems to be its original feature, is the faculty of manufacturing artificial objects, especially tools to make tools, and of indefinitely varying the manufacture. (Bergson, 1911, p. 146)[9]

In other words, human intelligence is to be understood solely in terms of that type of intelligence embodied in instrumentation and manufacture of artefacts, and in the scientific reasoning which informs these activities. All other forms of intelligence displayed in activities such as joke-telling or storytelling are written off as marginal. It is the intelligence of instrumentation and manufacture, belonging to human consciousness alone, which ensures that 'man comes to occupy a privileged place'.[10]

In the second quotation Bergson writes:

> We have said that intelligence is modelled on matter and that it aims in the first place at fabrication. But does it fabricate in order to fabricate, or does it not pursue involuntarily, and even unconsciously, something entirely different? Fabricating consists in shaping matter, in making it supple and in bending it, in converting it into an instrument in order to become master of it. It is this mastery that profits humanity, much more even than the material result of the invention itself. Though we derive an immediate advantage from the thing made, as an intelligent animal might do, and though this advantage be all the inventor sought, it is a slight matter compared with the new ideas and new feelings that the invention may give rise to in every direction, as if the essential part of the effect were to raise us above ourselves and enlarge our horizon. Between the effect and the cause the disproportion is so great that it is difficult to regard the cause as producer of its effect. It releases it, whilst settling, indeed, its direction. Everything happens as though the grip of

intelligence on matter were, in its main intention, *to let something pass*, that matter is holding back. (Bergson, 1911, pp. 192–3)

It is significant that nature is only of instrumental value to humans. But for Bergson, it is even more significant that human consciousness and intelligence, as embodied in instrumentation and manufacture as well as the scientific reasoning which stands behind these, so effectively breaks down any recalcitrance and resistance of non-human nature against the penetration and imposition of human intentions upon it. In other words, the transformation of the natural into the artefactual truly affirms humanity's mastery of nature. Homo faber reigns supreme.

The humanisation of biotic nature: the supersession of natural evolution

We have seen in the last two chapters that the vista for manipulating biotic nature opened up by biotechnology is both tempting and immense. To supplement the remarks already made, only one further major point will be highlighted, namely, its potential to supersede natural evolution and its processes, a point already raised en passant in earlier chapters.

Living organisms, as naturally occurring beings, are evolved beings. According to Darwin, natural selection of genetic variations as shown by such beings is the fundamental mechanism at work in natural evolution. The insights of Mendelism have been incorporated into such a framework leading to what is referred to as Neo-Darwinism. The major technology – hybridisation – spawned by the gene-chromosome theory has been confined largely to manipulating domesticated plants and animals. The more recent insights of molecular genetics are also not seen to have any radical implications for the Darwinian theory of natural selection. However, the same may not be true of the biotechnology which molecular genetics and other related molecular biological sciences have induced. Biotechnology may be seen as posing a far more serious and radical challenge to natural evolution itself than the relatively less deep technology spawned by Mendelian genetics.

Humankind may now outdo natural evolution in at least several respects. In natural evolution, there is a distinction between those organisms that reproduce sexually and those that reproduce asexually. The offspring of an organism that reproduces asexually simply inherits the genetic material from its one parent; the simplest form is exemplified by the amoeba, which reproduces by splitting down the middle, a method called binary fission. The offspring of those organisms that reproduce sexually develops from two cells coming from two different individuals, half the genetic inheritance having come from each of the two parents. With genetic engineering, organisms that reproduce asexually can have genetic material spliced into their genes from individuals other than themselves. The same holds also for those that reproduce sexually. Animals, on the whole, reproduce sexually, while some plants reproduce asexually. This means that under genetic engineering a major difference between some plants and most animals can be obliterated.

In sexual reproduction, varieties in a species (other things being equal) may transfer genetic material, but there is relatively little transfer between species.[11] But routine transfer is now possible in principle between species. The inter-specific barrier is crossed in a very radical way – as we have already emphasised, not only may the genetic material of one animal (or plant) species be transferred to another animal (or plant) species, but the material of an animal (or plant) may be transferred to another plant (or animal). In other words, the plant/animal kingdom distinction may be broken down. This, of course, includes breaking down the barrier between the human and other species – a human gene could be introduced into an animal/plant and an animal gene could be introduced into the human individual.[12]

The temporal dimension may also be tampered with. Natural evolution is based on actual encounters between individual organisms, which must, therefore, necessarily coexist temporally and spatially for the purpose of genetic transfer and transmission.[13] While it remains fanciful to talk about the re-creation of extinct organisms and species, it is, now, in principle, possible to transfer DNA remains of extinct organisms to living ones, given that an ancient gene could be isolated and then introduced into an existing species such that these organisms could mimic an aspect of the extinct species.[14]

To appreciate the next possibility, one must be reminded that genetic engineering is only one aspect of biotechnology. Included in that armoury are, for instance, protoplast fusion and protoplast culture, developments stemming from molecular or cell biology. A recent dramatic breakthrough came with the announcement in February 1997 that scientists at the Roslin Institute and the pharmaceutical company PPL Therapeutics, both based in Edinburgh, had successfully cloned Dolly the sheep.[15] The interest it aroused instantaneously worldwide sprang from the fact that Dolly was cloned from the DNA originating in a cell from the udder of an adult sheep. The year before, the same institute had already successfully produced two identical lambs, called Megan and Morag, which originated from different cells of the same embryo.[16]

Up to now, in evolutionary terms, a significant difference has existed between those cells which retain the potential to produce all the cell types of the organism they belong to, and those which can at best produce only some of the cell types but not all. The first kind of cells is said to be toti-potent and the second, pluri-potent. Plant cells (belonging to multi-cellular plants) are toti-potent and can, therefore, in principle be turned into a whole new plant. But few animal cells are toti-potent once past the early embryo stage – the eight-cell stage of division – so that in most adult animals, even the most versatile variety of cells are at best only pluripotent. This means that they are capable of giving rise to only a few kinds of new cells – the cells in the bone marrow would yield the various red and white blood cells but could not yield liver cells. Most mammalian cells refuse to divide further after a certain age, like nerve cells, or in the case of liver cells they are capable of only producing further liver cells.

But the Dolly achievement seems to show that the distinction between toti-potent (plant) cells and non-toti-potent animal cells can be technologically overcome.[17] The developmental clock has been 'wound back', showing that the biological development of cells is not as irreversible as was held to be, up to 1997, in molecular biology – this constitutes the crux of the radical nature of the experiment. The team led by Ian Wilmut put the udder cell from the donor sheep in a salt solution with just enough nutrients in it to keep the cell alive but in a state of hibernation, so that it stopped dividing and replicating its own DNA. The donor DNA was fused with a nucleus-free egg from another sheep to form an embryo, which was then implanted in a surrogate sheep to carry the developing embryo to full term.

Looking beyond present achievements, in principle it is even possible to build 'unnatural' amino acids into a protein, thus transcending the 20 amino acids now found and used in all living organisms.[18] As Cherfas (1982) puts it:

> The 20 amino acids used in life are all very well, but sometimes changing a couple of amino acids in a protein will enhance the efficiency of, say, a hormone. At the moment this has to be done chemically, because living systems can use only the words in the genetic code, and that means the 20 vital amino acids. But it might in future be possible to rewrite the genetic code, create transfer RNAs that will carry unnatural amino acids, and slot them into the correct place on an engineered RNA message, transcribed from an engineered gene. The cell itself would then be building a totally novel protein with tools you have supplied, to instructions you have written. What sorts of things might be made this way I have no idea, but I'm sure the organic chemists have a few ideas they would like to try. (p. 234)

Or consider the possibility of designing virtually a new kingdom of organism which could be said to be as significantly different from naturally evolved organisms up to now as plants are from animals. Colin Tudge has suggested the creation of a chemosynthetic plant where the new organism has been given genes from chemosynthetic bacteria, the kind which can process hydrogen sulphide for generating energy, unlike naturally evolved plants, which can only process water and carbon dioxide out of the atmospheric components.[19] Tudge envisages this as an entirely 'altruistic gift to nature' from humankind, should ever the day come when the atmosphere would have dramatically changed such that neither human, animal nor conventional plant life could be sustained.

Biotechnology has therefore tempted many to consider putting right what they perceive to be severe limitations in nature itself. One such limitation which 'designer proteins' and transgenic organisms hope to overcome is that natural evolution can capitalise only on the appearance of chance mutations, which originate in copying errors during DNA replication. Furthermore, natural evolution necessarily is a slow process, favouring those individual organisms with mutations which bestow an advantage on their possessors. Like Tudge, these thinkers are eager to 'help' nature during anticipated periods of extreme atmospheric or ecological stress when the necessary random mutation may not be forthcoming.

Yet others, such as Easterbrook, go even further to talk about overcoming 'design flaws' in nature, replacing nature with 'New Nature'. For instance, the New Nature envisaged is one in which predation by animals against animals would have been eliminated. He says:

> is the destructive life-pattern of the predator a necessity of biology or a flaw of nature awaiting correction? . . . It is possible at least in theory that through genetic intervention, present-day predators could become herbivores, continuing to live as wild bears or wolves or weasel, except leaving out the gruesome part. Nature might long for such a reform. Surely nature's prey species, a vast 'silent majority' in biosphere demographics, would be pleased by an end of predation. (Easterbrook, 1996, p. 671)

Modern civilisation holds it to be axiomatically correct that pain is an absolute evil, and the removal (or diminution) of pain an absolute good.[20] Other things being equal, and assuming the means are available, we have moral duties to fellow human beings to relieve them of their pain. However, Easterbrook has gone beyond the common confines of this axiom within inter-human conduct by confusing pain in nature with pain in culture.[21] But one point needs immediate clarification: pain in nature may be either anthropogenically or non-anthropogenically caused.[22] In the former context, other things being equal, we have a moral duty to avoid causing unnecessary pain to other sentient beings such as certain animals. But in the latter context where the pain exists even in the absence of human intervention and intention, it is not obvious that we have a moral duty to prevent such pain from occurring even if we could.[23] But Easterbrook implies that we have such a duty. If we do, the price to be paid is the supersession of natural evolution by cultural evolution. Not only would we turn those living organisms which are naturally occurring beings into biotic artefacts, we would also, if successful, be overturning millions of years of evolutionary history, and in the process we would be undermining the very processes of natural evolution themselves. This amounts to redesigning the existing biosphere in which carnivores operate at the top of the food chains to an entirely herbivoric biosphere.[24] This amounts to humanising nature with a vengeance.

To sum up: natural evolution is in danger of being superseded by human control and manipulation of biotic nature. Instead of natural selection, it is now possible to have human selection of characteristics deemed to be desirable spliced into the genomes of different life forms.[25] Sophisticated as Mendelian genetics and the technology it induced may be, they, nevertheless, operate within the framework of the transmission of inherited characteristics through reproduction, whether sexual or asexual. But this framework is being rapidly transcended by molecular genetics and its induced technology. Biotechnology makes it possible (at least in principle) for homo faber to rearrange genetic material in ways which please it. Organisms need no longer inherit genetic material from their parents (under sexual reproduction); instead, their genetic material can even come from other unrelated species.[26] Their genetic composition can be humanly designed and engineered in the laboratory.

The naturalisation of humans: humans as biotic artefacts

One needs to distinguish two aspects regarding the naturalisation of humans. The first is about the pervasiveness of a humanised world within which the human agent acts, and the second the actual transformation of the human being, as organism, into a biotic artefact.[27] Although the former is not of direct relevance to the preoccupation in this section, however, a few comments may be in order.

In a world heavily transformed by human fabrication, human existence itself cannot escape being transformed by its own fabrication in all its diverse activities. In other words, the homo which plays or daydreams acts in a world that has been humanised by humankind's continuous process of creative fabrication through its labour and its tools/technology.

As the case is sometimes put, the cultural history of humankind is indeed the history of its technology and the different artefacts which different forms of technology bring forth. Bergson (1911) articulated it well:

> In thousands of years, when, seen from the distance, only the broad lines of the present age will still be visible, our wars and our revolutions will count for little, even supposing they are remembered at all; but the steam-engine, and the procession of inventions of every kind that accompanied it, will perhaps be spoken of as we speak of the bronze or of the chipped stone of prehistoric times: it will serve to define an age. (p. 146)

The thesis that the identity and essence of humanity are constituted by the activity of fabrication amounts to this: it is not the claim that humans only manufacture artefacts and never play, make love, eat, write novels outside of the activity of fabricating things. Rather, it is to say that even when people play, eat, make love, or write novels, they are doing these things in the context of a fabricated, artefactual world. On the back of homo faber rides *homo ludens*. Take writing. In the past, it was done with reed and papyrus, equipment with a low level of artefacticity. Today many (including this author) use the computer as a word-processing machine, which is *par excellence* a highly technologised artefact. Fabrication penetrates every activity people engage in, including the act of breathing, as what they breathe may increasingly be air-conditioned and purified. As technology develops more radically and powerfully, homo faber structures and creates a more and more artefactual world within which all human activities necessarily take place. Even the activity of walking in the mountains or in the wilderness is not exempt, although walkers may convince themselves that it is. It is true that they are using their feet, their own power of locomotion. But the boots on their feet, the socks which cover the feet, the waterproof they wear, the sleeping bag they crawl into at night, the rucksack on their back are probably made of synthetic substances of one kind or another. As walkers, workers, lovers or whatever, we are what we are capable of doing through our labour, our science and our technology. The procedure of fabrication and its products transform non-human nature, and in so doing, also transform ourselves. Whereas other civilisations at other times in human history have chosen some other route to self-realisation, be it political or theological and, as a result, have subordinated the activity of fabrication to these other ends, modern civilisation has committed humankind to self-realisation via fabrication itself. The price paid for being homo faber is, increasingly, in the terminology of Marx and others, the near-total, if not the total, humanisation of nature and the naturalisation of humanity itself.

The second theme about the naturalisation of humanity by transforming the human organism into a (potential) biotic artefact is embodied in the Human Genome Project (HGP).[28] Robert Sinsheimer, a leading molecular biologist and a key figure in the initiative to establish the project, wrote in 1969: 'For the first time, a living creature understands its origin and can undertake to design its future.'[29] Up to the last quarter of the 20th century, by and large, humankind has relied on cultural evolution as the means to bring about what are perceived to be desirable traits in people. Custom and practice, on the one hand, and religion and law, on the other, circumscribe institutions such as courtship, marriage, reproduction and property inheritance, which in turn determine the size and nature of the gene pool of any population and the genetic information transmitted to the next generation. Some of that genetic inheritance may turn out to be unwelcome – for instance, Tay-Sachs disease is a common disorder among some groups of

Ashkenazi Jews in North America who, through many generations of marrying within the groups, have increased the chances of their offspring inheriting the deleterious gene from both parents, who might each be a heterozygous Tay-Sachs carrier.

On the whole, up to now, we have refrained from using either the craft-based technology of plant and animal breeding or the technology of double-cross hybridisation directly to ensure that undesirable traits are bred out and desirable ones bred in, as far as humans are concerned.[30] Such technologies, including the latest biotechnology, have been confined largely to agriculture and husbandry. Their *raison d'être* is the improvement of (domesticated) plants and animals considered to have only instrumental value for humankind. Humans who are said to be uniquely intrinsically valuable have not thought it appropriate to use such technologies to improve themselves.

However, of late, new currents have appeared which are breaking down the barrier previously erected. The least controversial of the uses of biotechnology is as diagnostic and therapeutic tools in medicine. The overarching goal of modern science and technology, as we have seen in Chapter 2, is promoting human material/physical well-being, of which good health is clearly a part. Furthermore, the axiomatic goal in medicine itself is to save and prolong life, to remove pain and suffering when the means are available. Society, in general, and medicine, in particular, consider it unproblematic to use biotechnology to achieve such highly desirable and desired goals. Tay-Sachs disease, earlier mentioned, is a disorder of fat metabolism involving the degeneration of the nerve cells which leads to blindness, paralysis and death within the first year of life. This highly distressing disease is a single-gene disorder. Genetic counselling is used to prevent the occurrence of the disorder. Beyond identifying the carriers, increasingly, genetic counselling also implies detecting the homozygous state of the embryo (one which has inherited two alleles of the defective gene, one from each parent) *in utero*. The parents would then be given the choice of abortion. Such a programme has been effective in North America.[31]

The next step beyond identification of defective genes *in utero* is fertilisation in vitro. Eggs released through super-ovulation induced by hormone treatment would be fertilised with the donor's sperm in vitro. At the blastocyst (eight-cell) stage, cells from the fertilised eggs would be analysed. Only an embryo without the deleterious gene would then be implanted. The other healthy ones would be saved under deep-freeze for future implantations, should the need arise. This constitutes embryo selection at the simplest.

A step beyond genetic counselling and embryo selection is gene replacement (somato-) therapy, when it is confined to correcting the defects within the affected cells of the person carrying it. This technique works best for those tissues that are continuously renewed through the division of stem cells. By altering the stem cells, they would give rise to healthy cells.

Sickle-cell anaemia falls into this category. The red (as well as the white) blood cells come from stem cells in the bone marrow. If some of these are removed and genes that code for normal haemoglobin are inserted into them before putting them back, then the individual should be rid of the original affliction for quite some time, if not for life.[32]

In Chapter 2 we saw that, in theory, the next 'deep' step involves germ-line therapy, with the possibility of eradicating from the human gene pool defective genes giving rise to highly distressing conditions. Techniques are already available and regularly used to carry out germ-line manipulation of domesticated animals. However, this technological possibility for humankind has in principle been rejected so far by all the ethical committees which have addressed this issue.[33] It is true that what works in the case of mammals such as sheep and cows may not work in the case of humans. But this does not mean that already established techniques might not be modified and perfected to render the manipulation of human germ cells sufficiently precise to tempt humankind down this path. However, the ethical problems raised are not the real concern of this book. Suffice it here to remind readers that in principle humans themselves could be transformed to become biotic artefacts to the same degree of artefacticity as they have transformed other living organisms.[34]

The HGP is a necessary though not sufficient condition of more precise genetic manipulation at different levels. However, this project is anxious to distance itself from the socially and politically unacceptable implications of eugenics in the last century, such as Nazi eugenics (in Germany), racist eugenics (in the USA) and classist eugenics (in Britain and even in some Scandinavian countries). Scientists today could claim that these earlier eugenic programmes were based on too simplistic an understanding of the genetic basis of human behaviour anyway. This means that the science of genetics itself, as we know it today, is neither implicated nor discredited by the previous poor science.[35] Furthermore, as Evelyn Fox Keller (1992) has argued, the scientists who advocate the human genome project have transformed the old nature/nurture controversy itself.

The old eugenics aspired to transform society genetically while still relying on crude social engineering ultimately to deliver the utopian results. In its most extreme form, the Nazis had to kill off (in today's language, by 'engaging in ethnic cleansing') those considered unfit to contribute to the gene pool of their good society. The new eugenics made possible by biotechnology induced by molecular biology is presented differently; it is said to enlarge individual choice and to extend the range of possible human intervention.[36] Take the latter possibility. We know that physical stature is affected by nurture. For instance, the average height of European medieval males is much less than that of today's white males residing in the affluent economies, as evidenced by the size of the average medieval suit of armour in museums. Similarly, post-Second World War

Japanese children, age for age, are taller than their pre-war counterparts. Biotechnology raises the possibility of an alternative route, the genetic one, should it perfect the knowledge about the identification of genes and the precise ways in which these express themselves; the gene for height when identified could then, in principle, be altered or modified.[37]

Nature in the nature/nurture controversy has been understood until recently to refer to a variable regarded as beyond human control and manipulation, and therefore, to imply fate or destiny, while nurture is taken to imply freedom. However, biotechnology has challenged this; it gives rise to the view that humans could control nature directly or just as readily, if not more readily and simply than nurture. It promises eventually to deliver us 'designer' babies in terms both of physical and mental characteristics.[38] However, at least for the time being, going down this route overtly is ethically frowned upon, unless it is medically framed, as we saw earlier. It is morally acceptable to ensure that people do not suffer from distressing conditions caused by defective genes and, perhaps, to eradicate such genes eventually from the human gene pool, but it is not morally acceptable to manipulate genetic material to ensure that only 'perfect' babies are born embodying whatever society (or a section of it) deems to be desirable traits. The narrower medical remit renders the new eugenics morally palatable by presenting such a use of genetics as a 'guarantee to all human beings an individual and natural right, the right to health' (Keller, 1992, pp. 294–5). As Keller also points out, the Office of Technology Assessment (USA) in its 1988 report on the HGP endorsed the argument that 'individuals have a paramount right to be born with a normal, adequate hereditary endowment' (United States National Research Council, 1988, p. 86).

The project poses the basic question: 'in genetic terms, what makes us human?' or 'what actually specifies the human organism?' But in trying to answer this question, the project will also sequence the genomes of other simpler organisms; all this knowledge is expected to act as a powerful research tool to tackle a variety of other fundamental problems. Molecular biology holds the view that the organism is defined by its DNA, and that its DNA molecule can be sequenced to reveal information defining the type of organism it is, and hence the species. Molecular biologists have estimated that there are 100,000 to 300,000 genes which make up a human being. The lower estimate assumes about 30,000 base pairs per gene; but as some genes may only be 10,000 base pairs long, there could be as many as 300,000 genes, according to the highest estimate. This means that the human DNA sequence is composed of three billion base pairs.[39] But whatever the estimate of the number of genes, the number alone underestimates the complexity of the human organism, because many genes encode ten to twenty different functions in different tissues.[40]

The project of studying the human genome envisages three distinct phases. The first involves a process called physical mapping, taking the

DNA itself, which is two metres long, and breaking it into smaller but ordered fragments. The second consists of determining the sequence of all the base pairs of all the chromosomes. (These two have been more or less completed since June 2000.)[41] The final phase, estimated to take a hundred years of research, involves understanding all the genes, the interrelationships between them and their environments, their functions in coding for proteins as well as an understanding of the proteins themselves.

The results from the first two phases are expected soon to throw light on those genes that cause rare genetic disease. More importantly, genes for common diseases will also be identified with the help of a detailed genetic map and the human DNA sequence. Molecular biologists are expecting to find sets of genes for susceptibility to cancer, conditions that predispose people to heart ailments or high blood pressure, and more generally, genes which affect how the body grows or fails to function properly.

Although the medical frame for sanctioning biotechnological intervention with humans at the moment rules out other culturally affected desiderata, one cannot be too sure how long society would hold out against breaching the narrower frame laid down by medical genetic engineering. We have already seen that biotechnology is currently presented via the language of the individual right to freedom of choice and of self-realisation.[42] This framework has so far been able to accommodate biotechnological intervention which falls strictly speaking outside the more narrowly defined concept of physical good health. For instance, menopausal women, women who cannot produce eggs or who cannot carry developing embryos are already being helped to realise their deeply seated desire to have children.

But whatever moral reservations there may be about extending freedom or self-realisation in this context, such extension, from the technological point of view, appears to present no special problems.[43] In principle a woman who has had a hysterectomy could arrange for eggs earlier collected from her ovaries to be fertilised in vitro with a donor's sperm. The fertilised egg(s) could be implanted in her own mother's uterus acting as a surrogate womb, after her mother herself has been given hormonal treatment to offset the effects of her menopause.[44] Such a birth upsets most of the known biological and conventional procedures governing human reproduction, and therefore, all the categories humankind in its long evolutionary history has developed to characterise the relationship between parent and offspring. This sort of case raises certain intriguing issues. The aspect considered no longer intriguing since the acceptance of artificial insemination by donor is that the biological father (the sperm donor) is not necessarily the 'sociological' father (indeed, the infant may never come to have one). The intriguing aspect is that it is not obvious who counts as the infant's biological mother. Normally, the birth mother is the biological mother; in most cases of surrogacy, the birth mother is not genetically related to the biological mother. In this case, however, the birth mother though not the biological mother is the genetic grandmother, as the birth mother has contributed only a quarter of her own genetic endowment towards the genetic make-up of the infant, while the biological mother has contributed a half. In genetic terms, it is clear that the birth mother is the infant's grandparent, not its parent. The birth mother (having passed her natural reproductive age) has given birth to her own grandchild; the infant is in one sense her child, and in another sense, her grandchild.[45] The infant; clearly, is a biotic artefact with a degree of artefacticity which far exceeds that of in vitro conception via artificial insemination by donor, or when that technique is combined with surrogacy in cases where the surrogate is genetically unrelated to the biological mother.[46]

Reproduction and production

This concluding section will look briefly at the distinction between reproduction and production and its associated issues raised by the recent technological innovations in the context of human reproduction.

It has earlier been commented on that until the appearance of biotechnology, humankind has relied, in the main (and still does), on cultural means to regulate and determine human reproduction. Once the cultural selection is in place, the only technique relied on is copulation, helped in some instances by subsidiary techniques, which vary from culture to culture, like eating the right foods, or saying the right prayers in the hope that there would be success in conception and that the offspring turn out to have certain desired characteristics. Traditionally, fertility is regarded as a gift of some deity or nature.

In Chapter 1 we distinguished between techniques and technologies, and argued that although the use of techniques leads to creations such as songs and poems, it does not on its own lead to artefacts. The former falls into the domain of doing things; the latter into that of making things. Each domain requires deliberate and intentional creation, but only the making of things leads to the production of an artefact which is defined as the material embodiment of human intentionality.

Between humans, the technique of copulation may be used intentionally to bring about reproduction or more often, it may not.[47] But as is well known, the intention alone is not sufficient in ensuring that reproduction would take place. It is precisely in cases of persistent failure that the recently established biotechnological innovations have been put to use to rectify some of these failures. In so doing, these innovations appear to have transformed the processes of reproduction to become procedures of production.

Take cake-making as the paradigm of production, issuing in an artefact. The confectioner (the efficient cause) chooses the quantity and type of ingredients, the kind of oven and temperature (the material cause), guided by the kind of cake that he or she desires to make (the formal cause) for the purpose of celebrating a birthday or a wedding (the final cause). In contrast, human reproduction, under non-technological conditions, does not approximate or satisfy at least two of these conditions. The man and woman attempting to reproduce may at best be characterised as the efficient cause; they may even be said to have a final cause in mind, in the sense that they would like to cement their relationship by having a child.[48] But as they have no control over the sex or the genetic inheritance – the material cause – of any offspring they may eventually have, they cannot be said to be the formal cause either. The formal cause and the material cause appear to lie within the union of a particular sperm and a particular egg to form the embryo, which develops into the infant born nine months later.

But under biotechnological conditions, reproduction is superseded by production. The efficient cause includes the woman or man who desires a child, the donor of the sperm or egg, the team of doctors and technicians, and in some cases, another woman willing to act as surrogate birth mother.[49] The person who desires to have a child is able, in principle, to choose its sex and some, if not all, of its genetic inheritance – the material cause. The choice in turn is guided by the kind of offspring deemed to be desirable – the formal cause. The final cause is the desire for a child, using whatever technological means are available that society has sanctioned.

Chapter 1 argued that when Maturana and Varela, as theoretical biologists, regard organisms as 'autopoietic machines', they have confused the ontological status of organisms as naturally occurring beings with that of machines as artefactual entities. 'Autopoiesis' may be loosely translated 'as self bringing forth'; when used to characterise organisms, it refers to their capabilities for self-maintenance, self-renewal and self-generation. Self-generation in the case of asexually reproducing, single-celled organisms – such as amoebas – takes the simple form of dividing into two exactly identical cells. In multi-cell, sexually reproducing organisms, self-generation involves the exchange of genetic material between the male and female sex cells, leading to the formation of a zygote. But 'autopoiesis' means precisely what it says, namely, that the various processes which the organisms undertake, including those involved in reproduction, are self-determining and self-controlling, without the intervention of external agencies. They embody intrinsic/immanent teleology.

In contrast, machines, as normally defined, are artefacts *par excellence* embodying extrinsic/imposed teleology. They have come into existence, continue to exist and function in certain ways only because humans have designed, made and maintained them to serve certain specific human ends. Organisms as evolved beings, on the other hand, have come into existence, continue to exist and reproduce themselves independently of human purpose and intervention. That is why when Maturana and Varela put forward the view that organisms are 'autopoietic machines', one is tempted to accuse them of having failed to appreciate that organisms and machines belong to two very different ontological categories. One could see why they invoke their new terminology, as it is meant to reflect their determination to open the way for the technological manipulation and control of organisms so that organisms will no longer be naturally occurring, autopoietic beings but will be transformed to become artefactual ones.

In Chapter 1 the argument was advanced that both biotic and abiotic entities may be said to exist 'by themselves' in the sense that they follow their respective trajectories independently of human interests and intervention. It further points out that only biotic entities may be said to exist 'for themselves' in the sense that they, unlike abiotic ones, can be seen to strive to maintain their own functioning integrity and to realise their own respective *tele*. As naturally occurring beings, organisms in existing 'by themselves' also at the same time exist 'for themselves'. However, it is left to the unique genius of humankind to prise these two aspects of existence apart, and in doing so, to undermine them both, for they, like Aristotle's four causes in naturally occurring entities, can only be separated in thought but not in reality.[50] Technology today has succeeded to do just that – Maturana's and Varela's autopoietic machines reflect precisely this already spectacular degree of success, and aspiration of even greater success to come. In principle, as we have seen, humans need no longer reproduce themselves but simply arrange for their offspring to be produced by taking advantage of the technological possibility that any organism, whether non-human or human, may no longer exist 'for itself' as understood till now. This is for the precise reason that the mechanisms and processes involved in existing 'for itself', including those intimately connected with reproduction, have been captured and hijacked by technology itself to serve certain ends which have been collectively sanctioned by society. As a result, the human organism as the developing embryo embodies an extrinsic/imposed teleology, not an intrinsic/imminent teleology, which the embryo would have done if it were a naturally occurring being. At the same time, because of this hijack, the developing embryo has also lost its status as a being which exists 'by itself'. It has come into existence through the deliberate intervention of others, and its trajectory enfolds largely, though not necessarily in a strict deterministic way, according to the ground plan of such intervention.

The production, unlike the reproduction, of human offspring literally involves the making of babies, just as the production of cakes involves the making of cakes.[51] Such babies, like cakes, are true artefacts except that one is biotic and human, whereas the other is abiotic. The supersession (in principle) of reproduction by production even in the context of human reproduction is the true measure of the ontological transformation humankind has effected, and of the extent to which it has not only humanised nature but in the process, using the same technologies, has also naturalised humanity itself.

Notes

1 See also Keekok Lee (1996a).
2 For a discussion of the concepts of sufficiency and abundance, see Nicolas Xenos (1989).
3 However, Martha Nussbaum (1986, pp. 373–7) points out that while the Platonic Aristotle maintained this view, the Aristotelian Aristotle, so to speak, was not so single-minded in elevating the purely contemplative life as the supreme good.
4 However, one must not forget that ancient Greek civilisation was based on slavery.
5 The Latin term itself – *homo faber* – appears to have been introduced by Henri Bergson in his *L'Évolution Créatrice* (1907; translated as *Creative Evolution*, 1911). According to Jean Leclercq (1950, p. 3) it was Bergson who 'threw the concept of *homo faber* into the circulation of ideas' (Arendt, 1958, p. 341).

   However, Arendt herself takes a different view about homo faber from the account given here. She sees its central significance to lie in Man's attempt to create a permanent world for himself out of fabrication, but at the expense of doing violence to nature. However, permanence is only secured if fabrication results in objects which, strictly speaking, have neither use nor exchange value. Hence, for Arendt, the paradigmatic product of fabrication is art, not craft – paintings, sculptures, literary works, which undoubtedly have been commodified under capitalism but which, in principle, may have no monetary value. Homo faber is engaged with doing, rather than contemplating, *vita activa* having displaced *vita contemplativa*. But this reversal of the classical hierarchy by homo faber is only one stage in the history of modernity. The next stage, according to Arendt, consists of the very defeat of homo faber himself by the principle of happiness, and through that, the final victory of the *animal laborans* in modernity.
6 On this point, Locke greatly influenced Marx. However, while Locke may be said to have used the labour theory of value to lay the philosophical foundation of modern (bourgeois) economics, in Marx's thinking that same theory led to his damning critique of that very subject. (See Keekok Lee, 1989b, pp. 161–72, 198–203; 1996a).
7 The labour theory of value, in Locke's hands, therefore, plays a dual role. It functions as a principle of distributive justice in his political philosophy – one is entitled to, and rightfully owns, what one has mixed one's labour with. But it also serves to justify the modern world-view in its insistence that nature only has instrumental value for humankind, leaving the way open for science and technology to appropriate and manipulate nature to promote solely human goals, particularly that of improving material well-being.
8 Hegel (1942, edited by Knox, p. 41).
9 However, to be fair to Bergson, when he talked about the ever-expanding realm of manufacturing, he was, nevertheless, of the opinion that fabrication must be confined to abiotic and exbiotic nature only. In this, he was not far-seeing enough; the biotic has now firmly been drawn into the domain of manufacturing.
10 The intelligence of instrumentation and fabrication as the essence of modernity is once again reflected in a recent publication by Steven Weinberg (1994). It con-

tains a chart captioned 'The emergence of intelligence'. Of the eighteen land-marks highlighted, from 1.9 million years BP to 1993, twelve are distinctly tools, instruments, machines of one kind or other. Of the remaining six, four are inventions as techniques leading to the production of material artefacts, namely, rock engraving, writing (first on papyrus, then on paper) money (the first coins) and the earliest farming which could refer to the practices of agriculture and domestication of plants and animals, as well as to tools and implements to assist such practices. The remaining two refer to fundamental theoretical break-throughs in scientific thought, namely, the theory of relativity in 1905 and the structure of DNA in 1953. These may have been included, perhaps, because they obviously lead to radical technological innovations, such as the communications satellite in the case of the former (one of the landmarks mentioned) and biotechnology in the case of the latter (however, biotechnology itself does not figure in the list of highlights).

This little chart implies that human intelligence is a history of progress, by and large, in tool making, from the first simple stone tools of 1.9 million years BP to the extremely complex and sophisticated communications satellite of 1993. Furthermore, it betrays a predilection for modern devices – nine out of the twelve tools and machines highlighted come from the period 1440–1993. This seems to imply that while human intelligence was tardy and intermittent pre-1440, it suddenly assumed great leaps forward in the last five hundred years of human history. One may conclude from this attempt at deconstruction that the chart is a clear reflection of the spirit of modernity.

In Western thought, the earliest hint of the idea that instrumentation is a measure of human intelligence may be traced to Anaxagoras, as reported by Aristotle. Anaxagoras is said to be of the view 'that it is his possession of hands that makes man the wisest of living things' (Kirk and Raven, 1977, p. 393).

11 Hybrids that do form tend to be sterile; they fail to form new species in the absence of reproductive success.

12 The latter possibility may be unacceptable for ethical, social or political reasons but that is another matter. However, the former has certainly been carried out, of late, in the creation of transgenic and 'knockout' mammals, in particular, mice, beginning with the oncomouse patented by Harvard University, in which human cancer genes have been inserted into the mice – see also Culliton (1993, p. 755). Furthermore, of late, even whole human chromosomes have been successfully spliced into the mouse genome.

13 Some plants are aided by the wind or by animals to carry their seeds further afield for fertilisation.

14 See Pääbo (1993).

15 The results were originally published in *Nature* (27 February 1997, pp. 810–13). But see also *New Scientist* (1 March 1997, pp. 4–5).

16 As early as the 1970s, scientists at the University of Cambridge had already transplanted nuclei from the skin cells of adult frogs into frog eggs whose own nuclei had been removed. Some of these embryos developed into tadpoles, though none became frogs. But the ABC Biotechnology Company based in Cambridge more recently produced identical quads from four-cell sheep embryos, and even more impressively, quintuplets from five of the eight cells of an eight-cell sheep embryo – see Coghlan and Concar (1997).

17 Initially, two caveats were entered about the Dolly experiment: (a) the experiment was not immediately successfully repeated in other laboratories worldwide;

(b) as a result, an unresolved matter remained, namely, whether the transferred nucleus was from a differentiated mammary gland cell or a stem cell of the adult donor sheep. See HGAC (1998), *Cloning Issues in Reproduction, Science and Medicine* (a consultation document issued in January 1998 by the Human Genetics Advisory Commission and Human Fertilisation & Embryology Authority, UK). However, in the light of further forensic DNA-testing, since July 1998, the scientific community became convinced that Dolly is a real clone; furthermore, another successful cloning of mice has also been reported. See Solter (1998).

But later research – reported in September 1999 – appears to have shown that Dolly might not after all be the perfect genetic clone she was thought to be. This is because of the role played by the few genes contained in an organism's mito-chondria, the powerhouses of cells. In the fusion of the nucleus of the donor udder cell, which contains nearly all the DNA, with the egg of the second sheep from which its own nucleus had been removed, though not its mitochondria, it remained unclear whether Dolly's mitochrondria came from the udder cell or the denucleated egg. Eric Shon of Columbia University and Ian Wilmut of the Roslin Institute have now established that the 37 genes in Dolly's mitochondria differ from those of the donor cell; in other words, they come from the mitochrondria of the denucleated egg instead. As mitochondria play a significant role in cells, Dolly and others like her created by nuclear transfer technology may differ in significant ways physically from their donors. This finding in turn may have two practical implications: (a) it might hold out hope for embryos which have faulty mitochondrial genes, as the DNA nucleus of such an affected embryo could be removed and then fused with a new (denucleated) egg with healthy mitochondria; (b) it might, however, limit the application of the technology to create human tissue for transplants, by fusing human cells with cow eggs to form an embryonic clone, from which stem cells may be har-vested. But if cow mitochondria are passed on to the embryo, then this would be problematic. (Critics who argue that today's biotechnology is based on poor science have already pointed out in advance of this experiment that Dolly is not a proper – 100 per cent – clone, precisely because, among other reasons, of the contribution of the genes from the mitochondria of the denucleated egg – see, for example, Ho, 1998, pp. 177–9.)

18 Of course, scientists still do not know as much as they would like about how pro-teins fold; neither can they predict precisely how a protein of any particular shape will behave, although work on these fronts is going on apace. But now that the first draft of the Human Genome Project has been completed (in June 2000), scientists are turning their attention to proteomics, the new 'Human Proteome Project' to which IBM is committing nearly 100 million dollars. This project will build the world's fastest computer and presumably enable biologists to find their next 'holy grail'. It will try to discover how cells in the human body build up each amino acid (of which proteins are made) atom by atom, using the genetic information pro-vided by DNA and RNA; it will also tackle the problem of protein folding itself – see *The Economist (Technology Quarterly)* (9 December 2000, pp. 31–9).

19 See Tudge (1993, p. 320).

20 However, even within culture, this axiom has attracted dissent – a life without pain is not necessarily a good life; neither is a life with an appreciable amount of pain necessarily a non-worthwhile one. In other words, the absence of pain is neither a necessary nor a sufficient condition for what constitutes a worthwhile human life.

21 An instance to illustrate a related confusion recently appeared in the British press. It concerned a three-year-old English bull terrier, called Lucy, which chased and killed a cat, called Fluffy, belonging to a neighbour of her owner. Lucy was 'arrested' by the police and detained, facing a possible death sentence under the Dangerous Dogs Act, on a charge of having been 'dangerous and out of control'. Lucy's arrest as well as her potential death sentence set a precedent – up to then, the Dangerous Dogs Act had been interpreted as applying only to dogs behaving aggressively to humans. (See Pilkington, 21 August 1995.) But as the story eventually turned out, Lucy was released after five days of detention, following the ruling that the police had been holding the animal unlawfully – see Wright (24 August 1995).

A dog is a domesticated animal, and so, a biotic artefact to a great extent. Bull terriers, as a breed, have been specially selected for their hunting ability. As they are, by and large, humanly created and designed, it would stand to reason that their creators and owners should be held liable for their vicious characteristics, and not the dogs themselves. The police seemed to be hopelessly muddled and confused. First, they failed to appreciate that according to modern thinking it makes no conceptual sense to hold animals, even domesticated ones, to be responsible for their behaviour. Second, that while there is a justification for putting down dogs which kill humans, one would be hard put to find any justification for putting down dogs which kill other animals. Third, if a justification were to be found, then by the same logic, cats which kill birds would also have to be put down. This kind of moral policing among animals smacks of misplaced zeal, the main source of which may be traced to the transposition of culture onto nature both domesticated and wild. However, in the case of the bull terrier, though a biotic artefact, nevertheless, it still has a residual *telos* of its own, that is to say, given its biological origin, being descended from wolves, and being the kind of biotic artefact that it has become, it is 'in its nature' to kill anything that runs away from it. More generally speaking, dogs and cats have been known since the dawn of their domestication to fight, and occasionally to kill each other.

For another example of confused thinking about the killing of animals by animals, see the editorial of *The Guardian* (1 February 2001, p. 21), which exhorted animal rights activists to stop harassing research institutions for their animal experimentation, and to turn their attention to stopping cats from 'murdering' (*sic*) fellow animals such as mice, rats, voles, shrews and birds.

22 One example (reported in *Natural History*, January 1984) should suffice to illustrate this confusion – cited by Stone (1988, pp. 155–6); Rolston (1994, pp. 110–11). A bison bull in February 1983 fell through the ice in Yellowstone River and could not get himself out. The park authorities decided not to intervene on the grounds that this was a natural occurrence. A group of snow-mobilers that came upon the scene was outraged by such a decision. About half of the party returned later, with a rope, to try to extricate the animal. However, they did not succeed, and when the night drew in, they abandoned their rescue. By the morning, the animal had frozen to death. (Coyotes and ravens soon lighted upon the carcass. In the following spring, after the snow melted, a grizzly bear was observed further downstream feeding on its remains.) One of the rescuers wrote to a radio commentator who said, in denouncing the Park Service's cruelty: 'The reason Jesus came to earth was to keep nature from taking its course.' A curious interpretation of the divine mission perhaps, but the comment neatly encapsulates the confusion between nature and culture. If the

snow-mobilers and the radio commentator had paused to substitute, perhaps, a water rat for the bison, they might not have been so righteously outraged, and might not have so readily convinced themselves that it is the bounden duty of humans (in accordance with 'Jesus' will) 'to keep nature from taking its course'.

For a discussion about the philosophical implications of the distinction between anthropogenic and non-anthropogenic, see Keekok Lee (1999, chapter 5).

23   Pain in nature is morally neither good nor bad. Pain serves the biological function of informing the organism that its physiological well-being is under stress, and to take action to avoid the stressful situation or to attenuate the activity which has caused the pain. For instance, an animal would instinctively withdraw its paw from a very hot surface upon experiencing the pain from the burn; without the information coming from the pain, the limb could be irreparably damaged. This mechanism holds true for humans as well.

24   Presumably, Easterbrook would consistently have to alter genetically insect-eating plants. Or would he only be interested in modifying animals which are sentient? But this in turn raises another interesting issue: he has a choice, to alter the prey or the predator. It may be just as possible in theory to turn a carnivore into a herbivore as it is to render a herbivore insensitive to the pain afflicted by the carnivore – a gene could be inserted into the herbivore genome, capable of rendering it insensitive to pain. One might argue that such manipulation would have even more radical implications for natural evolution than to stop predators from being predators altogether. Such genetically modified herbivores would not be well equipped for survival; should many die off before successful reproduction, their species could eventually become extinct, bringing with them in turn the extinction of the carnivores which prey on them. This would cause even greater disruption of evolutionary history and evolutionary processes than the other alternative of transforming predators into non-predators – the latter manipulation would produce a new 'herbivoric' biosphere, the former a solely photosynthetic one. But from the human/cultural standpoint, why is the herbivoric-cum-photosynthetic world necessarily preferable to the photosynthetic one? For Easterbrook, the answer can only be given in anthropocentric terms – we humans prefer the former world, perhaps for entirely aesthetic reasons.

25   An attempt is now afoot to create a new species of genetically engineered mosquitoes in the wild with the aim of wiping out malaria, by transforming the malaria-carrying mosquito – 60 out of the 380 mosquito species can transmit malaria, although one of them, the *Anopheles gambiae*, is in fact the principal carrier of death to 2.7 million people each year – into a different species of non-carrier. Malaria is transmitted by female mosquitoes with the parasite plasmodium which lives in the insect's saliva; when the mosquito drinks the blood of the human it has bitten, the parasite enters and infects the blood of the victim. Scientists have succeeded in manufacturing a synthetic gene which makes it impossible for the mosquito to be a host to the parasite. (An international conference in September 2001 at Imperial College, London, was held to discuss the possibility of releasing the transgenic mosquitoes in the wild, so that after numerous generations, the original malaria-carrying species would be replaced by the non-lethal blood-sucking genetically modified species.) They have come up with two strategies to do so. The first is to insert the synethetic gene into a bacterium called *Wolbachia*, which is then made to infect mosquitoes, such that the genetically modified bacterium becomes a part of the insects, thereby rendering them into transgenic organisms themselves. The effect of the gene is such that when the transgenic female mosquitoes mate with

males, they produce transgenic offspring, whether the males are transgenic or not; but when transgenic males mate with non-transgenic females, the females are sterile. In this way, transgenic females will always have more offspring, eventually driving out their non-transgenic competitors. The second is to attach the synthetic gene to a piece of DNA, a transposable element, which can jump across chromosomes during reproduction. In normal sexual reproduction, an offspring stands a fifty–fifty chance of inheriting either parental allele of any one gene. However, aided by the genetically modified transposable element, the transgenic mosquito will always pass on the synthetic gene to more than 50 per cent of its offspring; sooner or later it would spread through the entire population.

Wolbachia strategy		*Transposable element strategy*	
Female + Male	= Normal Offspring	Female + Male	= Normal Offspring
Female + TrMale	= Sterility	TrFemale + TrMale	= TrOffspring
TrFemale + TrMale	= TrOffspring	Female + TrMale	= +50%TrOffspring
TrFemale + Male	= TrOffspring		

(See James Meek, 3 September, 2001.)

26 Just one example of what Matt Ridley (1999) has called the 'triumph of the digital hypothesis' which underpins molecular genetics. This is the technique known as genetic rescue: 'so close are the similarities between genes that geneticists can now do, almost routinely, an experiment so incredible that it boggles the minds. . . . They can knock out a gene in a fly by deliberately mutating it, replace it by genetic engineering with the equivalent gene from a human being and grow a normal fly' (p. 180).

27 For an account of the disagreement among experts about the end of human evolution, see P. Cohen (2001). See also Johnjoe McFadden (2001).

28 For a technical, but nevertheless, accessible account behind the project, see Thomas Lee (1991). See also Ridley (1999).

29 One could say that implicit in the discovery of the structure of DNA are the HGP and the study of other genomes. Up to then, biologists working within the framework of Mendelian genetics could only infer the presence and the interactions of genes from the phenotypical characteristics of the organisms brought to light by breeding experiments. But since 1953, they could conceive (at least in principle) of analysing the growth and functioning of organisms by identifying base sequences and figuring out what these determine in the living organism.

30 Instead, societies at different times have resorted to such measures as killing female or deformed babies outright, or through neglect so that they die soon after birth. Furthermore, proposals, like Plato's, to ensure that philosopher-kings only mate with philosopher-queens have been condemned as utopian, totalitarian social engineering.

For the numerous ethical and social issues, both short- and long-term, posed by the application of genetic engineering techniques to humans, see, for instance, Kitcher (1996). For an account of what a society might look like which cares to practise the new eugenics, see Silver (1998).

31 This case is not tangled with other socially thorny problems, which could smack of either racism or 'ethnic cleansing'. For example, in the USA, people who are carriers of the sickle-cell trait and sufferers of sickle-cell anaemia are predominantly Americans of African descent. In the 1970s the US Department of Defense had a policy of excluding such carriers from the Air Force Academy,

even if they did not manifest the disease. This would appear to amount to racial discrimination. Neither does Tay-Sachs disease present any biological complexities like those associated with other single-gene disorders such as the thalassaemias. Beta-thalassaemia which affects the peoples of the Mediterranean also provides some protection against malaria – in other words, the gene has deleterious as well as good effects.

The National Institutes of Health in the USA has of late recommended another single-cell disorder for genetic counselling. One in 30 white Americans is said to carry the recessive allele for cystic fibrosis. This means a 1 in 900 chance of an average couple carrying the defective gene, and a 1 in 4 chance that any offspring will have cystic fibrosis. See Kleiner (26 April 1997).

32 For technical details, see Suzuki and Knudtson (1990, pp. 168–78). See also Kitcher (1996, especially chapter 2). Problems of a serious technical kind have not all been solved. For instance, scientists still do not know really enough about gene expression, which may involve the role played by long stretches found within genes (the introns) that are sometimes dismissed as 'junk' DNA, as we have seen. By inserting only exons (those containing the non-junk DNA), these may not be expressed at all.

One must also bear in mind that the success of this kind of therapy is confined in the main to single-gene disorders. However, not all distressing disorders are thus caused.

33 Johnjoe McFadden (2001) points out that modern medical treatment, by enabling people with genetic disabilities to survive to the age of reproduction, has undermined natural selection. To counterbalance this transmission of defective genes, society will soon have no choice but to endorse germ-line therapy.

34 Xeno-transplantation has been accepted primarily to overcome the shortfall between the demand and the supply of suitable organs from human donors for transplantation. But there is dissent; one type of criticism focuses on the possibility of the transplanted animal organs infecting human cells. For instance, pigs have been genetically manipulated with human DNA to produce organs to make them more suitable for human transplantation. But these pigs also carry at least two retroviruses incorporated in their DNA, one of which has the potential to infect human cells. It is not easy to remove them from the pig's DNA to prevent them from crossing the species barrier – see Brown (1997); Day (1997). However, the fear of cross-species infection has led some scientists to advocate abandoning the project.

The recent radical breakthrough in the Dolly sheep-cloning research tempts scientists to see if the same techniques could be applied in the case of humans, and if they do not, to modify or alter them to overcome the problems confronted. Again, as in germ-line therapy, the direct ethical issues thrown up by human cloning are not the concern of this discussion; however, such cloning both from early embryonic cells or adult mature cells has been rejected on ethical grounds so far. In some countries, such as the UK, it is illegal to clone humans; in the USA, federal funds cannot be used for human cloning, but there is nothing to prevent a privately funded body carrying out such a venture – see Borger (2000). But it is predicted that as technological breakthroughs appear thick and fast in this decade or so, the resistance on the part of scientists, governments and the public to human cloning or germ-line engineering would eventually break down – see Taylor (1998), and Silver (1998), who argues that no compelling moral constraints exist against human cloning.

35 See Kevles (1995).
36 Also referred to as laissez-faire eugenics – see Kitcher (1996, pp. 99 and 196–200). However, although there may be a legitimate distinction to be made between the (morally and politically) discredited old-style state eugenics and the (morally and politically fragrant) new-style laissez-faire eugenics, it may be worthwhile entering three caveats:

1. Firstly, regarding the latter. Its advocates, while disavowing genetic determinism of a crude kind, must nevertheless be committed to some form of genetic primacy, if not determinism; otherwise, it is difficult to accommodate the claim they make about the good effects which are said to ensue from genetic choice and biogenetic intervention. For instance, if such selection and intervention were not a more efficient means of preventing the occurrence of certain deleterious conditions in human beings, then why bother to advocate it quite so strenuously? It is true that even those with two mutant copies of a certain gene, might still not, for instance, suffer from PKU, provided genetic diagnosis is made as soon as the child is born and the appropriate diet is applied. In other words, environmental manipulation alone is sufficient in this kind of case to prevent the gene manifesting itself phenotypically. This then seems to provide evidence for the view that genes do not absolutely determine the course of events. While this may be true, it remains the case that it is less efficient as a method of removing the manifestation of disease conditions than the removal of the mutant gene entirely from those embryos which carry either one or both mutant alleles. The total absence of the mutant allele in the human population would guarantee the absence of the disease condition itself. The presence of the mutant alleles is a necessary, though not a sufficient, condition for the presence of the disease condition, but the total elimination of the mutant allele is jointly necessary and sufficient for the absolute absence of the disease condition. To bring about the latter appears to be a far more efficient way of eradicating the disease condition than tolerating the former. When the embryo possesses two mutant alleles, and there is failure of early diagnosis followed by implementation of an inappropriate diet, the disease condition would manifest itself, as such a combination of circumstances constitutes its jointly necessary and sufficient conditions. So ultimately, it may be argued that genes seem to enjoy a primacy over certain environmental variables.

2. State-sponsored eugenics in the past (up to the 1970s, for instance, in the state of Vermont – see Gallager, 1999) might have relied on either bad or inadequate science/technology. However, now that molecular biology and biotechnology are in place, there is no reason to believe that state-sponsored eugenics in the future would rely on outmoded science and outmoded technology. It is simply facilely asserted or assumed that the world today appears to be safe from such state political activity, given the current ascendancy of freedom and democracy, of the market and of individual consumer choice – see Kevles (1995, p. xii) and Silver (1998, pp. 158–62 and 216–17).

3. The end results of state-sponsored and laissez-faire eugenics, using the same science and the same technologies now available, may be similar – both could issue, under certain conditions, in a society whose genetic fault-line coincides with its class fault-line. That is to say, society would be divided into those who have been genetically enhanced or who are gene-rich (to use

Silver's terminology) and those who are not gene-rich; the former would enjoy higher income, prestige and status, while the latter would be the excluded class or the underclass. If this situation were to persist over a certain length of time, it could even be the case that the two classes would undergo speciation – the genetically enhanced would no longer want, and eventually be unable, to reproduce with the non-genetically enhanced. Silver admits this possibility under laissez-faire eugenics. But if so, then the only difference between state-sponsored and laissez-faire eugenics is that while the former issues a command (backed up by sanctions) to ensure that no reproduction takes place between the two classes, the latter issues no explicit dictat, but simply permits individual citizens (with the financial means and desire) genetically to enrich themselves and/or their offspring. The failure to reproduce between the two classes, initially, would be a socially induced lack of sexual attraction. This failure of sexual attraction and reproduction combined with further genetic enhancement on the part of the privileged would ultimately render the two classes no longer physically capable of successful reproduction (to produce offspring which would survive and whose offspring could successfully reproduce themselves).

(For the view that eugenic goals played an important role in the design of the molecular biology programme as conceived in the USA from the 1930s, see Kay, 1993.)
37 Robert Sinsheimer wrote in 1969:

It is a new horizon in the history of man. Some may smile and may feel that this is but a new version of the old dream, of the perfection of man. It is that, but it is something more. The old dreams of the cultural perfecting of man were always sharply constrained by his inherent, inherited imperfections and limitations . . . To foster his better traits and to curb his worse by cultural means alone has always been, while clearly not impossible, in many instances most difficult . . . We now glimpse another route – the chance to ease the internal strains and heal the internal flaws directly, to carry on and consciously perfect far beyond our present vision this remarkable product of two billion years of evolution.

38 Today, genetic clinics in some countries enable parents to choose the sex of their offspring. In north India, parents often choose to abort female foetuses (identified as such via amniocentesis) for cultural/social reasons. But ethics committees attached to hospitals and clinics in the mature industrial economies do not tolerate such a practice.
39 However, rather surprisingly, the latest research shows that the human genome has just slightly double the number of genes as the fruit fly. The HGP's consortia claim (*Nature*, 15 February 2001) to have found between 30,000 and 40,000 genes, while the Celera Genomics scientists (*Science*, 16 February 2001) have estimated between 26,000 and 38,000; the original prediction was 70,000 to 140,000 – see McKie (2001).
40 For scientists and science writers who argue against simplistic genetic determinism, see Jones (1994) and Ridley (1999).
41 Remember though that the June 2000 announcement is only the first draught, said to contain 90 per cent of the genome. There are still lots of gaps to be filled.

42 In Chapter 2 we saw how germ-line therapy is now practised under certain conditions, such as the Nash case in the USA, as reported in the media in October 2000, as well as the operation which University College Hospital, London, intended to carry out a few days after the Nash announcement. These humanitarian cases are feared to have opened the floodgates to designing babies with specific genetic traits. (See Borger and Meek, 2000; Meek, 4 October 2000) Indeed, the day after the American couple had publicised their case, the press in the UK reported a British couple who intended to take their case to the highest court for permission to have another daughter. They did have a daughter but she had died in an accident; they desperately wanted another in order to restore 'the female dimension' to their existing family of four sons. This case has nothing to do with the prevention of disease – see Scott, 5 October 2000; Meek, 5 October 2000.

43 A case which seems to cause moral unease involves a couple in California whose granddaughter died (in 1996) from leukaemia. However, before she received chemotherapy, she had ensured that some of her eggs were fertilised in vitro with an anonymous donor's sperm. Before her death she had made her relatives promise to find a surrogate mother for the fertilised eggs. Although the relatives secured legal custody of the zygotes, they had difficulty in getting surrogate agencies in America to agree to undertake implantation. But they continued to find ways round this obstacle. (See Craig and Bourne, 1996.) *New Scientist* in an editorial (6 December 1997, p. 3) reported that the grandparents had found a 23-year-old woman to be the surrogate mother.

44 The earliest reported case is a South African one in which a 48-year-old woman (Pat Anthony) in 1987 acted as gestational surrogate for her daughter, Karen (who has had a hysterectomy), and gave birth to two boys and a girl. Under ovarian stimulation Karen produced eleven eggs which were fertilised in vitro with her husband's sperm, resulting in four embryos two days later. These were introduced into Pat Anthony's uterus, with three successful implantations, much to the surprise of the doctors, given the woman's age. Immediately after the birth, Karen was able to breast-feed the babies as she had already received hormones to stimulate milk production. (See Silver, 1998, p. 143.) In Britain, in December 1996, a 51-year-old woman (called Edith Jones), whose menopause had occurred five years earlier, gave birth to a girl by Caesarian section on behalf of her daughter, who was born without a uterus. Her daughter was given injections to stimulate her ovaries; the eggs collected were fertilised in vitro with sperm from her daughter's husband. Two zygotes were then implanted in Mrs Jones's uterus. The pioneers of these techniques, Professors Ian Craft and Robert Winston, each had reservations about the particular case. The philosopher Baroness Warnock, who chaired the Committee of Inquiry into Human Fertility in the UK, approved; the ethics committee of the hospital involved in the case had given permission. (Laurance, 1996.)

45 A recently published case involves a post-menopausal woman who lied about her age to receive fertility treatment. She was 63 years old when she gave birth to a baby girl by Caesarian section in 1996 in Los Angeles. According to doctors, this made her the oldest person known to have given birth. The doctors used her husband's sperm to fertilise eggs from an anonymous donor in vitro before transplanting the zygotes into her uterus. (See A. D. Smith, 1997, p. 2.) Before this case, a British woman aged 59 had given birth to twins after receiving treatment by an Italian doctor, Severino Antinori. Another patient of the same doctor became pregnant at the age of 64, but her pregnancy was not successful.

Some cases have also come to light of male sterility in Britain, but even more so in Japan, where the solution involves the impregnation of the woman with sperm donated by the father of the sterile male partner. The offspring in such cases is (genetically) the half-brother of the male partner who, however, is the sociological father, while his own father is the biological father of the child. (See Burke and Harris, 2000.)

46   However, up to now, humankind has not yet sanctioned exploring the possibility of implanting a human embryo into a suitably treated surrogate uterus of perhaps a related species. In the case of rare animals belonging to endangered species, zoos have implanted their fertilised embryos in the uterus of more commonly available ones. Elands have successfully carried bongos, and elands are not even particularly closely related to bongos as a species.

However, Amrad, an Australian biotech company, took out a Europe-wide patent in January 1999 which has since been sold to Chemicon International, a US company, on a procedure which permits 'chimeric' embryos to be formed from humans, mice, sheep, pigs, cattle, goats or fish. Ironically, even as late as October 2000, the European Patent Office had claimed it would never grant a patent on mixed-species embryos on the grounds that it would be against 'public order and morality'. However, in November 2000, Greenpeace's German Office had uncovered just such a patent procedure. Greenpeace has now called on the European Patent Office to withdraw the patent. (See Barnett, 2000.)

47   To prevent conception, technological means such as contraceptive pills or the intrauterine device are, of course, available. Sterilisation, however, does not count as a technological device, but a technique. Sterilisation is analogous to breaking someone's leg except that the former today is done with a high-tech tool under high-tech conditions in a medical context, whereas the latter (in the eyes of the law) is frowned upon, whether accomplished with a kick or a rod of steel.

48   In the days before the easy availability of mass contraceptive measures, reproduction was often, if not invariably, the unintended outcome of sexual intercourse.

49   Lesbian and gay couples have also resorted to such technological means of production to achieve parenthood. In 1996 two gay men in Edinburgh announced to friends the birth of their daughter. One of them, an American citizen, had used his sperm to fertilise eggs donated by a paid surrogate, a fellow American, who carried the pregnancy successfully. (See Mega, 1996.)

50   This, undeniably, is an impressive achievement, whatever one's reservations from a philosophical – whether ethical or ontological – point of view. For details of an assessment from the ontological perspective, see Keekok Lee (1999).

51   Under normal conditions of reproduction (or procreation), the expression 'making babies' is not meant to be understood literally.

Conclusion

The exploration in this book of the notion of biotic artefact has been conducted in terms of the intimate interplay between the contributions of philosophy, science and its technology. To chart the emergence and development of the notion, it has drawn upon various disciplines and sub-disciplines such as philosophy and its history, the history of science and technology by way of case studies, the philosophy of technology, the philosophy of biology and environmental philosophy.

If the arguments deployed in this exploration are sound, then they have established several theses crucial to the understanding of modern civilisation itself. Central to the identity of modernity is the notion of homo faber, aided and abetted by science and its induced technologies. At its very inception in the 17th century, modern science programmatically declared its goal to be the control and manipulation of nature for the advancement of human material well-being (and, later, under Idealist influence, of human freedom and self-realisation). This goal is philosophically embedded in the metaphysics of Scientific Naturalism which permits nature to exist only within the ontological space granted to it as *res extensa* in terms of its primary qualities. This severe ontological reduction of nature to inert, homogeneous matter (as atoms and molecules and their varied arrangements) paves the way ultimately for a universal mode of fabrication and production. The first wave of success was based on the theoretical breakthroughs of chemistry and physics in the 19th century. But the second wave, in the 20th and 21st centuries, has been based on the breakthroughs of biology, in particular, of genetics. Today, at the very beginning of the 21st century, the triumph of molecular genetics and molecular biology together with their induced technology, biotechnology, has made absolutely clear that modern science's research programme can finally fulfil its pledge to transform whatever is natural (at least at the level of so-called natural kinds, such as *canis lupus*) to become the artefactual – biotic nature is not, after all, exempt from this systematic humanisation of nature in all its manifestations.

This book has argued that naturally occurring organisms exist 'by themselves'. By this is meant that they are beings which have come into existence, continue to exist and go out of existence entirely independent of human design and manipulation; this entails the denial that they have come into existence to serve any human purpose. At the same time, unlike abiotic entities which only exist 'by themselves', naturally occurring biotic beings in existing 'by themselves' also exist 'for themselves'. By this is meant that they are beings which strive to maintain, to renew and to reproduce themselves. But biotechnology has spectacularly shown that biotic beings can be stripped of their ontological status as beings which exist 'by themselves' to become biotic artefacts, their capability to exist as beings 'for themselves' having in the process been hijacked by homo faber to serve human ends, not to unfold their own *tele*. The preparation and the ground for this ontological shift in theoretical biology itself may be detected in the works of Maturana and Varela, who define organisms as 'autopoietic machines'. This definition nicely catches the point just made, namely, that the ontological status of naturally occurring organisms has been distorted in their conceptualisation as machines, which paradigmatically are artefacts. Admittedly, unlike more standard machines, these 'machines' conveniently are capable of keeping themselves going, under their own steam, without any external input apart from the nutrition they require. Such beings, that is to say, 'autopoietic machines', are ripe for homo faber to appropriate, making them serve not their own but human ends. In other words, in the terminology of this book, intrinsic/immanent teleology has been displaced by extrinsic/imposed teleology.

Admittedly, the procedures which began this shift of ontological status have been a long drawn out affair. The beginning went back to the dawn of domestication and agriculture using craft-based technology. However, impressive though the achievements of traditional breeding methods undoubtedly were, their control and manipulation of biotic nature could be said to be (relatively) imprecise, and their success little understood. A proper theoretical understanding of the transmission of inherited characteristics only came with the so-called rediscovery of Mendelian genetics (at the beginning of the 20th century), whose technology of hybridisation enabled homo faber to create biotic artefacts with a far greater degree of artefacticity than traditionally bred ones. Roughly half a century later, molecular genetics, an even 'deeper' science than Mendelian genetics, has induced an even more powerful technology, enabling homo faber, for the first time in the history of the human manipulation of biotic nature, to bypass the transmission of inherited characteristics itself, thereby creating biotic artefacts with an even greater degree of artefacticity than Mendelian ones. There is, therefore, nothing unintelligible about the notion of patenting biotic artefacts; on the contrary, as the material embodiment of human intentionality, biotic artefacts are no different from abiotic artefacts.[1] The oncomouse belongs to the same ontological category as Michaelangelo's *David*. One should not be distracted by the fact that the oncomouse appears to be a being which exists 'for itself'; instead, one should focus on the crucial fact that it and the statue are not beings which exist 'by themselves'. The mouse by becoming the oncomouse has lost its status as a being which exists 'by itself', thereby also losing its status as a being which exists 'for itself'.

As we have also seen, biotechnology, for the first time in human history, makes it not only possible, but also thinkable in numerous contexts, for homo faber to turn *Homo sapiens* itself into biotic artefacts; thus, in humanising biotic nature, humanity has naturalised itself. Cultural evolution (which, by and large, governs human development) is opposed to natural evolution (which governs the development of non-human life forms). For humans, societal norms of one kind or another determine the time and manner of sexual intercourse and procreation as well as the partners for sex and procreation. But today human reproduction is superseded by production, that is, the fabrication of the child, which is its end product.[2] The techniques employed are no different in principle from those used in producing the prize cow or sow.

The evolution of life on earth is supported by two pillars: the transmission of inherited characteristics through reproduction of organisms, and the determination of what characteristics would be transmitted and inherited through natural selection. However, natural evolution would be superseded were the twin pillars themselves rendered superfluous. Human selection (in principle) from now could determine the characteristics to be spliced into the genome of different life forms. The pig, as a biotic artefact, can possess human or mouse characteristics. Furthermore, should we humans perceive any 'flaw' in nature, we could (and should?) remedy it. For instance, *Homo sapiens* may increasingly perceive the prey–predator relationship to be deeply 'flawed' as an affront to its moral or aesthetic sensibility; homo faber could one day (perhaps sooner rather than later) turn carnivores into herbivores. To do so would be entirely in keeping with the spirit of homo faber, the fundamental ontological category of modernity.

As closing remarks, it is worth while to remind the reader yet again that the remit of this book is necessarily a very limited one. It has four mutually related aims. First, it is to lay bare the philosophical framework within which modern biology and its accompanying technologies (especially in genetics and cell biology) have made it possible for homo faber to transform naturally occurring biotic beings into biotic artefacts. Second, it is to set out, in brief outline, how that transformation occurs via the case studies of Mendelian genetics and hybridisation technology, on the one hand, and DNA genetics and biotechnology, on the other. Third, it is to demonstrate how biotechnology has effected a quantum leap in the depth of artefacticity through its fabrication of transgenic organisms. Finally and most importantly, it is to highlight the shift of ontological status involved in the transformation of the naturally occurring organism into a biotic artefact. The transgenic organism is the paradigmatic embodiment of human intentionality; as such it is ontologically appropriate to regard it as a human invention and, therefore, eminently patentable. As this book focuses mainly on the ontological dimension to our technological transformation of the biotic world, it is beyond its remit to examine critically the much wider issue, whether the ontological change itself involves any loss or gain of value or, indeed, the kinds of value that may be lost or gained.[3]

Notes

1   However, recall that according to the perspective argued for in this book, DNA sequences themselves, either as partial or complete gene sequences, are not artefacts and, therefore, are not patentable.
2   By talking about supersession in this context, it is not intended to deny that reproduction worldwide still takes place in the same manner as it has done since the beginning of *Homo sapiens*. It is intended to mean no more than that it is technologically possible (and even increasingly becoming acceptable, socially, politically and ethically) to bypass physical constraints such as those imposed by age and its attendant conditions, such as the menopause, or the mere lack of a uterus.
3   For a detailed critical examination of these and related points, see Keekok Lee (1999).

References and Select Bibliography

Allen, Garland E. *Life Science in the Twentieth Century* (Cambridge: Cambridge University Press, 1979).

—. 'The Transformation of a Science: T. H. Morgan and the Emergence of a New American Biology', in *The Organization of Knowledge in Modern America, 1860–1920*, ed. Alexandra Oleson and John Voss (Baltimore and London: Johns Hopkins University Press, 1980).

American Breeders Association. *Proceedings of the First and Second Annual Meetings of the American Breeders Association, 1903 and 1904* (Washington, DC: American Breeders Association, 1905).

Aquinas, Thomas. *Summa Contra Gentiles*, trans. Vernon J. Bourke (Notre Dame: Notre Dame University, 1975).

Arendt, Hannah. *The Human Condition* (New York: DoubleDay Anchor, 1958).

Aristotle. *Physics* in *The Basic Works of Aristotle*, ed. Richard McKeon (New York: Random House, 1941a).

—. *Politics* in *The Basic Works of Aristotle*, ed. Richard McKeon (New York: Random House, 1941b).

Armbruster, Paul, and Fritz Peter Hessberger. 'Making New Elements', *Scientific American* (September 1998) 50–5.

Arnold, David. *The Problem of Nature: Environment, Culture and European Expansion* (Oxford: Blackwell, 1996).

Ashoori, R. C. 'Single-Electron Capacitance Spectroscopy of a New Electron Box', *Physica B*, 189 (1993) 117–24.

Ashoori, R. C., H. L. Stormer, J. S. Weiner, L. N. Pfeiffer, S. J. Pearton, K. W. Baldwin, and K. W. West. 'Single-Electron Capacitance Spectroscopy of Discrete Quantum Levels', *Physical Review Letters*, 68 (18 May 1992) 3088–91.

Ashoori, R. C., H. L. Stormer, J. S. Weiner, L. N. Pfeiffer, K. W. Baldwin and K. W. West. 'Energy Levels of an Artificial Atom Probed with Single-Electron Capacitance Spectroscopy', *Surface Science*, 305 (1994) 558–65.

Astbury, W. T. 'Adventures in Molecular Biology', *Harvey Lectures*, Series 46 (1950).

Atkins, F. W. *The Second Law* (New York: Scientific American, 1984).

Attenborough, David. 'The Big Freeze', programme in the BBC TV series *Life in the Freezer* (London: BBC, 1993).

Attfield, Robin. 'Genetic Engineering: Can Unnatural Kinds be Wronged?', in *Animal Genetic Engineering: Of Pigs, Oncomice and Men*, ed. Peter Wheale and Ruth McNally (London: Pluto, 1995).

Baggot, Breffni. 'Patenting Transgenics in the European Union', *Nature Biotechnology*, 16 (1998) 299–300.

Barnes, Jonathan. 'Life and Work', in *The Cambridge Companion to Aristotle*, ed. Jonathan Barnes (Cambridge: Cambridge University Press, 1995a).

—. 'Metaphysics', in *The Cambridge Companion to Aristotle*, ed. Jonathan Barnes (Cambridge: Cambridge University Press, 1995b).

Barnett, Anthony. 'Patent Allows Creation of Man–Animal Hybrid', *The Observer*, (26 November 2000) 2.

Bateson, Patrick, and Paul Martin. *Design for a Life* (London: Jonathan Cape, 2000).

Bateson, William. 'Practical Aspects of the New Discoveries in Heredity', in *Proceedings of the International Conference on Plant Breeding and Hybridization, Memoirs of the Horticultural Society of New York*, 1 (New York: Horticultural Society of New York, 1902).

—. Review of *The Mechanism of Mendelian Heredity* by T. H. Morgan, A. H. Sturtevant, H. J. Muller and C. B. Bridges, *Science*, 44 (1916) 536–43.

Becker, Gay. *The Elusive Embryo*. (San Francisco: University of California Press, 2001).

Ben-Ami, Leora, Patricia A. Carson and Kent M. Rogers. 'Biotech Patent Law Developments', 573, *Practising Law Institute*/Pat 555 (1999) [cite as: 573 PLI/PAT 555].

Bendall, Kate. 'Genes, the Genome and Disease', *New Scientist: Inside Science* (17 February 2001) 1–4.

Bent, Stephen A., Richard L. Schwaab, David G. Conlin, and Donald D. Jeffrey. *Intellectual Property Rights in Biotechnology Worldwide* (New York: Stockton, 1991).

Berardi, Gigi M., and C. C. Geisler (editors). *The Social Consequences and Challenges of New Agricultural Technologies* (Boulder: Westview, 1984).

Bergson, Henri. *Creative Evolution*, trans. Arthur Mitchell (London: Macmillan, 1911).

Bird, Elisabeth Ann R. 'The Social Construction of Nature: Theoretical Approaches to the History of Environmental Problems', *Environmental Review*, 11 (1987) 255–64.

Bishop, Jerry E. and Michael Waldholz. *Genome: The Story of the Most Astonishing Scientific Adventure of Our Time, The Attempt to Map All the Genes in the Human Body* (New York and London: Simon and Schuster, 1991).

Borger, Julian. 'Alarm as Cult Announces Plan to Clone Humans', *The Guardian*, (11 October 2000) 16.

Borger, Julian, and James Meek, 'Test-tube Child Designed in US as Cell Transplant Donor: Parents Create Baby to Save Sister,' *The Guardian* (4 October 2000) 1.

Borgmann, Albert. 'The Nature of Reality and the Reality of Nature', in *Reinventing Nature? Responses to Postmodern Deconstruction*, ed. Michael E. Soulé and Gary Lease (Washington, DC,. and California: Island, 1995).

Bowler, Peter J. *The Mendelian Revolution: The Emergence of Hereditarian Concepts in Modern Science and Society* (London: Athlone, 1989).

Brennan, Andrew. 'The Moral Standing of Natural Objects', *Environmental Ethics*, 6 (1984) 35–56.

Bright, Chris. *Life Out of Bounds* (New York: W. W. Norton/Worldwatch, 1998).

Brockway, Lucille. H. *Science and Colonial Expansion: The Role of the British Royal Botanic Gardens* (New York: Academic, 1979).

Brown, Phyllida. 'Pig Transplants "Should be Banned", *New Scientist* (1 March 1997) 6.

Browne, Anthony, and Robin Mckie. 'How Far Will the Genetic Manipulation of Embryos Go?' *The Observer* (8 October 2000) 20.

Bud, Robert. *The Uses of Life: A History of Biotechnology* (Cambridge: Cambridge University Press, 1993).

Bunge, Mario. 'Philosophical Inputs and Outputs of Technology', in *The History and Philosophy of Technology*, ed. George Bugliarello and Dean B. Doner (Urbana: University of Illinois Press, 1979).

—. 'Toward a Philosophy of Technology', in *Philosophy and Technology: Readings in the Philosophical Problems of Technology*, ed. Carl Mitcham and Robert Mackey (New York and London: Free, 1983).

Burke, Jason, and Paul Harris. 'Infertile Men Turn to Fathers for Sperm', *The Observer* (19 November 2000) 1.

Burke, Jason and Robin McKie. 'GM Goats Will Yield Super "Spider-Fibre"', *The Observer* (27 August 2000) 8.

Busch, Lawrence, William B. Lacy, Jeffrey Burkhardt and Laura Lacy. *Plants, Power, and Profit: Social, Economic, and Ethical Consequences of the New Biotechnologies* (Oxford: Basil Blackwell, 1991).

Callicott, J. Baird. 'The Role of Technology in the Evolving Concept of Nature', in *Ethics and Environmental Policy: Theory meets Practice*, ed. Frederick Ferré and Peter Hartel (Athens, GA: University of Georgia Press, 1994).

Capra, Fritjof. *The Turning Point* (New York: Simon and Schuster, 1982).

Caspar, Max. *Kepler*, ed. and trans. C. Doris Hellman (London and New York: Aberlard-Schuman, 1959).

Cavalieri, L. F. *The Double-Edged Helix* (New York: Columbia University Press, 1981).

Chang, Shing, and Cohen, Stanley N. '*In Vivo* Site-specific Genetic Recombination Promoted by the Eco RI Restriction Endonuclease', *Proceedings of the National Academy of Science*, 74 (November 1977) 4811–15.

Cherfas, Jeremy. *Man Made Life: A Genetic Engineering Primer* (Oxford: Basil Blackwell, 1982).

Clark, Andrew. 'Gene Discovery Boosts Shares', *The Guardian* (6 October 2000) 26.

Clark, Andrew, and James Meek. 'Drug Firms Laying Claim to Our Genes', *The Guardian* (18 February 2000) 31.

Coghlan, Andy. 'One Small Step for a Sheep', *New Scientist* (1 March 1997a) 4.

—. 'Clotted Milk', *New Scientist* (27 September 1997) 10 [first reported in *Nature Biotechnology*, 15, 1997, 971].

—. 'Sensitive Flower', *New Scientist* (26 September 1998) 24–8.

—. 'It's a Wonderful Weed', *New Scientist* (16 December 2000) 14–15.

—. 'Against the Grain', *New Scientist* (3 February 2001) 6.

Coghlan, Andy, and David Concar. 'How the Clock of Life was Turned Back', *New Scientist* (1 March 1997) 5.

Coghlan, Andy, and Emma Young. 'Too Close for Comfort', *New Scientist* (20 January 2001) 6.

Cohen, Philip. 'Dolly's Mixture: Clones Are Not the Perfect Replicas We Thought', *New Scientist*, (4 September 1999) 5.

—. 'Dinner With Destiny: Will Culture and Technology End Human Evolution or Accelerate It to a Furious Pace? *New Scientist*, (13 January 2001) 25–9.

Cohen, S. N. 'The Manipulation of Genes', in *Recombinant DNA*, ed. David Freifelder (San Francisco: W. H. Freeman, 1978).

Collingwood, R. G. *The Idea of Nature* (Oxford: Clarendon, 1945).

Collins, Francis S., and Karin G. Jegalian. 'Deciphering the Code of Life', *Scientific American* (December 1999) 50–5.

Comstock, Gary L. *Vexing Nature: On the Ethical Case Against Agricultural Biotechnology* (Boston/Dordrecht/London: Kluwer Academic, 2000).

Comte, Auguste. *Cours de Philosophie Positive*, 6 vols. (Paris, 1830–1842).

—. *The Essential Comte*, ed. S. Andreski, trans. M. Clarke (London: Croom Helm, 1974).

Cossons, Neil, Andrew Nahum and Peter Turvey. *Making the Modern World: Milestones of Science and Technology* (London: John Murray in association with the Science Museum, 1992).

Craig, Olga, and Brendan Bourne. 'Baby Love', *Sunday Times* (29 December 1996) 10.

Crick, Francis. H. C. *Of Molecules and Men* (Seattle and London: University of Washington Press, 1966).

Culliton, Barbara J. 'A Home for the Mighty Mouse', *Nature*, 364 (1993) 755.

Dasgupta, Subrata. *Technology and Creativity* (New York and Oxford: Oxford University Press, 1996).

Dastgheib-Vinarov, Sara. 'A Higher Nonobviousness Standard for Gene Patents: Protecting Biomedical Research from the Big Chill', 4 *Marquette Intellectual Property Law Review,* 143 (2000) [cite as: 4 Marq. Intell. Prop. L. Rev. 143].

Davies, Hunter. *George Stephenson* (Middlesex: Hamlyn, 1980).

Dawkins, Richard. *The Selfish Gene* (Oxford: Oxford University Press, 1976).

——. *The Extended Phenotype* (San Francisco: Freeman, 1982).

Day, Michael. 'Tainted Transplants', *New Scientist,* (18 October 1997) 4.

Derwent GENESEQ, http://www.derwent.co.uk/geneseq [database]

Descartes, René. 'Discourse on the Method', in *The Philosophical Writings of Descartes,* trans. John Cottingham, Robert Stoothoff and Dugald Murdoch, vol. 1 (Cambridge: Cambridge University Press, 1992).

Diamond, Jared, M. *Guns, Germs and Steel* (London: Vintage, 1998).

Dijksterhuis, E. J. *The Mechanization of the World Picture,* trans. C. Dikshoorn (Oxford: Clarendon, 1961).

Doeleman, J. A. 'Environment and Technology: Speculating on the Long Run', in *Technology and the Environment,* Research in Philosophy and Technology, vol. 12, ed. Frederick Ferré (Connecticut and London: JAI, 1992).

Donnelly, Strachan, Charles R. McCarthy and Rivers Singleton Jr. 'The Brave New World of Animal Biotechnology', *Hastings Center Report,* 24 (February–January 1994) S1–S31.

Drake, Stillman. *Discoveries and Opinions of Galileo* (New York: Doubleday Anchor, 1957).

——. *Galileo* (Oxford: Oxford University Press, 1980).

Drake, Stillman, and C. D. O'Malley (translators). *The Controversy on the Comets of 1618* (Philadelphia: University of Pennsylvania Press, 1960).

Draper, Elaine Alma. 'Social Issues of Genome Innovation and Intellectual Property', *Risk: Health, Safety and Environment,* 201 (Summer 1996) [cite as: 7 Risk: Health, Safety & Env't 201].

Drexler, Eric K. *Engines of Creation: The Coming Era of Nanotechnology* (New York: Doubleday; Oxford: Oxford University Press, 1992 [originally published New York: Doubleday, 1986]).

Drexler, K. Eric, Chris Petersen and Gayle Pergamit. *Unbounding the Future* (London: Simon & Schuster, 1992).

D'Silva, Joyce. 'A Critical View of the Genetic Engineering of Farm Animals', in *Animal Genetic Engineering: Of Pigs, Oncomice and Men,* ed. Peter Wheale and Ruth McNally (London: Pluto, 1995).

Durant, John. 'Genetically Engineered Mice', in *Making of the Modern World: Milestones of Science and Technology,* ed. Neil Cossons, Andrew Nahum and Peter Turvey (London: John Murray in association with the Science Museum, 1992).

East, E. M., and D. F. Jones. *Inbreeding and Outbreeding: Their Genetic and Sociological Significance* (Philadelphia, PA: J. B. Lippincott, 1919).

Easterbrook, Gregg. *A Moment on the Earth: The Coming Age of Environmental Optimism* (London: Penguin, 1996).

Eckersley, Robyn. *Environmentalism and Political Theory: Toward an Ecocentric Approach* (London: University College Press, 1992).

The Economist: Technology Quarterly (9 December 2000) 31–9.

Elliot, Robert. *Faking Nature* (London: Routledge, 1997).

Emmott, Steve. 'No Patents on Life: The Incredible Ten-year Campaign against the European Patent Directive', in *Redesigning Life?,* ed. Brian Tokar (London and New York: Zed, 2001).

espacenet, http://ep.espacenet.com/ [European Patent Office database]
European Community Directive 98/44/EC of the European Parliament and of the Council of 6 July 1998 on the Legal Protection of Biotechnological Inventions.
European Union, *Official Journal,* C-378 (5 December 1998) 13.
Feenberg, Andrew. *Critical Theory of Technology* (Oxford and New York: Oxford University Press, 1991).
—. *Questioning Technology* (London and New York: Routledge, 1999).
Ferkiss, Victor. *Nature, Technology and Society: Cultural Roots of the Current Environmental Crisis* (New York and London: New York University Press, 1993).
Ferré, Frederick. *Philosophy of Technology* (Englewood Cliffs, NJ: Prentice Hall, 1988).
— (editor). *Technology and the Environment,* Research in Philosophy and Technology, vol. 12 (Connecticut and London: JAI, 1992).
Ferré, Frederick, and Peter Hartel (editors). *Ethics and Environmental Policy: Theory Meets Practice* (Athens, GA: University of Georgia Press, 1994).
Fichte, Johann Gottlieb. *The Vocation of Man,* trans. William Smith (London: John Chapman, 1848).
Fox, Barry, and Andy Coghlan. 'Patently Ridiculous', *New Scientist* (9 December 2000) 4.
Fox, Michael. 'Transgenic Animals: Ethical and Animal Welfare Concerns', in *The Bio-Revolution: Cornucopia or Pandora's Box?,* ed. Peter Wheale and Ruth McNally (London: Pluto, 1990).
Fox, Warwick. *Toward a Transpersonal Ecology: Developing New Foundations for Environmentalism* (Boston: Shambhala, 1990).
Fruton, J. S. *Molecules and Life* (New York: Wiley-Interscience, 1972).
Galileo, Galilei. *Discoveries and Opinions of Galileo,* trans. with an introduction and notes by Stillman Drake (New York: Doubleday Anchor, 1957).
—. 'The Assayer', in *The Controversy on the Comets of 1618,* ed. Stillman Drake and C. D. O'Malley (Philadelphia: University of Philadelphia Press, 1960).
Gallagher, Nancy L. *Breeding Better Vermonters: The Eugenics Project in the Green Mountain State* (Vermont: University Press of New England, 1999).
Gare, Arran E. *Postmodernism and the Environmental Crisis* (London and New York: Routledge, 1995).
Golden, Frederic, and Michael D. Lemonick (reported by Dick Thompson). Washington. 'Mapping the Genome', *Time Magazine* (3 July 2000).
Gosling, William. 'We Do It: Just Don't Ask How', *The Guardian,* Science Section (30 November 2000) 3.
Gotthelf, Allan. 'Aristotle's Conception of Final Causality', in *Philosophical Issues in Aristotle's Biology,* ed. Allan Gotthelf and James G. Lennox (Cambridge and New York: Cambridge University Press, 1987).
Gotthelf, Allan, and James G. Lennox (editors). *Philosophical Issues in Aristotle's Biology* (Cambridge and New York: Cambridge University Press, 1987).
Grant, Edward. *The Foundations of Modern Science* (Cambridge and New York: Cambridge University Press, 1997).
Greising, David. 'Gene Researcher Mapped Own Way to Vital Discovery', *Chicago Tribune* (28 June 2000).
Griliches, Z. 'Research Costs and Social Returns: Hybrid Corn and Related Innovations', *Journal of Political Economy,* 66 (1958) 419–31.
Grove, Richard H. *Green Imperialism* (Cambridge: Cambridge University Press, 1995).
The Guardian. Patenting Life (15 November 2000).

—. Editorial (1 February 2001) 21.

Halfpenny, Peter. *Positivism and Sociology: Explaining Social Life* (London: Allen and Unwin, 1982).

Hall, Nina. 'Heavy Metal Mystery', *Observer,* Life Section (12 February 1995) 67.

Hankinson, R. J. 'Philosophy of Science', in *The Cambridge Companion to Aristotle,* ed. Jonathan Barnes (Cambridge: Cambridge University Press, 1995a).

—. 'Science', in *The Cambridge Companion to Aristotle,* ed. Jonathan Barnes (Cambridge: Cambridge University Press, 1995b).

Harlan, Jack R. *Crops and Man* (Madison, WI: American Society of Agronomy, 1975).

Hegel, G. W. F. *The Philosophy of Right,* ed. T. Knox (London: Oxford University Press, 1942).

Heidegger, Martin. 'The Question Concerning Technology', in *The Question Concerning Technology and Other Essays,* trans. William Lovitt (New York: Harper & Row, 1982).

Hettinger, Ned. 'Patenting Life: Biotechnology, Intellectual Property, and Environmental Ethics', *Environmental Affairs,* 22 (1995) 267–305.

HGAC. *Cloning Issues in Reproduction, Science and Medicine* (London: Human Genetics Advisory Commission and Human Fertilisation & Embryology Authority, January 1998).

Hilpinen, Rosto. 'Belief Systems as Artifacts', *Monist,* 28 (1995) 136–55.

Ho, Mae-Wan. *Genetic Engineering: Dream or Nightmare? The Brave New World of Bad Science and Big Business* (Bath: Gateway, 1998).

Hobbes, Thomas. *Leviathan,* ed. Michael Oakshott (New York: Collier, 1962).

Holdrege, Craig. *A Question of Genes: Understanding Life in Context* (Hudson, NY: Lindisfarne/Floris, 1996).

Hood, Leroy. 'Biology and Medicine in the Twenty-First Century', in *The Code of Codes: Scientific and Social Issues in the Human Genome Project,* ed. Daniel J. Kevles and Leroy Hood (Cambridge, MA: Harvard University Press, 1992).

Hubbard, R. and E. Wald. *Exploding the Gene Myth* (Boston: Beacon, 1993).

Ihde, Don. *Instrumental Realism: The Interface between Philosophy of Science and Philosophy of Technology* (Bloomington: Indiana University Press, 1991).

—. *Philosophy of Technology: An Introduction* (New York: Paragon House, 1993).

Iltis, H. H. 'From Teosinte to Maize: The Catastrophic Sexual Transmutation', *Science,* 222 (25 November 1983) 886–94.

Jantsch, Erich. *The Self-Organizing Universe: Scientific and Human Implications of the Emerging Paradigm of Evolution* (Oxford: Pergamon, 1980).

Jonas, Hans. *The Phenomenon of Life: Toward a Philosophical Biology* (New York: Harper & Row, 1966).

Jones, Steve. *The Language of the Genes* (London: Flamingo/HarperCollins, 1994).

Judson, H. F. *The Eighth Day of Creation: Makers of the Revolution in Biology* (New York and London: Simon and Schuster, 1979).

—. 'A History of the Science and Technology Behind Gene Mapping and Sequencing', in *The Code of Codes: Scientific and Social Issues in the Human Genome Project,* ed. Daniel J. Kevles and Leroy Hood (Cambridge, MA, and London: Harvard University Press, 1992).

Katz, Eric. 'Artefacts and Functions: A Note on the Value of Nature', *Environmental Values,* 2 (1993) 223–32.

—. *Nature As Subject: Human Obligation and Natural Community* (Lanham: Rowman and Littlefield, 1997).

Kay, Lily E. *The Molecular Vision of Life: Caltech, the Rockfeller Foundation and the Rise of the New Biology* (Oxford and New York: Oxford University Press, 1993).

Keller, Evelyn Fox. 'Nature, Nurture, and the Human Genome Project', in *The Code of Codes: Scientific and Social Issues in the Human Genome Project*, ed. Daniel J. Kevles and Leroy Hood (Cambridge, MA, and London: Harvard University Press, 1992).

Kevles, Daniel J. *In the Name of Eugenics: Genetics and the Uses of Human Heredity* (Cambridge, MA, and London: Harvard University Press, 1995).

Kevles, Daniel J. and Leroy Hood (editors). *The Code of Codes: Scientific and Social Issues in the Human Genome Project* (Cambridge, MA, and London: Harvard University Press, 1992).

Kirk, G. S. and J. E. Raven. *The PreSocratic Philosophers* (Cambridge: Cambridge University Press, 1977).

Kitcher, Philip. *The Lives to Come: The Genetic Revolution and Human Responsibilities* (New York and London: Penguin, 1996).

Kleiner, Kurt. 'US Urges Routine Genetic Testing', *New Scientist* (26 April 1997) 12.

Kloppenburg, Jack Ralph, Jr. 'The Social Impacts of Biogenetic Technology in Agriculture: Past and Future', in *The Social Consequences and Challenges of New Agricultural Technologies*, ed. Gigi M. Berardi and Charles C. Geisler (Boulder and London: Westview, 1984).

—. *First The Seed: The Political Economy of Plant Technology, 1492–2000* (Cambridge and New York: Cambridge University Press, 1990).

Kolakowski, Lezek. *Positivist Philosophy* (UK: Penguin, 1972).

Kolata, Gina. *Clone: The Road to Dolly and the Path Ahead* (New York and London: Penguin, 1997).

Krimpenfort, P. 'Generation of Transgenic Dairy Cattle Using "in vitro" Embryo Production', *Bio/Technology*, 9 (1991) 844–7.

Krimsky, Sheldon. *Genetic Alchemy: The Social History of the Recombinant DNA Controversy* (Cambridge, MA, and London: MIT Press, 1982).

—. *Biotechnics & Society: The Rise of Industrial Genetics* (New York and London: Praeger, 1991).

Kuhn, Thomas S. *The Structure of Scientific Revolutions* (Chicago: University of Chicago Press, 1962).

Kullman, Wolfgang. 'Different Concepts of the Final Cause in Aristotle', in *Aristotle on Nature and Living Things*, ed. Allan Gotthelf (Pennsylvania and Bristol: Mathesis/Bristol Classical Press, 1985).

Laurance, Jeremy. 'Grandmother's Surrogate Birth Will Not Get Out of Hand', *The Times* (9 December 1996) 4.

Leclercq, Jean. 'Vers La Société Basée Sur Le Travail', *Revue du Travail*, 51 (1950) 3.

Lee, Keekok. 'Popper's Falsifiability and Darwin's Natural Selection', *Philosophy* (1969) 291–302.

—. *The Positivist Science of Law*, Avebury Philosophy Series (Aldershot: Avebury, 1989a).

—. *Social Philosophy and Ecological Scarcity* (London: Routledge, 1989b).

—. *The Legal-Rational State: A Comparison of Hobbes, Bentham and Kelsen*, Avebury Philosophy Series (Aldershot: Avebury, 1990).

—. 'Awe and Humility: Intrinsic Value in Nature. Beyond an Earthbound Environmental Ethics', in *Philosophy and the Natural Environment*, ed. Robin Attfield and Andrew Belsey (Cambridge: Cambridge University Press, 1994; Royal Institute of Philosophy Supplement: 36).

—. 'Beauty For Ever?', *Environmental Values*, 4 (1995) 213–25.

—. *'Homo faber:* The Ontological Category of Modernity', in *Contemporary Political Studies*, vol. 1, ed. Iain Hampsher-Monk and Jeremy Stanyer (Belfast: Political Studies Association of the United Kingdom, 1996a).

—. 'Source and Locus of Intrinsic Values: A Re-examination', *Environmental Ethics*, 18 (1996b) 297–309.

—. 'Designer Mountains: The Ethics of Nanotechnology', *Terra Nova*, 2 (1997) 127–34.

—. 'Biodiversity', *Encyclopedia of Applied Ethics*, vol. 1, ed. Ruth Chadwick (San Diego: Academic, 1998), 285–304.

—.*The Natural and the Artefactual: The Implications of Deep Science and Deep Technology for Environmental Philosophy* (Lanham: Lexington/Rowman and Littlefield, 1999).

Lee, Thomas, F. *The Human Genome Project: Cracking the Genetic Code of Life* (New York and London: Plenum, 1991).

—. *Gene Future: The Promise and Perils of the New Biology* (New York and London: Plenum, 1993).

Leiss, William. *Under Technology's Thumb* (Montreal and London: McGill-Queen's University Press, 1990).

Lewis, C. S. *Studies in Words*, 2nd edn (Cambridge: Cambridge University Press, 1967).

Lewontin, R. C. 'Agricultural Research and the Penetration of Capital', *Science for the People*, 14 (1982) 12–17.

—. *The Doctrine of DNA: Biology as Ideology* (London: Penguin, 1993).

Lloyd, G. E. R. 'Empirical Research in Aristotle's Biology', in *Philosophical Issues in Aristotle's Biology*, ed. Allan Gotthelf and James G. Lennox (Cambridge and New York: Cambridge University Press, 1987).

—. 'Greek Antiquity: The Invention of Nature', in *The Concept of Nature: The Herbert Spencer Lectures*, ed. John Torrance (Oxford: Clarendon, 1992).

Locke, John. *Two Treatises of Government*, ed. Peter Laslett (Cambridge: Cambridge University Press, 1988).

Maclachlan, James. 'Drake v. the Philosophers', in *Nature, Experiment, and the Sciences: Essays on Galileo and the History of Science in Honor of Stillman Drake*, ed. Trevor H. Levere and William R. Shea, Boston Studies in the Philosophy of Science, vol. 120 (Dordrecht/Boston/London: Kluwer Academic, 1990).

Magner, Lois N. *A History of the Life Sciences* (New York and Basel: Marcel Dekker, 1979).

Manfield, Edwin. 'Intellectual Property, Technology and Economic Growth', in *Intellectual Property Rights in Science, Technology and Economic Performance: International Comparisons*, ed. Francis W. Rushing and Carole Ganz Brown (Boulder: Westview, 1990).

Marchant, Joanna. 'Know Your Enemy', *New Scientist*, 168 (4 November 2000) 46–50.

Mathews, Freya. *The Ecological Self* (London: Routledge, 1991).

Maturana, Humberto R. and Francisco J. Varela. *Autopoiesis and Cognition: The Realization of the Living* (Dordrecht/Boston: D. Reidel, 1980).

—. *The Tree of Knowledge: The Biological Roots of Human Understanding* (Boston: Shambhala, 1988).

Mayer, Sue. 'Environmental Threats of Transgenic Technology', in *Animal Genetic Engineering: Of Pigs, Oncomice and Men*, ed. Peter Wheale and Ruth McNally (London: Pluto, 1995).

Mayr, Ernst. *Animal Species and Evolution* (Cambridge, MA: Belknap Press of Harvard University Press, 1963).

—. *The Growth of Biological Thought* (Cambridge, MA: Belknap Press of Harvard University Press, 1982).

—. *Toward a New Philosophy of Biology* (Cambridge, MA, and London: Belknap Press of Harvard University Press, 1988).

McClellan, James, and Harold Dorn. *Science and Technology in World History* (Maryland: Johns Hopkins University Press, 1999).

McFadden, Johnjoe. *Quantum Evolution* (New York: HarperCollins, 2001).

McKibben, Bill. *The End of Nature* (New York: Random House, 1989).

McKie, Robert. 'Medicine Man at the $100m Biotech Temple', *The Observer,* Business Section (9 October 1994) 6.

—. 'Slim Hopes for Fat of the Land', *The Observer* (19 March 1995) 7.

—. 'Revealed: The Secret of Human Behaviour', *The Observer* (11 February 2001) 1.

McNeilly, F. S. *The Anatomy of Leviathan* (London: Macmillan, 1968).

Meek, James. 'Now Genetic Ethics Begin At Home', *The Guardian* (4 October 2000) 12.

—. 'Agency Under Fire As IVF Storm Gathers Pace', *The Guardian* (5 October 2000) 5.

—. 'Sons Created to Beat Blood Disease', *The Guardian* (17 October 2000).

—. 'Scientist Plant Alien Gene in Monkey for First Time', *The Guardian* (12 January 2001) 1–2.

—. 'Scientists Plan to Wipe Out Malaria with GM Mosquitoes', *The Guardian* (3 September 2001) 3.

Meek, James, and Paul Brown. 'How US Muscle Bent the Rules in Europe', in *The Guardian*, Patenting Life (15 November 2000) 11.

Meek, James, and Michael Ellison. 'On the Path of Biology's Holy Grail', *The Guardian* (5 June 2000) 3.

Mega, Marcello. 'Two Homosexual Men Raise Surrogate Baby Daughter' *The Sunday Times* (1 September 1996).

Mendel, Gregor. *Experiments in Plant Hybridization,* ed. J. H. Bennet (Edinburgh: Oliver and Boyd, 1965).

Messelson, Matthew, and Robert Yuan. 'DNA Restriction Enzyme from E. coli', *Nature,* 217 (1968) 1110–14.

Mill, John Stuart. 'Nature' in *John Stuart Mill: Autobiography and other Writings*, ed. Jack Stillinger (Boston: Houghton Mifflin, 1969).

Mitcham, Carl. 'Philosophy and the History of Technology', in *The History and Philosophy of Technology*, ed. George Bugliarello and Dean B. Doner (Urbana and London: University of Illinois Press, 1979).

—. 'Three Ways of Being-With Technology', in *From Artifact to Habitat: Studies in the Critical Engagement of Technology,* Research in Technology Series, vol. 3, ed. Gayle L. Ormiston (London and Toronto: Associated University Press, 1990).

—. *Thinking Through Technology: The Path between Engineering and Philosophy* (Chicago: Chicago University Press, 1994).

— (editor). *Social and Philosophical Construction of Technology*, Research in Philosophy and Technology Series, vol. 15 (Greenwich, CT, and London: JAI, 1995).

Mitcham, Carl, and Robert Mackey (editors). *Philosophy and Technology: Readings in the Philosophical Problems of Technology* (New York and London: Free, 1983).

Monbiot, George. 'Patent Nonsense', *The Guardian* (12 March 2002) 15.

Mooney, P. R. *Seeds of the Earth: A Private or Public Resource?* (Ottawa: Inter Pares, 1979).

—. 'The Law of the Seed', *Development Dialogue*, 1–2 (1983) 1–172.

Morgan, Thomas Hunt. *Evolution and Adaptation* (New York: Macmillan, 1903).

Mumford, Lewis. *Technics and Civilization* (London: George Routledge, 1946).

—. *The Myth of the Machine: Technics and Human Development* (London: Secker and Warburg, 1967).

National Research Council. *Genetic Engineering of Plants* (Washington, DC: National Academy Press, 1984).

—. *Mapping and Sequencing the Human Genome* (Washington, DC: National Academy, 1988).

New Scientist, Editorial: 'The Point of No Return' (1 March 1997) 3.

—, Editorial: 'Fasten Your Seat-belt' (6 December 1997) 3.

—. (22 April 2000) 5.

—, 'Seeds of Discontent' (21 October 2000) 66–8 [interview with Richard Jefferson].

—. 'Beyond the Genome' (4 November 2000) 28–50.

Nott, Robin. '"You Did It!": The European Biotechnology Directive At Last', *European Intellectual Property Review*, 20 (1998) 347–51.

Nussbaum, Martha. *The Fragility of Goodness* (Cambridge: Cambridge University Press, 1986).

Nye, David E. *American Technological Sublime* (Cambridge, MA: MIT Press, 1996).

The Observer (10 October 1993) 13 on *Science in China*.

Olby, Robert C. *Origins of Mendelism* (London: Constable, 1966).

—. *The Path to the Double Helix* (London: Macmillan, 1974).

—. 'The Revolution in Biology', in *Companion to the History of Modern Science*, ed. Robert C. Olby, Geoffrey Cantor, John Christie and Jonathon Hodge (London and New York: Routledge, 1990a).

—. 'The Emergence of Genetics', in *Companion to the History of Modern Science*, ed. Robert C. Olby, Geoffrey Cantor, John Christie and Jonathon Hodge (London and New York: Routledge, 1990b).

Ormiston, Gayle L. (editor). *Studies in the Critical Engagement of Technology*, Research in Technology Series, vol. 3 (Bethlehem: Lehigh University Press; London and Toronto: Associated University Press, 1990).

Oser, Andreas. 'Patenting (Partial) Gene Sequences Taking Particular Account of the EST Issue', *International Review of Industrial Property and Copyright Law*, 30 (1999) 1–18.

Pääbo, Svante. 'Ancient DNA', *Scientific American*, 269 (November 1993) 60–6.

Pacey, Arnold. *Technology in World Civilization: A Thousand Year History* (Cambridge, MA: MIT Press, 1990).

Palladino, Paolo. 'Between Craft and Science: Plant Breeding, Mendelian Genetics, and British Universities, 1900–1920', *Technology and Culture*, 34 (1993) 300–22.

—. 'Wizards and Devotees: On the Mendelian Theory of Inheritance and the Professionalization of Agricultural Science in Great Britain and the United States, 1880–1930', *History of Science*, 98 (1994) 409–44.

Phillips, Jeremy (editor). *Patents in Perspective: A Collection of Essays* (Oxford: ESC, 1985).

Phillips, Jeremy, and Alison Firth. *Introduction to Intellectual Property Law* (London: Butterworths, 1995).

Pilkington, Edward. 'Fur Starts to Fly as Police Arrest Bull Terrier Which Killed a Cat', *The Guardian* (21 August 1995) 1.

Plato. *The Republic*, vol. 1, Books 1–4, trans. by Paul Shorey (Cambridge, MA, and London: Harvard University Press/William Heinemann, 1982).

Plumwood, Val. *Feminism and the Mastery of Nature* (London: Routledge, 1993).

Popper, Karl. *Conjectures and Refutations* (London: Routledge and Kegan Paul, 1969).

Preus, Anthony. *Science and Philosophy in Aristotle's Biological Works* (New York and Hildesheim: Georg Olms, 1975).

Prigogine, Ilya, and Isabelle Stenger. *Order Out of Chaos: Man's New Dialogue with Nature* (New York: Bantam, 1984).

Rabinow, Paul. *Making PCR: A Story of Biotechnology* (Chicago: University of Chicago Press, 1996).

Radford, Tim. 'A Leaf From Life's Book', *The Guardian*, Science Section, (14 December 2000) 1–3.

Ramage, R. T. 'Heterosis and Hybrid Seed Production in Barley', in *Heterosis*, ed. R. Frankel (New York: Springer, 1983).

Reed, Peter. 'Man Apart: An Alternative to the Self-Realization Approach', *Environmental Ethics*, 11 (1989) 53–69.

Regis, Edward. *Nano!* (London and New York: Bantam, 1995).

Reiss, Michael J. and Roger Straughan. *Improving Nature? The Science and Ethics of Genetic Engineering* (Cambridge: Cambridge University Press, 1996).

Rescher, Nicholas. *Unpopular Essays on Technological Progress* (Pittsburgh: University of Pittsburgh Press, 1980).

Ridley, Matt. *Genome: Autobiography of a Species* (London: Fourth Estate, 1999).

Rifkin, Jeremy. *Algeny: A New World* (London: Pelican, 1984).

—. *The Biotech Century* (London: Gollancz, 1998).

—. 'The Price of Life', *The Guardian* (15 November 2000) 22.

—. 'Shopping for Humans', *The Guardian* (29 March 2001) 21.

Rindos, David. *The Origins of Agriculture: An Evolutionary Perspective* (Orlando and London: Academic, 1984).

Roberts, H. F. *Plant Hybridization Before Mendel* (Princeton: Princeton University Press, 1929).

Rolston, Holmes. *Conserving Natural Values* (New York: Columbia University Press, 1994).

Roy, D. J., B. E. Wynne and R. W. Old (editors). *Bioscience Society* (Chichester and New York: John Wiley, 1991).

Rushing, Francis W., and Carole Ganz Brown. *Intellectual Property Rights in Science, Technology and Economic Performance* (Boulder: Westview, 1990).

Russell, N. *Like Engend'ring Like: Heredity and Animal Breeding in Early Modern England* (Cambridge: Cambridge University Press, 1986).

Ryerson, K. A. 'The History and Significance of Plant Introduction Work in the United States Department of Agriculture', *Agricultural History*, 2 (1933): 110–28.

Sagoff, Mark. 'Process or Product? Ethical Priorities in Environmental Management', *Environmental Ethics*, 8 (1986) 121–38.

—. 'Zuckerman's Dilemma: A Plea for Environmental Ethics', *Hastings Center Report*, 21 (September–October 1991) 32–40.

Schatz, Ulrich. 'Patentability of Genetic Engineering Invention in European Patent Office Practice', *International Review of Industrial Property and Copyright Law*, 29 (1998) 2–16.

Schiff Eric. *Industrialization Without National Patents:* The Netherlands, 1869–1912; Switzerland, 1850–1907 (Princeton: Princeton University Press, 1971).

Schrödinger, Erwin. *What is Life?* (Cambridge: Cambridge University Press, 1945).

Schueller, Gretel H. 'But Is It Art?', *New Scientist* (6 January 2001) 34–7.

Scientific American: Key Technologies for the 21st Century (New York: W. H. Freeman, 1996).

Scott, Kirsty. 'Bereaved Couple Demand Right to Baby Girl', *The Guardian* (5 October 2000) 5.

—. 'Cloning Scientists Breed Chickens to Aid Cancer Fight', *The Guardian* (7 December 2000) 10.

Shapere, Dudley. *Galileo: A Philosophical Study* (Chicago and London: Chicago University Press, 1974).

Shapiro, K. J. 'The Death of the Animal: Ontological Vulnerability', *Between the Species*, 5 (1989) 183–94.

Shrader-Frechette, Kristin, and Laura Westra (editors). *Technology and Values* (Lanham and Oxford: Rowman and Littlefield, 1997).

Shull, George H. 'The Composition of a Field of Maize', *Annual Report of the American Breeders Association*, 4 (1908) 296–301.

—. 'A Pure-line Method in Corn Breeding', in *Annual Report of the American Breeders Association*, 5 (1909) 51–9.

Silver, Lee, M. *Remaking Eden: Cloning and Beyond in a Brave New World* (London: Weidenfeld and Nicolson, 1998).

Simmonds, Norman W. *Principles of Crop Improvement* (New York: Longman, 1979).

Sinsheimer, Robert. 'The Prospect of Designed Genetic Change', *Engineering and Science*, 32 (1969) 8–13.

Smith, Alex Duval. 'Mother, 63, "Deceived Fertility Unit"', *The Guardian* (25 April 1997) 2.

Smith, Bruce D. *The Emergence of Agriculture* (New York: Scientific American Library, 1995).

Sober, Elliott, and Richard Lewontin. 'Artifact, Cause and Genic Selection', *Philosophy of Science*, 49 (1982) 157–80.

Solter, Davor. 'Dolly *is* a clone and no longer alone', *Nature*, 394 (23 July 1998) 315–16.

Soulé, Michael E. 'The Social Siege of Nature', in *Reinventing Nature? Response to Postmodern Deconstruction*, ed. Michael E. Soulé and Gary Lease (Washington, DC, and California: Island, 1995).

Staudenmaier, John M. *Technology's Storytellers: Reweaving the Human Fabric* (Massachusetts and London: Society for the History of Technology/MIT Press, 1985).

Stevenson, Peter. 'Patenting of Transgenic Animals: A Welfare/Rights Perspective', in *Animal Genetic Engineering: Of Pigs, Oncomice and Men*, ed. Peter Wheale and Ruth McNally (London: Pluto, 1995).

Stone, Christopher D. *Earth and Other Ethics: The Case for Moral Pluralism* (New York: Harper and Row, 1988).

Sulston, John. 'Forever', *New Scientist* (1 April 2000) 46–7.

Sulston, John and Georgina Feroy. *The Common Thread* (London: Bantam Press, 2002).

Suzuki, David and Peter Knudtson. *Genethics: The Ethics of Engineering Life* (London: Unwin, 1990).

Sylvester, E. J., and L. C. Klotz. *The Gene Age: Genetic Engineering and the Next Industrial Revolution* (New York: Charles Scribner, 1983).

Taylor, Robert. 'Superhumans', in *New Scientist* (3 October 1998) 24–9.

Tenner, Edward. *Why Things Bite Back: Technology and the Revenge Effect* (London: Fourth Estate, 1997).

Tiles, Mary, and Hans Oberdiek. *Living in a Technological Culture: Human Tools and Human Values* (London and New York: Routledge, 1995).

Tokar, Brian (editor). *Redesigning Life? The Worldwide Challenge to Genetic Engineering* (London and New York: Zed, 2001).

Toolis, Kevin. 'DNA: It's War', *The Guardian*, Weekend (6 May 2000) 8–19.

Torrance, John. *The Concept of Nature: The Herbert Spencer Lectures* (Oxford: Clarendon, 1992).

Tudge, Colin. *The Engineer in the Garden: Genes and Genetics* (London: Jonathan Cape, 1993).

—. *In Mendel's Footnotes: An Introduction to the Science and Technologies of Genes and Genetics from the Nineteenth Century to the Twenty-Second* (London: Jonathan Cape, 2000).

UK Patent Office, http://www.patent.gov.uk/search/[database]

United States National Research Council. *Mapping and Sequencing the Human Genome* (Washington, DC: National Academy, 1988).

United States Patent Office. *United States Patent 4,237,224: Process for Producing Biologically Functional Molecular Chimeras* (Washington, DC: US Patent Office, 1980).

Van de Graaf. *Patent Law and Modern Biotechnology* (Rotterdam: Gouda Quint, 1997).

Varela, Francisco J. *Principles of Biological Autonomy* (New York and Oxford: North Holland, 1979).

Varner, Gary E. *In Nature's Interests? Interests, Animal Rights and Environmental Ethics* (New York and Oxford: Oxford University Press, 1998).

Verhoog, H. 'The Concept of Intrinsic Value and Transgenic Animals' *Journal of Agricultural and Environmental Ethics*, 5 (1992) 147–60.

Vidal, John, and John Carvel. 'Lambs to the Gene Market', *The Guardian* (13 November 1994) 25.

Vines, Gail. 'One Giant Leap into the Unkown', *New Scientist* (1 March 1997) 5.

Vries, H. de. *Intracellular Pangenesis*, trans. by C. S. Gager (Chicago: Open Court, 1910).

Watson, James. *The Double Helix: A Personal Account of the Discovery of the Structure of DNA* (London: Weidenfeld and Nicholson, 1968).

Weinberg, Steven. 'Life in the Universe', *Scientific American*, 271 (1994) 22–7.

Weisheipl, James A. 'Aristotle's Concept of Nature: Avicenna and Aquinas', in *Approaches to Nature in the Middle Ages*, ed. Lawrence D. Roberts (New York: State University of New York at Binghamton, 1982).

Westfall, Richard S. 'The Scientific Revolution of the Seventeenth Century: The Construction of a New World View', in *The Concept of Nature: The Herbert Spencer Lectures*, ed. John Torrance (Oxford: Clarendon, 1992).

Wheale, Peter and Ruth McNally. *Genetic Engineering: Catastrophe or Utopia?* (Hemel Hempstead and New York: Harvester, Wheatsheaf/St Martin's Press, 1988).

— (editors). *The Bio-Revolution: Cornucopia or Pandora's Box?* (London: Pluto, 1990).

— (editors). *Animal Genetic Engineering: Of Pigs, Oncomice and Men* (London: Pluto, 1995).

Wick, Warner. 'Aristotelianism', in *The Encyclopedia of Philosophy*, vol. 1, ed. Paul Edwards (London: Collier-Macmillan, 1967).

Wilkerson, T. E. *Natural Kinds* (Aldershot: Avebury, 1995).

Wilkie, Tom. *Perilous Knowledge: The Human Genome Project and its Implications* (London and Boston: Faber and Faber, 1994).

Wilmut, Ian, Keith Campbell and Colin Tudge. *The Second Creation: The Age of Biological Control by the Scientists Who Cloned Dolly* (London: Headline, 2000).

Wilson, E. O. (editors). *Biodiversity* (Washington, DC: National Academy, 1988).

—. 'Address to the American Association for the Advancement of Science', as reported in *The Guardian* (18 February 1995) 8.

Wright, H. E., and D. G. Frey (editors). *The Quaternary of the United States* (Princeton: Princeton University Press, 1965).

Wright, Nick. 'Lucy, the Cat Killer, Released', *The Guardian* (24 August 1995) 7.

Xenos, Nicolas. *Scarcity and Modernity* (London: Routledge, 1989).

Yoxen, Edward. *The Gene Business: Who Should Control Biotechnology?* (London: Pan, 1983).

Zimmerman, Michael. *Heidegger's Confrontation with Modernity: Technology, Politics, Art* (Bloomington: Indiana University Press, 1990).

Index